METHODS IN
MICROBIOLOGY

METHODS IN
MICROBIOLOGY

Volume 17
Plasmid Technology

Edited by

P. M. BENNETT

*Department of Microbiology, University of Bristol, Medical School,
Bristol, UK*

and

J. GRINSTED

*Department of Biology, University of Bristol, Medical School,
Bristol, UK*

1984

ACADEMIC PRESS
(Harcourt Brace Javanovich, Publishers)
London   Orlando   San Diego   San Francisco   New York
Toronto   Montreal   Sydney   Tokyo   São Paulo

ACADEMIC PRESS INC. (LONDON) LTD.
24–28 Oval Road
London NW1 7DX

U.S. Edition published by
ACADEMIC PRESS INC.
(Harcourt Brace Jovanovich, Inc.)
Orlando, Florida 32887

British Library Cataloguing in Publication Data

ISBN   0–12–521516–9
LCCCN 68–57745
ISSN   0580–9517

Filmset in Monophoto Times New Roman by Latimer Trend & Company Ltd, Plymouth
Printed in Great Britain by St Edmundsbury Press,
Bury St Edmunds, Suffolk

CONTRIBUTORS

P. M. Bennett   Department of Microbiology, University of Bristol, Medical School, University Walk, Bristol BS8 1TD, UK

N. L. Brown   Department of Biochemistry, University of Bristol, University Walk, Bristol BS8 1TD, UK

H. J. Burkardt   Department of Microbiology and Biochemistry, University of Erlangen, Federal Republic of Germany

L. Caro   Department of Molecular Biology, University of Geneva, 1211 Geneva 4, Switzerland

M. Chandler   Department of Molecular Biology, University of Geneva, 1211 Geneva 4, Switzerland (Present address: Institut de Recherche en Biochemie et Genetique Cellulaire de CNRS, 118 Route de Narbonne, 31062 Toulouse cedex, France)

G. Churchward   Department of Molecular Biology, University of Geneva, 1211 Geneva 4, Switzerland

W. P. Diver   Department of Microbiology, University of Bristol, Medical School, University Walk, Bristol BS8 1TD, UK (Present address: Molecular Biology Unit, Research School of Biological Sciences, Australian National University, Canberra ACT, Australia)

A. Docherty   Department of Microbiology, University of Bristol, University Walk, Bristol BS8 1TD, UK (Present address: Celltech Ltd, 250 Bath Road, Slough, UK)

G. Dougan   Microbiology Department, Trinity College, Dublin 2, Ireland (Present address: Department of Bacteriology, Wellcome Research Laboratories, Beckenham, Kent, UK)

T. J. Foster   Microbiology Department, Trinity College, Dublin 2, Ireland

J. Grinsted   Department of Microbiology, University of Bristol, Medical School, University Walk, Bristol BS8 1TD, UK

G. O. Humphreys   Department of Microbiology, University of Liverpool, Liverpool L69 3BX (Present address: Celltech Ltd, 250 Bath Road, Slough, Berkshire, UK)

M. Kehoe   Microbiology Department, Trinity College, Dublin 2, Ireland (Present address: Department of Microbiology, University of Newcastle-upon-Tyne, NE1 7RU, UK)

A. Pühler   Department of Genetics, Faculty of Biology, University of Bielefeld, Postfach 8640, 4800 Bielefeld, Federal Republic of Germany

J. R. Saunders   Department of Microbiology, University of Liverpool, Liverpool L69 3BX, UK

V. Stanisich   Department of Microbiology, La Trobe University, Bundoora 3083, Australia

C. M. Thomas   Department of Genetics, University of Birmingham, P.O. Box 363, Birmingham B15, UK

N. Willetts   Department of Molecular Biology, University of Edinburgh, King's Building, Mayfield Road, Edinburgh EH9 3JR, UK (Present address: Biotechnology Australia Pty Ltd, 28 Barcoo Street, P.O. Box 20, Roseville, New South Wales 2069, Australia)

PREFACE

While initiating many students into the mysteries of plasmid biology during the last few years it has become increasingly obvious that there is a need for an introductory methodology text that deals with the techniques used to investigate bacterial plasmids. This volume is an attempt to fill that gap. The techniques covered range from those that are relatively simple and demand no sophisticated equipment to those now used routinely in molecular biology. We hope that both the novice and the experienced research worker will find something of use within the pages of this text.

P. M. Bennett
J. Grinsted

January 1984

CONTENTS

1

Introduction

P. M. BENNETT AND J. GRINSTED

Department of Microbiology, University of Bristol, Medical School, Bristol, UK

Plasmids are double-stranded circular DNA molecules that replicate independently of the host cell's chromosome. In bacteria, plasmids constitute a major pool of genetic information. Indeed, in recent years it has become apparent that many of the features of bacteria that interest microbiologists are conferred by plasmid-borne genes. Hence, the study of bacterial plasmids has become an important aspect of molecular biology. More recently, bacterial plasmids have acquired major importance as a cornerstone of the technology popularly referred to as genetic engineering.

Plasmids vary in size enormously; they can be as small as 1000 base pairs (1 kb) or greater than 400 000 base pairs (400 kb). They can be considered as mini-chromosomes; but, unlike chromosomes, most, if not all, are dispensable as far as the bacteria are concerned, except under particular circumstances. For example, if a cell can grow and survive in the presence of ampicillin because it contains a resistance plasmid encoding a beta-lactamase, it follows that the plasmid is indispensable in the presence of the drug. However, the plasmid is not necessary for growth on a drug-free medium and can be lost from the cell without affecting cell survival.

The first plasmid to be identified was the *Escherichia coli* fertility factor F, which was discovered because of its ability to mediate transfer of chromosomal markers from one strain of *E. coli* to another (Hayes, 1968). These initial genetic experiments established that the fertility factor was physically separate from the bacterial chromosome, and some years after it was shown that the factor is a circular, double-stranded DNA molecule (Hayes, 1968). The discovery of F was of fundamental importance for the development of bacterial genetics but generated little interest outside certain academic circles. However, the discovery of infectious resistance to antibiotics in epidemic strains of *Shigella* in the late 1950s in Japan, and the fact that this was encoded by plasmids (Watanabe, 1963) changed people's awareness. The tempo of plasmid research accelerated dramatically as the clinical importance of the elements was appreciated. Throughout the next two decades much plasmid research centred on drug-resistance plasmids, particularly on their epidemiology and the mechanisms of drug resistance. During this period, however,

METHODS IN MICROBIOLOGY
VOLUME 17 ISBN 0–12-521517–7

it became apparent that plasmids are responsible for conferring a much greater variety of cell phenotypes than just fertility or drug resistance (Chapter 2).

Because bacterial plasmids can transfer between bacterial cells, they are responsible for much of the genetic versatility displayed by bacteria, and for their ability to adapt rapidly to new environmental conditions. Thus, the genetic pool that is available in a population of bacteria may be greater than the chromosomal complement of the individuals. This flexibility is increased by the fact that transposable elements (Chapters 10 and 11) can use transferable plasmids as vectors. So, the combination of transferable plasmids and transposable elements provides a rapid method for distributing genetic information and is thus a potent force in evolution.

In recent years, plasmid research has taken an entirely new turn with the advent of gene cloning and the use of plasmids as cloning vectors (i.e. they are important in genetic engineering). Thus, DNA sequences of interest can be isolated from one organism, inserted *in vitro* into a bacterial plasmid, which is then introduced, by transformation (Chapter 4), into a bacterial cell, where the gene and its expression can be examined more easily. The technique allows, in principle, any DNA to be introduced into a bacterial cell. This allows molecular biologists to bring to bear a whole range of experimental techniques on it, because of the ease with which bacterial cultures can be manipulated. It also provides the opportunity of expressing the foreign gene in the bacteria; this, of course, has led to the recent industrial interest in the technique. An admirable introductory text to genetic manipulation is written by Old and Primrose (1982). Therefore, now, the study of plasmids is not only of academic interest but also of great practical importance, commercially, socially and ecologically.

This volume is not concerned directly with the plasmids themselves but rather with how they are studied. For information concerning plasmids and their biology the reader is referred to Hayes (1968) for a description of the early studies on F, and then to Falkow (1975) and Broda (1979). In this volume, some of the basic experimental techniques used to study plasmids are introduced, together with one or two more recent developments which can be used to examine, in much more detail, a particular gene(s) carried on a plasmid. It is not a comprehensive treatise of experimental techniques to be applied to plasmid studies. Rather it is intended to be a simple practical guide to the basic methodology used to study plasmids. Nonetheless, we hope that the more experienced worker will find it useful. We do not deal specifically with genetic engineering techniques, although some aspects are dealt with in particular chapters. These techniques are comprehensively dealt with by Grossman and Moldave (1980), Wu (1979) and Maniatis *et al.* (1982).

References

Broda, P. (1979). "Plasmids". Freeman, San Francisco, California.
Falkow, S. (1975). "Infectious Multiple Drug Resistance". Pion, London.
Grossman, L. and Moldave, K. (Eds) (1980). "Methods in Enzymology," Vol. 65. Academic Press, New York and London.
Hayes, W. (1968). "The Genetics of Bacteria and their Viruses," 2nd edn. Blackwell, Oxford.
Maniatis, T., Fritsch, E. F. and Sambrook, J. (1982). "Molecular Cloning. A Laboratory Manual". Cold Spring Harbor, New York.
Old, R. W. and Primrose, S. B. (1981). "Principles of Gene Manipulation. An Introduction to Genetic Engineering," 2nd edn. Blackwell, Oxford.
Watanabe, T. (1963). *Bacteriol. Rev.* **27**, 87–115.
Wu, R. (Ed.) (1979). "Methods in Enzymology," Vol. 68. Academic Press, New York and London.

2

Identification and Analysis of Plasmids at the Genetic Level

V. A. STANISICH

Department of Microbiology, La Trobe University, Bundoora, Australia

I. Introduction

Many bacteria of diverse type and habitat are now known to harbour plasmid DNA. This observation lends credence to the view that these elements are ubiquitous among procaryotes and are likely to be detected in any species in which a thorough search for them is made. In recent years the demonstration of plasmids in an increasing variety of bacteria has been striking and directly the result of the development of techniques that allow the physical demonstration, isolation and molecular characterization of plasmid DNA. Thus, plasmids in bacteria in which genetic analysis is presently limited or impossible are as amenable to detailed molecular study as those from genetically well-characterized bacteria. Such investigations are satisfactory where the primary concern is the molecular characterization, comparison and *in vitro* manipulation of plasmids for specific purposes such as the construction of cloning vectors. They may, however, be less appropriate for studies directed towards an evaluation of the contribution made by plasmids to the properties and adaptability of the host bacterium. Thus, a list of plasmid-carrying bacteria such as that shown in Table I includes many species in which extrachromosomal DNA has been detected by physical methods but no functions or host-expressed phenotypes ascribed to it. In most instances, such "cryptic" DNAs will be typical plasmids, but in others they may represent bacteriophage DNAs comparable to the coliphages of the P1 type that exist intracellularly as extrachromosomally replicating molecules (Falkow, 1975). The bacteria screened for extrachromosomal DNA have often been chosen because of some distinctive property that they display. This may be a pathogenic capability, an unusual metabolic capability or the ability to survive in an extreme environment. In these instances it has been usual to attempt to correlate plasmid carriage with the particular distinctive property of interest. Thus, while the physical characterization and manipulation of plasmid DNA is an essential aspect of their study, this cannot be divorced from the microbiological and genetic investigations that provide additional information regarding the plasmid's contribution to host phenotype. This chapter is concerned with analyses of the latter type and deals with the primarily genetic procedures that can be used, first to identify a plasmid-encoded phenotype, and then to characterize further the element involved.

II. Evidence for plasmid-determined phenotypes

The first bacterial plasmids were identified among members of the Enterobacteriaceae (Meynell, 1972). The plasmids were recognized by the fact that they were responsible for particular properties displayed by the bacterium, that their replication was independent of that of the bacterial chromosome and that they could be lost from the bacterium by an irreversible process. The properties recognized were those of chromosome mobilization, conjugal transmissibility (and associated properties), antibiotic resistance and colicin production. As can be seen from Table II, this list has now been expanded to include a wide array of properties in different bacterial species and many examples can be cited of plasmids that determine combinations of these properties (Jacob et al., 1977).

The observation of an unusual phenotype in an isolate of an otherwise well-characterized bacterial species is often the first indicator that the property is plasmid determined. Many examples of this have been found involving the properties used for the rapid diagnostic identification of clinically significant bacteria. Thus, plasmid-mediated lactose fermentation (Guiso and Ullman, 1976), H_2S production (Ørskov and Ørskov, 1973), citrate utilization (Ishiguro et al., 1978) and other properties have all been found among atypically responding members of the Enterobacteriaceae. Some of the

TABLE I

Genera of bacteria in which plasmids or extrachromosomal DNA have been detected

---

Phototrophic bacteria and blue–green algae

Rhodopseudomonas[1]
Chromatium[1]
Anacystis[1]
Agmenellum[1]
Synechococcus[2]
Synechocystis[2]
Nostoc[3]

Gliding bacteria

Myxococcus[4]

Spiral and curved bacteria

Campylobacter

Gram-negative aerobic rods and cocci

Pseudomonas[6]
Xanthomonas[7]
Rhizobium[8]
Agrobacterium[9]
Halobacterium[10]
Alcaligenes[11]
Bordetella[12]
Thermus[13]

Gram-negative facultatively anaerobic rods

Escherichia[12]
Salmonella[12]
Shigella[12]
Klebsiella[12]
Enterobacter[12]
Serratia[12]
Proteus[12]
Yersinia[14]
Erwinia[15]

Vibrio[12]
Providencia[12]
Aeromonas[12]
Haemophilus[16]
Citrobacter[17]

Gram-negative anaerobic bacteria

Bacteroides[18]

Gram-negative cocci and coccobacilli

Neisseria[19]
Acinetobacter[20]

Gram-positive cocci

Staphylococcus[21]
Streptococcus[22]

Endospore-forming rods

Bacillus[23]
Clostridium[24]

Gram-positive asporogenous rod-shaped bacteria

Lactobacillus[25]

Actinomycetes and related organisms

Corynebacterium[26]
Mycobacterium[27]
Streptomyces[28]

Mycoplasmas

Mycoplasma[29]
Acholeplasma[29]

---

[1]Saunders (1978); [2]van den Hondel *et al.* (1979); [3]Reaston *et al.* (1982); [4]Kaiser and Manoil (1979); [5]Taylor *et al.* (1981); [6]Jacoby (1979); [7]Kado and Liu (1981); [8]Dénarié *et al.* (1981); [9]Dellaporta and Pesano (1981); [10]Weidinger *et al.* (1979); [11]Fisher *et al.* (1978); [12]Jacob *et al.* (1977); [13]Eberhard *et al.* (1981); [14]Silver *et al.* (1979); [15]Coplin *et al.* (1981); [16]Kaulfers *et al.* (1978); [17]Taylor and Summers (1979); [18]Privitera *et al.* (1979); [19]Sox *et al.* (1978); [20]Hinchliffe *et al.* (1980); [21]Lacey (1975); [22]Clewell (1981); [23]Le Hagarat and Anaguostpoulous (1977); [24]Rood *et al.* (1978); [25]Hofer (1977); [26]Schiller *et al.* (1980); [27]Mizuguchi *et al.* (1981); [28]Chater (1979); [29]Razin (1978).

TABLE II
Properties determined by bacterial plasmids[a]

---

1. **Resistance properties**
   (a) Resistance to antibiotics
       —Aminoglycosides (e.g. streptomycin, gentamicin, amikacin—as a result of enzymic modification by N-acetylation, O-nucleotidylation or O-phosphorylation)
       —Chloramphenicol (as a result of enzymic modification by O-acetylation)
       —Fusidic acid
       —Furans
       —β-Lactam antibiotics (e.g. benzy penicillin, ampicillin, carbenicillin—as a result of enzymic cleavage of the lactam ring)
       —Sulphonamides, trimethoprim (as a result of alternative drug-resistant target enzymes)
       —Tetracyclines (as a result of altered transport system)
       —Erythromycin (as a result of altered ribosome binding site)
   (b) Resistance to heavy-metal cations
       —Mercury and organomercurials (as a result of reductases and hydrolases)
       —Nickel, cobalt, lead, cadmium, bismuth, antimony, zinc, silver, thallium
   (c) Resistance to anions
       —Arsenate, arsenite, tellurite, borate, chromate
   (d) Other resistances
       —Radiation (e.g. u.v., X-rays)
       —Phage and bacteriocin resistance (e.g. Inc P2 plasmids)
       —Plasmid-specified restriction/modification systems (e.g. Inc N plasmids)

2. **Metabolic properties**
       —Antibiotic and bacteriocin production (e.g. by *Streptomyces, Escherichia, Pseudomonas, Bacillus, Streptococcus*)
       —Metabolism of simple carbohydrates (e.g. lactose, sucrose, raffinose)
       —Metabolism of complex carbon compounds (e.g. octane and other *n*-alkanes, *p* or *m*-xylenes, *p* or *m*-toluenes, camphor, nicotine)
       —Metabolism of proteins (e.g. casein, gelatin)
       —Metabolism of opines (by Ti$^+$ *Agrobacterium*)
       —Nitrogen fixation (by *Rhizobium*)
       —δ-Endotoxin by sporulating *B. thuringiensis*
       —Other properties (e.g. citrate utilization, H_2S production, leucine biosynthesis)

3. **Properties contributing to pathogenicity or symbiosis**
       —Antibiotic resistance and bacteriocin production
       —Toxin production (e.g. enterotoxins of *Escherichia coli* and *Staphylococcus aureus*, exfoliative toxin by *S. aureus*, haemolysins by *Escherichia, Staphylococcus* and *Streptococcus*)
       —Colonization antigens of *E. coli* (e.g. K88, K89, CFAI, CFAII)
       —Tumorigenicity (by Ti$^+$ *Agrobacterium*)
       —Host specificity (of *Agrobacterium* and *Rhizobium*)
       —Nodulation (by *Rhizobium*)

4. Conjugal properties
   —Sex-pili and associated sensitivity to pilus-specific phages
   —Surface exclusion
   —Response to and inhibition of pheromones (in *Streptococcus*)
   —Fertility inhibition

5. Replication-maintenance properties
   —Sensitivity to curing agents
   —Incompatibility
   —Host range
   —Copy number
   —Temperature-sensitive replication

6. Other properties
   —Gas vacuole formation in *Halobacterium*
   —Interference in sporulation of *Bacillus pumilis*
   —Sensitivity to bacteriocins (in *Agrobacterium* and *Streptococcus*)
   —Translucent-opaque colony change in *Mycobacterium*
   —Regulation of melanin production in *Streptomyces*

---

a Modified from Davey and Reanney (1980) and Stanisich (1982).

properties used to classify bacteria at the species or even the genus level may also be properties determined by plasmids. For example, members of the Rhizobiaceae are assigned to the genus *Rhizobium* or *Agrobacterium* largely on the basis of their nitrogen-fixing or plant-pathogenic capabilities. Both properties have been found to be plasmid determined in the respective bacteria (Dénarié *et al.*, 1981; Dellaporta and Pesano, 1981). It would seem, therefore, that literally any bacterial property could be plasmid encoded. Such an assumption follows fairly naturally from the broad variety of plasmid-determined properties already defined (Table II), and from the knowledge that, at least in theory, some of the products of recombinational interchanges between DNAs in a single bacterium have the possibility of being transferred to other species or even genera of bacteria by the variety of gene transfer processes known (Starlinger, 1977; Brooks Low and Porter, 1978). Table III summarizes the way that the experimental approaches that are described in this section might be used to identify plasmid-encoded functions.

A. Plasmid instability and curing

Plasmids are defined as extrachromosomally replicating molecules of DNA. It is expected, therefore, that in any growing population of plasmid-carrying bacteria, plasmidless segregants will occasionally be produced as the result of an error in the processes of plasmid replication or partitioning to daughter bacteria. Such bacteria will survive provided that the plasmid lost does not

TABLE III

Criteria for determining whether the property A^+ in bacterium $B(A^+)$ is plasmid mediated

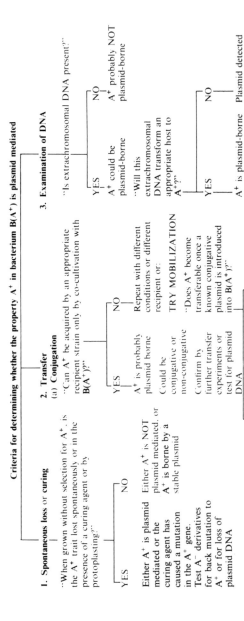

1. Spontaneous loss or curing

"When grown without selection for A^+, is the A^+ trait lost spontaneously or in the presence of a curing agent or by protoplasting?"

YES
Either A^+ is plasmid mediated or the curing agent has caused a mutation in the A^+ gene. Test A^- derivatives for back mutation to A^+ or for loss of plasmid DNA

NO
Either A^+ is NOT plasmid mediated, or A^+ is borne by a stable plasmid

2. Transfer
(a) Conjugation

"Can A^+ be acquired by an appropriate recipient strain only by co-cultivation with $B(A^+)$?"

YES
A^+ is probably plasmid borne
Could be conjugative or non-conjugative
Confirm by further transfer experiments or test for plasmid DNA

NO
Repeat with different conditions or different recipient or: TRY MOBILIZATION
"Does A^+ become transferable once a known conjugative plasmid is introduced into $B(A^+)$?"

YES
A^+ probably on a non-conjugative plasmid
Confirm by further transfer experiments or test for plasmid DNA

NO
A^+ probably NOT plasmid-borne

(b) Transduction or transformation

YES
A^+ could be chromosomal or plasmid-borne
Distinguish using recombination-deficient recipients or test for plasmid DNA

NO
Plasmid may be too large to be transferred intact

3. Examination of DNA

"Is extrachromosomal DNA present?"

YES
A^+ could be plasmid-borne
"Will this extrachromosomal DNA transform an appropriate host to A^+?"

YES
A^+ is plasmid-borne

NO
Plasmid detected DOES NOT specify A^+

NO
A^+ probably NOT plasmid-borne

encode functions vital for growth under the prevailing environmental conditions. Furthermore, the bacteria can only regain the lost functions by acquiring, from an external source, the necessary genes. Thus, the instability of a bacterial property, be it a common or uncommon feature of that species, can be an indicator of plasmid involvement. Clearly, such "spontaneous" instability will only be evident in those instances where it occurs at relatively high frequency, say $> 10^{-3}$, and is associated with an easily recognizable phenotype or one that is easily detected by testing individual colonies. The former would include changes in colonial morphology or pigmentation, and the latter, properties such as resistance to antimicrobial agents, antibiotic production or various metabolic capabilities.

In those instances where instability is infrequent or the loss of the property difficult to determine, the bacteria can be treated with "curing" agents (Table IV). These include chemical and physical agents, some of which can mutate DNA, interfere specifically with its replication or affect particular organelles or enzymes of the bacterial cell. Although all of these agents have been used to enhance the recovery of plasmidless derivatives of various bacteria, they are individually effective only against some plasmids, and their effect on a newly discovered plasmid cannot be predicted.

Thus, the inability to cure a phenotypic property is almost never used as evidence against plasmid involvement. The plasmid may simply be refractory to the curing agent used, or appear so because it carries functions vital for cell viability. This latter possibility is perhaps most likely for very large plasmids

TABLE IV
Examples of curing agents

Acridine orange[1]	Nitrosoguanidine[8]
Acriflavin	u.v.-Radiation[8]
Proflavine	Mitomycin C[9]
5-Amino acridine[3]	Thymidine starvation[10]
Ethidium bromide[4]	Atabrine[11]
Quinacrine[5]	Sodium dodecyl sulphate[12]
Quinine[5]	Urea[13]
Chloroquine[5]	Heat[14]
Berberine[5]	Ni^{2+} and Co^{2+} [15]
Miracil D[5]	Novobiocin[16]
Rifampicin[6]	Penicillin[17]
Sarkomycin[7]	Imipramine[18]
Ethyl methane sulphonate[8]	Guanidine hydrochloride[19]

[1] Hirota (1960); [2] Mitsuhashi et al. (1961); [3] Meynell (1972); [4] Bouanchaud et al. (1969); [5] Hahn and Ciak (1971); [6] Johnston and Richmond (1970); [7] Ikeda et al. (1967); [8] Willetts (1967); [9] Chakrabarty (1972); [10] Clowes et al. (1965); [11] Yoshikawa and Sevag (1967); [12] Tomoeda et al. (1968); [13] Tomoeda et al. (1970); [14] May et al. (1964); [15] Hirota (1956); [16] McHugh and Swartz (1977); [17] Lacey (1975); [18] Molnar et al. (1978); [19] Costa et al. (1980).

whose contribution to host function may be considerable. None of the "megaplasmids" of *Rhizobium* or *Agrobacterium* that exceed 250×10^6 daltons have yet been cured, although heat-induced deletions of parts of these plasmids or of smaller plasmids (90×10^6–160×10^6 daltons) resident in the same cell have been possible (Dénarié *et al.*, 1981). Curing of plasmids is discussed in more detail in Chapter 5, in which experimental procedures are presented.

B. Plasmid loss by protoplasting

Techniques that remove the cell wall from bacteria may provide an alternative method to that of standard curing experiments for the identification of plasmid-associated phentoypes. This is suggested by the observation that up to 80% of regenerated protoplasts from *Staphylococcus aureus* (Novick *et al.*, 1980) and 25% of those from *Streptomyces coelicolor* (Hopwood, 1981) did not carry plasmids present in the untreated bacteria. In *Staphylococcus aureus*, curing occurred with nine independently-carried small ($< 3 \times 10^6$ daltons) high copy number plasmids but not with four large ($> 15 \times 10^6$ daltons) low copy number plasmids. In *S. coelicolor* the two plasmids cured were both of the latter type (30×10^6 and 150×10^6 daltons). A similar effect was found with a Group B *Streptococcus* where conversion to a stable cell-wall-deficient L-form was associated with concomitant loss of an antibiotic-resistance plasmid (Schmitt-Slonska *et al.*, 1979). These observations suggest that plasmid loss can result directly from removal of the cell wall, perhaps because of the associated loss of mesosomal material. Alternatively, it may be the result of faulty partitioning of plasmids during the early cell divisions of the regeneration process (Novick *et al.*, 1980). Irrespective of the mechanism, this method would appear to be suitable for Gram-positive bacteria that are relatively easily converted to protoplasts by treatment with penicillin or lysozyme (including lysostaphin for *Staphylococcus*), and for those Gram-negative bacteria and *Streptomyces* for which more complex protoplasting procedures have already been developed (Hopwood, 1981).

C. Additional criteria

Several additional criteria may be appropriate for the primary identification of a plasmid or plasmid-associated phenotype in individual instances. These are the u.v.-inactivation kinetics of the property (Section II.D.2), displacement of the plasmid by introduction of an incompatible plasmid (Section III.D) and response of the bacterium to donor-specific bacteriophages (Section III.E). These aspects are discussed later as indicated.

D. Plasmid transfer

The ability of a property to be transferred from one bacterium to another provides good presumptive evidence of plasmid involvement, particularly if the frequency of transfer is high. Attempts to demonstrate such transfer can, therefore, be used as an initial means of identifying a plasmid-encoded property or of providing evidence to support this if plasmid involvement has already been indicated by curing or other experiments. In many instances the frequency of gene transfer will be low ($< 10^{-3}$) so that experiments to detect this are only feasible where a positive selection for inheritance of the plasmid-encoded property can be made. Transfer experiments that are conducted by simply mixing cultures of the test bacterium with a suitable recipient strain can give rise to progeny by conjugation, transduction or transformation (Brooks Low and Porter, 1978). Sometimes the interpretation of data obtained from transfer experiments can be facilitated by a knowledge of the type of process involved. This may be roughly gauged as follows: if treatment of the bacterial mixture with DNAase reduces the yield of progeny, transformation is indicated; if mixtures of the recipient with a culture supernatant of the test bacterium yields progeny, transduction is indicated and the presence of bacteriophage should be demonstrable; if neither transformation nor transduction can be demonstrated, transfer via cell-to-cell contact (i.e. conjugation) is indicated. Table V shows routes of gene transfer that have been discovered in various bacterial genera.

1. Conjugation

Many plasmids encode functions that allow their transfer from cell to cell by direct contact. This process, termed conjugation, is controlled by conjugative plasmids whose individual sizes vary over a wide range. Such plasmids of only 17×10^6 daltons have been found in *Streptococcus* (Clewell, 1981) and the Enterobacteriaceae (Jacob *et al.*, 1977), whereas others of more than 200×10^6 daltons occur in *Pseudomonas* (Hansen and Olsen, 1978) and the Rhizobiaceae (Dénarié *et al.*, 1981; Dellaporta and Pesano, 1981). Conjugation has been detected in many members of the Enterobacteriaceae and in other Gram-negative and Gram-variable bacteria (Table V). It also occurs in some Gram-positive species and plasmid transfer from *Streptococcus faecalis* to *Bacillus subtilis* and *Staphylococcus aureus* has been demonstrated under laboratory conditions (Clewell, 1981). Studies with F and F-like plasmids in *Escherichia coli* K12 have shown that the conjugation process and its genetic control is complex (Achtman and Skurray, 1977; Willetts and Skurray, 1980). Several features of these systems are common to

TABLE V
Gene transfer in bacteria[a]

Family or Genus	Conjugation[b]	Transduction	Transformation
Enterobacteriaceae	Jacob et al. (1977)	Brooks Low and Porter (1978)	Smith et al. (1981)
Acinetobacter	Hinchliffe et al. (1980)	Herman and Juni (1974)	Juni and Janik (1969)
Agrobacterium	Dellaporta and Pesano (1981)		Klein and Klein (1956)
Azotobacter			Page and Sadoff (1976)
Bacillus	Privitera et al. (1979)	Yasbin and Young (1974)	Smith et al. (1981)
Bacteroides	Taylor et al. (1981)		
Campylobacter			
Caulobacter		Poindexter (1981)	
Clostridium	Rood et al. (1978)		
Corynebacterium		Hirai and Yanagawa (1970)	
Erwinia	Chatterjee et al. (1979)		
Haemophilus	Kaulfers et al. (1978)		Smith et al. (1981)
Methylobacterium			O'Connor et al. (1977)
Methylococcus			Williams and Bainbridge (1971)
Micrococcus			Tirgari and Moseley (1980)
Micromonospora	Beretta et al. (1971)		
Moraxella			Bovre and Frohlm (1972)
Mycobacterium	Gelbart and Juhasz (1973)	Raj and Ramakrishnan (1970)	
Neisseria	Sox et al. (1978)		Biswas et al. (1977)
Nostoc			Trehan and Sinha (1981)
Pasteurella	Jacob et al. (1977)		Tyeryar and Lawton (1969)
Pseudomonas	Holloway et al. (1979)	Holloway et al. (1979)	Holloway et al. (1979)
Rhizobium	Kondorosi and Johnston (1981)	Kondorosi and Johnston (1981)	Kondorosi and Johnston (1981)
Staphylococcus		Lacey (1975)	Lacey (1975)
Streptococcus	Clewell (1981)	Clewell (1981)	Clewell (1981)
Streptomyces	Hopwood and Merrick (1977)	Lomovskaya et al. (1980)	Hopwood and Merrick (1977)
Vibrio	Jacob et al. (1977)	Wilke and Schlegel (1979)	
Xanthobacter	Wilke (1980)		
Xanthomonas			Corey and Starr (1957)

[a] Other systems of gene transfer are described by Brooks Low and Porter (1978).
[b] Conjugation mediated by Inc P plasmids in various genera is described by Holloway (1979).

other plasmids of the Enterobacteriaceae and the Pseudomonadaceae despite the fact that at the detailed genetic level each is unique (Willetts, 1977; Thomas, 1981; Carrigan and Krishnapillai, 1979). These plasmids all control the formation of a filamentous surface appendage, the sex pilus, that is required for pair formation; they have a special system of replication and transfer of plasmid DNA; and they have a mechanism of "surface exclusion" that reduces conjugal efficiency between bacteria carrying the same plasmid. These features may or may nor apply widely among Gram-negative bacteria but clear differences have already been identified in the conjugation systems of the Gram-positive *Streptomyces* (Hopwood *et al.*, 1973) and *Streptococcus* (Clewell, 1981). Conjugation and experimental procedures for its study are discussed in detail in Chapter 3.

2. Transduction

Transduction is the transfer of bacterial DNA from one cell (the donor) to another (the recipient) by a bacteriophage capsid. It proceeds because the entity involved, the transducing particle, retains the adsorption and DNA-infection mechanisms typical of the normal phage. Once the DNA has entered the recipient cell three pathways are possible: if the DNA is a replicon, for example a plasmid, it can be inherited intact by the recipient; if it is only a fragment of a chromosome or plasmid, stable inheritance of any part of it will require its recombination with DNA already carried by the recipient; if neither of these events occur the DNA can survive for a period without replication, but will eventually be degraded. In this last instance, the functions carried by the DNA can, however, be expressed during the interim period and the altered phenotype of the cells (abortive transductants) observed under special circumstances (Ozeki and Ikeda, 1968). The transductional processes that can give rise to these events fall broadly into two classes termed specialized and generalized transduction.

Specialized transduction occurs when the transducing particle carries the bacterial DNA as an insertion or substitution within the viral genome. The covalent linkage of the phage and bacterial DNAs occurs during the establishment of the prophage state in the donor bacterium. Subsequently, the induction of vegetative phage replication involves the detachment of the prophage from the bacterial DNA by an excision or "looping out" process. If this event is imprecise, bacterial DNA that adjoins the prophage can become part of the excised unit and thence enclosed in the phage capsid during the maturation process. Clearly, only bacterial DNA that occurs in the "special" regions flanking the prophage can be transduced in this way. For λ phage these are usually the *gal* and *bio* regions of the *E. coli* K12 chromosome adjacent to the λ-attachment site (Franklin, 1971). In contrast, generalized transduction appears to be the accidental packaging of bacterial DNA inside a phage capsid — the transducing particles contain only, or almost only, bacterial DNA and any segment of the bacterial genome can be encapsulated (Ozeki and Ikeda, 1968; Schmieger and Buch, 1975). While most transducing phages studied fall clearly into one or other category, the two forms of transduction are not mutually exclusive. This is seen in the ability of the classical transducing phages P22 and P1 to promote specialized transduction in their respective hosts, *Salmonella typhimurium* (Smith-Keary, 1960) and *E. coli* (Luria *et al.*, 1960), and of the specialized transducing λ to promote generalized transduction in *E. coli* under certain conditions (Sternberg and Weisberg, 1975).

Most examples of generalized transduction involve temperate phages that are able to associate with their host bacteria to establish a lysogenic or pseudolysogenic state. This is not, however, an essential requirement, as can be seen from the transductional capabilities of typical virulent phages such as T1 in *E. coli* (Drexler, 1970), SPP1 in *B. subtilis* (Yasbin and Young, 1974), E79 in *P. aeruginosa* (Morgan, 1979) and RL38 in *R. leguminosarum* (Buchanan-Wollaston, 1979), and in the common use of clear plaque mutants of P1 for transduction experiments in *E. coli* K12 (Lennox, 1955). This is not to suggest that all phages have transducing capability. In the first instance, DNA from the donor bacterium must be packaged—be it by an accidental or specific process—to produce the transducing particle. This may not occur or may not be possible in cases where phage infection leads to rapid and extensive degradation of the host DNA (Sadowski and Kerr, 1970). Second, the transducing particle must be able to absorb to the recipient bacterium and inject its DNA without otherwise interfering with cell viability. With some phages, adsorption is sufficient to cause cell death (Duckworth, 1970). Third, the injected DNA must survive the barrier posed by nuclease degradation in the recipient and become established, as previously outlined, to produce stable transductants. Bearing in mind that the phage lysates used for generalized transduction experiments contain only a minority of transducing particles, the conditions used must be such as to prevent excessive killing of potential transductants by lytic growth of the accompanying normal phage particles.

Phages containing double-stranded DNA range in size from 12×10^6 to 480×10^6 daltons and have been detected in a wide variety of bacteria (Reanney and Ackermann, 1981). Those capable of transduction have been detected in a more limited number of genera (Table V) and, with a few exceptions such as PBS1 (170×10^6 daltons) in *B. subtilis*, they have a smaller size range (about 20×10^6 to 70×10^6 daltons). Gene transfer by generalized transduction occurs at a frequency in the range 10^{-5}–10^{-7}, depending on the phage, and has been used to detect plasmid-associated properties, to separate individual plasmids from cells harbouring several different plasmids and to define the range of properties associated with a particular plasmid. Such studies are limited by the fact that the distribution of phages among bacterial species is far from even. Transductional studies may, therefore, be precluded, not only because of the unavailability of documented transducing phages, but also because of a lack of virulent or temperate phages whose transductional capabilities might be tested. In instances where phages are available, their individual host ranges determine the number of bacteria that can serve as recipients. Some phages such as PBS1 in *Bacillus* (Bramucci and Lovett, 1976), pf20 in *Pseudomonas* (Stanisich and Richmond, 1975), P1323mo in *Streptococcus* (Skjold *et al.*, 1979) and RL38 in *Rhizobium* (Buchanan-Wollaston, 1979) can infect or transduce several species. More usually, transduction is confined to the same species but can be extended to a larger number of strains if the effects of restriction can be overcome. Finally, the size of DNA that can be transduced is limited by the DNA capacity of the phage. Plasmids of similar or smaller size than the phage can be transduced intact and give rise to stable transductants. In contrast, larger plasmids are transduced as fragments and will not form stable transductants unless appropriate recipients are used that allow recombinational "rescue" of properties from the DNA (Stanisich *et al.*, 1976). The phenomenon of "transductional shortening" is sometimes observed with large plasmids (Falkow, 1975) and probably represents the packaging of spontaneously arising deleted derivatives of the plasmid that occur at low frequency within the population. Successful and frequent transduction of a plasmid-associated property, therefore, provides an upper limit on the size of the plasmid concerned.

Attempts to transduce a bacterial property will involve propagation of an appropriate generalized transducing phage on the donor or induction of a prophage already carried by it. The former is best carried out by co-cultivation of the phage and bacteria in soft-agar overlays on nutrient medium since this yields higher titres of phage than does propagation in broth. Bacteria (about 10^7 cells) and phage (10^4–10^5 p.f.u.) in about 1 ml are mixed with 2–3 ml of molten (45–48 C) soft agar, which is then poured onto the surface of a dried nutrient agar plate to set as a layer 1–2 mm in thickness. After appropriate incubation, near-confluent lysis of the bacterial lawn should be evident. The layer is scraped off, emulsified in about 5 ml of broth and the mixture then centrifuged to remove debris. The supernatant is then freed of viable bacteria by the addition of 0.1 ml of chloroform or by membrane filtration. Induction of prophage is usually by treatment with u.v.-radiation of wavelength about 260 nm. Growing bacteria are suspended in saline or some other inorganic medium at a density of about 10^8 per millilitre, then irradiated as a thin layer (1–2 mm) in a glass Petri dish. The dose used (between 10 and 100 joules mm^{-2}) will depend on the bacteria but should be sufficient to obtain 10–15% survival. After irradiation, the bacteria are concentrated, transferred to broth and allowed to grow for 1–2 h until lysis occurs. Alternatively, mitomycin C can be added to growing broth cultures (about 10^8 cells per millilitre) at a concentration of 0.5 μg ml^{-1}, then incubation continued in the dark until lysis occurs. In both procedures, residual contaminating bacteria are removed after lysis is completed. Additional details concerning these and other methods of phage propagation are described by Billing (1969), Kay (1972), Meynell and Meynell (1965) and Eisenstark (1966).

The transduction procedure involves mixing the transducing lysate with growing broth cultures of the recipient (about 10^9 cells per millilitre) at the temperature normally used for culture, allowing a period for phage adsorption (about 30 min), then concentrating the bacteria and plating on medium containing the selective agent in order to recover the transductants. If a period of expression seems appropriate for the particular property under study, the bacteria can be reincubated in fresh broth after the centrifugation stage and selection imposed later. A multiplicity of infection of between one to ten is usually used for transduction experiments with temperate phages. This leads to the recovery of lysogenic transductants that have arisen by simultaneous infection of the bacterium with both a transducing and normal phage particle or, more probably, by superinfection of the transduced cell during the course of its growth. When virulent phages are used, infections by normal phage particles must be avoided, since such events will kill the transductants. This is usually achieved by u.v.-irradiating the transducing lysate to reduce plaque-forming ability (i.e. phage viability), using a phage to bacterium ratio of < 1 and removing unadsorbed phage by thorough washing of the bacteria at the concentration stage or treating them with appropriate phage antiserum. An alternative method used for successful transduction by the virulent phage E79tv-1 in $P.$ $aeruginosa$ involved a plasmid-carrying recipient, where the plasmid concerned could interfere with phage propagation but not with either phage adsorption or DNA injection (Morgan, 1979).

The distinction between transduction of a plasmid-associated or chromosomally-associated property can be made in a number of ways: by examining the transductants for the inheritance of a unique species of plasmid DNA, by comparing the transductability of the property to Rec$^+$ and Rec$^-$ bacteria if the latter are available or by studying the effects of u.v.-irradiation of the lysate on the frequency of transduction. The latter approach is based on the observation of Arber (1960) and others (Garen and Zinder, 1955; Benzinger and Hartmen, 1962; Asheshov, 1966) that the transduction frequency of certain properties can be increased up to ten-fold or more by irradiation of the lysate with small doses of u.v., whereas for other properties irradiation causes only a progressive decline in both transduction frequency and plaque-forming ability. The former is characteristic of chromosomal properties and seems to be a result of stimulation of recombination events by irradiation-damaged DNA. The latter is characteristic of plasmid properties whose stable inheritance is not dependent on recombination. Irradiation, therefore, only leads to mutation of the property or of other plasmid functions required for survival in the recipient. This u.v.-inactivation test has been used extensively to identify plasmids in *Staphylococcus* (Lacey, 1975) and should be applicable to other bacteria in which plasmids can be transduced intact.

Two additional observations related to transduction are worthy of note. First, transduction can be used to separate the plasmids from a bacterium carrying several different plasmids, since the transducing particle packages only a single segment of DNA. Although this applies generally, there have been observations of the joint transduction of plasmids arising from a single transduction event (Grubb and O'Reilly, 1971; Stiffler *et al.*, 1974; Iordanescu, 1977; Novick *et al.*, 1981). Such joint transduction could arise from a high-frequency co-integration-type interaction between the plasmids, which is mediated either by a transposable element or some new type of specific interaction (Novick *et al.*, 1981). Packaging of a recombinant molecule could, therefore, occur which subsequently persists stably in the transductants or dissociate into its constituent replicons if the recombination event is a reversible one. Under these circumstances, transduction of a particular property could give rise to the unexpected finding that the transductants are heterogeneous with respect to the number and size of the plasmids that they carry.

The second observation concerns an unusual plasmid transfer system in *S. aureus*. Phages are implicated since transfer requires the presence of calcium ions (presumably for adsorption), a lysogenic donor and a phage-sensitive recipient. Typical transduction is not, however, involved since cell-to-cell contact of the bacteria is essential and no transfer occurs if the recipient is mixed only with culture supernatants of the donor. Indeed, in many instances, such supernatants contain little plaque-forming activity, suggesting that the phage may be cell bound, defective or highly unstable, so that cell apposition is required for adsorption and DNA transfer (Lacey, 1975). Unusual gene transfer processes that similarly appear to involve phage-like particles have been described in *Rhodopseudomonas capsulata* (Saunders, 1978) and *Streptococcus lactis* (McKay *et al.*, 1973; Klaenhammer and McKay, 1976). It would seem, therefore, that transfer experiments involving species in which phages are common should be attempted both by the procedures typically used for transduction and by the mixed-culture method more usually associated with conjugation.

3. Transformation

Transformation is the process by which DNA from one cell (the donor) is taken up by another (the recipient) directly from the surrounding medium.

Table V shows genera in which transformation has been successfully demonstrated. Although "competence" (the ability to be transformed) can arise naturally with some genera (Chapter 4), of much greater value in attempts to use transformation to demonstrate the plasmid association of a particular property are the artificial systems of competence induction. These favour transformation by plasmid rather than by chromosomal DNA and can be applied to bacteria irrespective of their natural transformability.

Confirmation of the plasmid association of a transformed property can be by a comparison of the efficiency of transformation to Rec^+ and Rec^- recipients, or by the identification of a unique plasmid species among the transformants. Bearing in mind that a competent bacterium can take up more than one molecule of DNA, the concentration of DNA used in the experiment should be adjusted to reduce this possibility. Alternatively, species of plasmid DNA can be individually recovered from the transformant and retested in the same bacterium to determine association with the property under study.

Transformation is discussed in detail in Chapter 4.

III. Phenotypic characterization of plasmids

Identification of a plasmid by physical or genetic means is usually accompanied by efforts to define its contribution to cell phenotype and to compare its properties and interactions with those of other plasmids identified in the same or related species. Such studies contribute to a broader understanding of the epidemiology and evolution of these molecules and of their control of many of the unique attributes displayed by bacteria. As far as possible, such genetic characterization should be undertaken by transfer of the plasmid to a bacterial host whose properties are well-defined and which carries no other plasmids. Table II lists the properties that have been found associated with plasmids in various bacteria. Combinations of several of these properties can occur on a single plasmid (Jacob et al., 1977; Jacoby and Shapiro, 1977; Novick et al., 1977; Clewell, 1981) and, in theory, all combinations may occur in natural isolates. In practice, only a limited number of tests are applied to characterize a new plasmid, the choice of these depending on the origin of the plasmid, the ease of the test, whether it is applicable in the host strain and the particular interests of the investigator. In Section III some of the main criteria used in plasmid characterization and classification are discussed.

A. Resistance properties

Plasmids that determine resistance to antibiotics (R-plasmids) are most common in bacteria from clinical and veterinary sources, where exposure to antibiotics is likely to be high (Linton, 1977; Smith, 1977). They also occur at low frequency in bacteria from water and other sources (Sizemore and Colwell, 1977; Gonzal et al., 1979; Talbot et al., 1980) and from healthy individuals living in urban or isolated communities (Falkow, 1975). R-plasmids have been detected in many members of the Enterobacteriaceae and in a variety of other clinically significant bacteria including species of *Bacteroides, Clostridium, Haemophilus, Neisseria, Pseudomonas, Staphylococcus* and *Streptococcus* (Table I for references). The antibiotic resistances conferred by plasmids broadly reflect the agents used against the bacteria in which the plasmids occur. Thus, erythromycin resistance occurs on plasmids from the Gram-positive cocci, *Clostridium* and *Corynebacterium*, whereas resistance to tetracycline and to certain penicillins and aminoglycosides occurs on plasmids from bacteria of either Gram type. Plasmids may also confer resistance to other antimicrobial agents. These include heavy metal ions such as mercury (II) [in *Staphylococcus* and *Pseudomonas* (Summers and Silver, 1978)], various anions such as arsenate, chromate and tellurite [in *Staphylococcus, Streptococcus* and *Pseudomonas*, respectively (Silver et al., 1981; Jacoby, 1979; Clewell, 1981)] and u.v.-radiation [in *Streptococcus, Pseudomonas* and the Enterobacteriaceae (Clewell, 1981; Jacoby and Shapiro, 1977; Jacob et al., 1977)]. The particular resistance properties conferred by a plasmid are of little value as an aid to establishing the relatedness of independent isolates, although in a few instances they may serve as a guide to plasmid type, for example tellurite resistance and u.v.-radiation resistance are common attributes of Inc P2 plasmids in *P. aeruginosa* and Inc N plasmids in *E. coli* K12, respectively.

The characterization of plasmids with respect to these properties generally poses no especial difficulties, and requires only the determination of the minimum inhibitory concentration of the agent against the R^- control and its R^+ derivative. The range of concentrations that are tested will depend on the medium used, the natural level of susceptibility of the R^- strain and whether an attempt is made to induce resistance by growth of the R^+ strain in subinhibitory concentrations of the agent. Most basal nutrient media should be suitable although certain antibiotics, such as the sulphonamides and trimethoprim, should be tested using diagnostic sensitivity testing agar or defined minimal medium, perhaps supplemented with casamino acids (about 1%). The addition of chemicals to test for anion or cation resistance can result in marked changes in the pH of the medium; this should be appropriately adjusted to avoid an inhibition of bacterial growth that could mask the presence of a resistance property. Resistance to u.v.-radiation can be determined by exposing bacteria on nutrient agar to varying doses of u.v.-radiation. This is best achieved by preparing a series of similar plates inoculated with a dilution series of a culture of the bacterium. The individual plates are then exposed to increasingly higher doses of u.v.-radiation (from about 10 to 100 joules mm^{-2}) and, after incubation in the dark, the effect of u.v.-radiation quantitated from the number of colony-forming bacteria.

B. Metabolic properties

Plasmids can confer a wide variety of metabolic properties on their host bacterium. This includes properties that may interfere with the rapid diagnostic identification of certain bacteria; for example plasmid-determined H_2S production (Ørskov and Ørskov, 1973) or utilization of lactose (Guiso and Ullman, 1976), sucrose (Wohlhieter et al., 1975), raffinose (Smith and Parsell, 1975) or citrate (Smith et al., 1978) occurs among members of the Enterobacteriaceae. Other properties are significant in the species designation of bacteria: for example plasmid-determined β-haemolysin production by *Streptococcus zymogenes* (Jacob et al., 1975) and citrate utilization by *Streptococcus diacetylactis* (Kempler and McKay, 1979) accounts for the distinction between these bacteria and *Streptococcus faecalis* and *S. lactis*, respectively. Metabolic versatility enables bacteria to occupy ecological niches not available to those with more stringent nutritional requirements. Many species of *Pseudomonas* can use a wide variety of compounds as sole carbon and energy sources (Stanier et al., 1966) and, in *P. putida* especially, this can be associated with the presence of "degradative" plasmids. Depending on the catabolic pathway encoded by the plasmids, compounds such as toluates, xylenes, naphthalene and salycilate can be degraded via the intermediate catechol, and thence further by plasmid-encoded (meta-cleavage) or chromosomally encoded (ortho-cleavage) pathways (Whellis, 1975; Chakrabarty, 1976; Broda, 1979). Other unusual compounds metabolized via plasmid-encoded pathways include the herbicide 2-methyl-4-chlorophenoxyacetic acid by *Alcaligenes* (Fisher et al., 1978) and opines (α-N-substituted amino acid derivatives) by Agrobacteria carrying Ti plasmids (Dellaporta and Pesano, 1981). In the latter situation the presence of Ti DNA stimulates crown gall tissue of the infected plant to produce one of the three major types of opine (octopine, nopaline or agropine). This is then available as a nutrient source for the bacteria since the Ti plasmid also encodes the pathway required for utilization of the specific opine induced by it. The properties indicated here are all readily tested on the appropriate diagnostic media or on chemically defined media in which the substance to be degraded is provided as the sole carbon source.

An additional plasmid-determined metabolic property is that of antibiotic production. Two groups of substances are involved: these are bacteriocins, which are usually active only against bacteria related to the producer strain, and true antibiotics that are active against diverse microbial genera (Hopwood, 1978). The former occur among members of the Enterobacteriaceae (Hardy, 1975; Tagg *et al.*, 1976), *Streptococcus* (Clewell, 1981), *Staphylococcus* (Warren *et al.*, 1975), *Rhizobium* (Dénarié *et al.*, 1981) and *Bacillus* (Bernhard *et al.*, 1978). Plasmid-determined antibiotic production includes the microcins from *E. coli* and *P. aeruginosa* (Bacquero *et al.*, 1978), methylenomycin A from *Streptomyces coelicolor* (Wright and Hopwood, 1976) and possibly nisin from *Streptococcus lactis* (Kozak *et al.*, 1974; Fuchs *et al.*, 1975). Production of these types of substances can be demonstrated by exposure of a sensitive bacterium to the producer strain or culture supernatants of the producer strain. For example, the producer strain can be grown as single colonies or as a streak on nutrient medium and then overlayed with agar containing the sensitive bacterium. Alternatively, bacteria-free culture supernatants of the producer strain can be spotted onto lawns of the sensitive bacteria. After appropriate incubation, inhibition of growth of the sensitive strain would indicate antibiotic production. In some cases the amount of bacteriocin produced can be increased by induction of the strain with mitomycin C or u.v.-radiation.

C. Pathogenic and symbiotic properties

Various aspects of the host–bacterium relationship are controlled by plasmids. Properties such as bacteriocin production, antibiotic resistance and haemolysin production (Lacey, 1975; de la Cruz *et al.*, 1979; Clewell, 1981) are likely to contribute to the establishment of the organism, its epidemic spread and the severity of the disease caused by it. Other properties are, however, more clearly implicated in the pathogenic state. This is seen in the cases of plasmid-determined glucan production by cariogenic *Streptococcus faecalis* (Oliver *et al.*, 1977), tumour production in plants by *Agrobacterium* (Dellaporta and Pesano, 1981) and toxin production by *E. coli* and *Staphylococcus aureus*. The latter includes the heat-stable and heat-labile enterotoxins produced by *E. coli* that cause diarrhoea (Gyles *et al.*, 1974; So *et al.*, 1979), and the enterotoxin B (Shalita *et al.*, 1977) and exfoliative toxin (Warren *et al.*, 1975) produced by *S. aureus* which cause food poisoning and scalded skin syndrome, respectively. The host specificity and colonization ability of bacteria may also be determined by plasmids. This is seen in the control of host range and nodulation specificity of *Rhizobium* (Dénarié *et al.*, 1981) and *Agrobacterium* (Dellaporta and Pesano, 1981) species, respectively, and in the adhesion of enteropathogenic *E. coli* to the intestinal mucosa brought about by specific colonization antigens that occur on their surface (Bak *et al.*, 1972; Evans and Evans, 1978).

Evaluation of most of the properties indicated here depend on *in vivo* animal or plant tests, or *in vitro* serological or tissue culture tests. Details of these procedures are given in the references cited here and by Cabello and Timmis (1979).

D. Incompatibility and exclusion properties

Certain plasmids are unable to coexist stably in the same cell line, whereas others are able to do so. The former are referred to as incompatible plasmids and where several exhibit this property (i.e. A is incompatible with B, B with C and C with A) they are assigned to the same incompatibility (Inc) group. Incompatibility is an inherent characteristic of all plasmids and can be demonstrated between homologous plasmids when experiments with appropriately marked derivatives are undertaken. It is generally accepted, therefore, that incompatibility between independently isolated heterologous plasmids reflects their similarity or evolutionary relatedness. This view is strengthened by the finding that incompatible plasmids usually share more sequence homology ($>60\%$) than do compatible plasmids ($<15\%$) (Falkow, 1975; Gorai *et al.*, 1979; Shalita *et al.*, 1980; de la Cruz *et al.*, 1980) and, in the case of conjugative plasmids, usually specify similar transfer systems (Willetts and Skurray, 1980; Bradley, 1981). The genetic control of incompatibility is complex and several distinct interactions seem to be involved (Novick and Hoppensteadt, 1978; Lane, 1981; Cowan and Scott, 1981). For the purpose of plasmid characterization, however, it is sufficient that incompatibility provides a feature of distinction that applies both to conjugative and non-conjugative plasmids (Datta, 1979) and to extrachromosomally maintained phages (Matsubara and Otsuji, 1978; Cowan and Scott, 1981). To date, 24 incompatibility groups have been defined in *E. coli* K12 for plasmids from the Enterobacteriaceae (Datta, 1979), 13 in *Staphylococcus aureus* (Iordanescu and Surdeanu, 1980), 10 in *P. aeruginosa* PAO (Jacoby, 1979) and 3 in *Streptococcus faecalis* (Romero *et al.*, 1979).

The incompatibility of two plasmids, A and B, can be determined if each controls a distinctive phenotype that allows its presence to be inferred. A can then be introduced into cells containing B (by conjugation, transduction or transformation) by imposing a selection *only* for A. The progeny so derived are purified two or three times in the presence of the selective agent, then tested for the distinctive property determined by B. If this is absent, displacement is indicated, and the two plasmids are considered to be incompatible. If the polarity of the cross is reversed so that B is transferred to A$^+$ cells, incompatibility should again be observed. This pattern of behaviour, in which a superinfecting plasmid invariably displaces a resident one, is the basis of definition of the Inc groups indicated above. An alternative, and formally more rigorous, test for incompatibility is to establish both plasmids in the same cell (usually a Rec$^-$ strain, to prevent recombination between the plasmids), and then to examine segregation. The cell containing both plasmids is constructed and purified with selection for both plasmids. It is then grown in non-selective conditions and plated to give single colonies. These colonies are then tested for the markers carried by the two plasmids; loss of one set or other of these markers indicates plasmid incompatibility.

Unfortunately, the situation is often less clear-cut than implied above, and many reports of anomalous incompatibility interactions exist. These include unidirectional incompatibility, where plasmid A can displace plasmid B but the two are compatible when B is the superinfecting element; dual incompatibility, where a plasmid is incompatible with members of more than one Inc group and "dislodgement" where low level incompatibility occurs with members of one or several groups (Datta, 1979). The basis of these interactions is not known but they will often prevent the unambiguous assignment of a new plasmid to a defined Inc group. Despite this, the particular interaction observed will be a reproducible property of the plasmid and hence serve to identify it if it is isolated again from independent sources. In those instances where incompatibility is observed in some but not all progeny of the cross, the latter should be repurified several times on non-selective medium and again tested for the distinctive phenotypes. If both are still present, the bacteria may be carrying the plasmids as a compatible pair or as a recombinant that has retained both the phenotypes. These possibilities can be distinguished by a further transfer and linkage analysis study, or by examining the DNA for one or two plasmid species.

The most commonly encountered limitation in incompatibility studies is the similarity of properties determined by the plasmids under study. This can be overcome by the tedious task of isolating specific plasmid mutants following mutagenesis, or screening cultures for spontaneously arising plasmid segregants. Alternatively, plasmids can be "labelled" with appropriate transposons (Finger and Krishnapillai, 1980) or suitable recombinants constructed in other ways. In the latter regard, Iordanescu and Surdeanu (1980) have developed an efficient method of labelling *Staphylococcus aureus* plasmids by co-integrating them with a temperature-sensitive Tc^r plasmid. When these are subsequently used in incompatibility experiments, they displace plasmids homologous or related to the Tc^s component of the co-integrate. Sasakawa *et al.* (1980) have simplified the task of incompatibility testing in *E. coli* K12 by isolating a series of strains each carrying a different plasmid integrated into the chromosome. Eleven Inc groups are represented. Conjugation is used to introduce the test plasmid into a control R^- strain and into the series of R^+ derivatives. Incompatibility is observed as a decreased yield of progeny ($< 10^{-2}$) in matings involving the incompatible plasmid pair. In other situations, where the plasmids under study differ in only a single selective property, incompatibility can be detected by purifying the progeny and directly examining their DNA for the two plasmid species (Palomares and Perea, 1980).

Surface exclusion is a property that is often observed when tests for incompatibility are carried out by conjugation (Chapter 3). The two phenomena are, however, quite distinct. Surface exclusion refers to the decrease in transconjugant yield that occurs when a donor is mated with a plasmid-carrying recipient compared to a plasmidless recipient. In the case of F, exclusion is controlled by several cistrons in the transfer operon that exert their effect by reducing the formation of stable mating aggregates (Willetts and Skurray, 1980). Exclusion of about 400-fold occurs in matings between two F-carrying bacteria and is bidirectional in that each bacterium used as the recipient will exclude the superinfecting plasmid. Since plasmids of the same Inc group often specify similar transfer systems, it is not surprising to find both exclusion and incompatibility when certain heterologous combinations are studied. Unfortunately, there are many examples of exclusion (bidirectional and unidirectional) between compatible plasmids, and of incompatible plasmids that do not exhibit exclusion (Jacob et al., 1977; Jacoby, 1979). Thus, while the observation of exclusion serves to define this characteristic of a plasmid it cannot be used alone to infer the relatedness of the plasmids involved. This may not apply in P. aeruginosa where good correlation was observed when FP plasmids were grouped by their exclusion or incompatibility response (Finger and Krishnapillai, 1980).

Exclusion can interfere with incompatibility testing if it abolishes completely or almost completely the yield of transconjugants. This effect can sometimes be overcome if stationary phase rather than log phase cultures of the recipient are used. If not, the required progeny will have to be obtained by transduction or transformation. Exclusion can also lead to spurious results in instances where the plasmid carried by the recipient is unstable. Any plasmidless segregants arising in the population will have a greater chance of mating with the donor than will their exclusion-proficient sibs. Particularly in instances where the effect of exclusion is strong, even the low frequency occurrence of such segregants can lead to a significant proportion (if not all) of the transconjugants arising from such matings. These progeny will appear to have resulted from displacement of the resident plasmid by the superinfecting one, and hence to the erroneous conclusion that the two plasmids under study are incompatible. Thus, when incompatibility is observed in combination with a strong exclusion effect it should be confirmed by demonstrating that it also occurs if the polarity of the conjugational cross is reversed or if the progeny are constructed by transduction or transformation. (It should be noted that, if incompatibility was tested by first establishing both plasmids in the same cell and then examining segregation, exclusion will not present a problem.)

Incompatibility testing is used to characterize a plasmid relative to others already defined in a particular host. The property could also be used to demonstrate the presence of a plasmid in a natural isolate by observing the loss of a phenotype associated with the displacement event. This approach has not been widely used because a successful outcome is limited by the large number of Inc groups that occurs. It may, however, be valuable in instances where screening for a particular plasmid type is being undertaken or where only one or a few plasmid types are indicated by the particular phenotype expressed by the bacterium.

E. Interactions with phages

Conjugative plasmids carried by Gram-negative bacteria determine a filamentous surface appendage, the sex pilus. The pili determined by plasmids of a particular Inc group are serologically related and usually distinguishable from those of other groups (Bradley, 1980). These differences in structure and morphology are also reflected in the adsorptional specificity of certain phages, which are termed sex-specific or donor-specific, and whose receptors occur on the sex pili. Such phages can, therefore, be used as a primary means of detecting a plasmid that encodes a sex pilus in a wild-type isolate, or of establishing the incompatibility type of such a newly identified plasmid. Sex pilus-specific phages and procedures for their use are described in Chapter 3.

Plasmids may also interfere with phage propagation. This phenomenon has been described in many bacteria, and a variety of mechanisms has been implicated (Duckworth et al., 1981). These include plasmid-mediated restriction/modification (Bannister and Glover, 1968), effects on phage transcription (Moyer et al., 1972) or translation (Blumberg et al., 1976), or more general effects on cell functions (Britton and Haselkorn, 1975; Condit, 1976). In *P. aeruginosa* PAO, such plasmid–phage interactions have been used as an effective guide to plasmid classification (Jacoby, 1979).

Acknowledgements

I am grateful to Jillian Bennett for assistance with the manuscript and to Oriella Lonni for preparation of the typescript. Research in the author's laboratory is supported by the Australian Research Grants Scheme.

References

Achtman, M. and Skurray, R. (1977). *In* "Microbial Interactions, Receptors and Recognition" (J. L. Reissig, Ed.), Series B, Vol. 3, pp. 233–279. Chapman & Hall, London.

Arber, W. (1960). *Virology* **11**, 273–288.
Asheshov, E. H. (1966). *Nature (London)* **210**, 804–806.
Bacquero, F., Bouanchaud, D., Martinez-Perez, M. C. and Fernandez, C. (1978). *J. Bacteriol.* **135**, 342–347.
Bak, A. L., Christiansen, G., Christiansen, C., Stenderup, A. and Ørskov, F. (1972). *J. Gen. Microbiol.* **73**, 373–385.
Bannister, D. and Glover, S. W. (1968). *Biochem. Biophys. Res. Commun.* **30**, 735–738.
Benzinger, R. and Hartman, P. E. (1962). *Virology* **18**, 614–626.
Beretta, M., Betti, M. and Polsinelli, M. (1971). *J. Bacteriol.* **107**, 415–419.
Billing, E. (1969). In "Methods in Microbiology" (J. R. Norris and D. W. Ribbons, Eds), Vol. 3B, pp. 315–329. Academic Press, London.
Biswas, G. D., Sox, T. and Sparling, P. F. (1977). *J. Bacteriol.* **129**, 983–992.
Blumberg, D. D., Mabie, C. T. and Malamy, M. H. (1976). *J. Virol.* **17**, 94–105.
Bouanchaud, D. H., Scavizzi, M. R. and Chabbert, Y. A. (1969). *J. Gen. Microbiol.* **54**, 417–425.
Bøvre, K. and Frøhlm, L. O. (1972). *Acta Pathol. Microbiol. Scand. Sect. B* **80**, 649–659.
Bradley, D. E. (1980). *Plasmid* **4**, 155–169.
Bradley, D. E. (1981). In "Molecular Biology, Pathogenicity and Ecology of Bacterial Plasmids" (S. B. Levey, R. C. Clowes and E. L. Koenig, Eds), pp. 217–226. Plenum, New York.
Bramucci, M. G. and Lovett, P. S. (1976). *J. Bacteriol.* **127**, 829–831.
Britton and Haselkorn (1975). *Proc. Natl. Acad. Sci. U.S.A.* **72**, 2222–2226.
Broda, P. (1979). "Plasmids". Freeman, San Francisco, California.
Brooks Low, K. and Porter, D. D. (1978). *Annu. Rev. Genet.* **12**, 249–287.
Buchanan-Wollaston, V. (1979). *J. Gen. Microbiol.* **112**, 135–142.
Cabello, F. and Timmis, K. N. (1979). In "Plasmids of Medical, Environmental and Commercial Importance" (K. N. Timmis and A. Pühler, Eds), pp. 55–69. Elsevier, Amsterdam.
Carrigan, J. M. and Krishnapillai, V. (1979). *J. Bacteriol.* **140**, 809–816.
Chakrabarty, A. M. (1972). *J. Bacteriol.* **112**, 815–823.
Chakrabarty, A. M. (1976). *Annu. Rev. Genet.* **10**, 7–30.
Chater, K. F. (1979). In "Genetics of Industrial Microorganisms" (O. K. Sebek and A. I. Laskin, Eds), pp. 123–133. American Society for Microbiology, Washington D.C.
Chatterjee, A. M., Behrens, M. K. and Starr, M. P. (1979). *Proc. Int. Conf. Plant Pathol. Bacteriol.* **4**, 75–79.
Clewell, D. B. (1981). *Microbiol. Rev.* **45**, 409–436.
Clowes, R. C., Moody, E. E. M. and Pritchard, R. H. (1965). *Genet. Res.* **6**, 147–152.
Condit, R. (1976). *Nature (London)* **260**, 287–288.
Coplin, D. L., Rowan, R. G., Chisholm, D. A. and Whitmoyer, R. E. (1981). *Appl. Environ. Microbiol.* **42**, 599–604.
Corey, R. R. and Starr, M. P. (1957). *J. Bacteriol.* **74**, 146–150.
Costa, M. L. P., Penido, E. and Costa, S. O. P. (1980). *J. Gen. Microbiol.* **118**, 543–547.
Cowan, J. A. and Scott, J. R. (1981). *Plasmid* **6**, 202–222.
Datta, N. (1979). In "Plasmids of Medical, Environmental and Commercial Importance" (K. N. Timmis and A. Pühler, Eds), pp. 3–12. Elsevier, Amsterdam.
Davey, R. B. and Reanney, D. C. (1980). In "Evolutionary Biology" (M. K. Hecht, W. C. Steere and B. Wallace, Eds), Vol. 13, pp. 113–147. Plenum, New York.
De la Cruz, F., Zabala, J. C. and Ortiz, J. M. (1979). *Plasmid* **2**, 507–519.

De la Cruz, F., Zabala, J. C. and Ortiz, J. M. (1980). *Plasmid* **4**, 76–81.
Dellaporta, S. I. and Pesano, R. I. (1981). *In* "Biology of the Rhizobiaceae" (K. L. Giles and A. G. Atherly, Eds), pp. 83–104. *Int. Rev. Cytol.* Suppl. 13.
Dénarié, J., Boistard, P. and Casse-Delbert, F. (1981). *In* "Biology of the Rhizobiaceae" (K. L. Giles and A. G. Atherly, Eds), pp. 225–246. *Int. Rev. Cytol.* Suppl. 13.
Drexler, H. (1970). *Proc. Natl. Acad. Sci. U.S.A.* **66**, 1083–1088.
Duckworth, D. H. (1970). *Bacteriol. Rev.* **34**, 344–363.
Duckworth, D. H., Glenn, J. and McCorquodale, D. J. (1981). *Microbiol. Rev.* **45**, 52–71.
Eberhard, M. D., Vasquez, C., Valenzuela, P., Vicuna, R. and Yudelevich, A. (1981). *Plasmid* **6**, 1–6.
Eisenstark, A. (1966). *In* "Methods in Virology" (K. Maramorosch and H. Koprowski, Eds), pp. 449–524. Academic Press, New York and London.
Evans, D. G. and Evans, D. J. (1978). *Infect. Immun.* **21**, 638–647.
Falkow, S. (1975). "Infectious Multiple Drug Resistance". Pion, London.
Finger, J. and Krishnapillai, V. (1980). *Plasmid* **3**, 332–342.
Fisher, P. R., Appleton, J. and Pemberton, J. M. (1978). *J. Bacteriol.* **135**, 798–804.
Franklin, N. C. (1971). *In* "The Bacteriophage Lambda" (A. D. Hershey, Ed.), pp. 175–194. Cold Spring Harbor Laboratory, New York.
Fuchs, P. G., Zajdel, J. and Dobrzanski, W. T. (1975). *J. Gen. Microbiol.* **88**, 189–192.
Garen, A. and Zinder, N. (1955). *Virology* **1**, 347–376.
Gelbart, S. M. and Juhasz, S. E. (1973). *Antonie van Leeuwenhoek; J. Microbiol. Serol.* **39**, 1–10.
Gonzal, S. M., Gerba, C. P. and Melnick, J. L. (1979). *Water Res.* **13**, 349–356.
Gorai, A. P., Heffron, F., Falkow, S., Hedges, R. W. and Datta, N. (1979). *Plasmid* **2**, 485–492.
Grubb, W. B. and O'Reilly, R. J. (1971). *Biochem. Biophys. Res. Commun.* **42**, 377–383.
Guiso, N. and Ullman, A. (1976). *J. Bacteriol.* **127**, 691–697.
Gyles, C., So, M. and Falkow, S. (1974). *J. Infect. Dis.* **130**, 40–49.
Hahn, F. E. and Ciak, J. (1971). *Ann. N.Y. Acad. Sci.* **182**, 295–304.
Hansen, J. B. and Olsen, R. H. (1978). *J. Bacteriol.* **135**, 227–238.
Hardy, K. G. (1975). *Bacteriol. Rev.* **39**, 464–515.
Herman, J. J. and Juni, E. (1974). *J. Virol.* **13**, 46–52.
Hinchliffe, E., Nugent, M. E. and Vivian, A. (1980). *J. Gen. Microbiol.* **121**, 411–418.
Hirai, K. and Yanagawa, R. (1970). *J. Bacteriol.* **101**, 1086–1087.
Hirota, Y. (1956). *Nature (London)* **178**, 92.
Hirota, Y. (1960). *Proc. Natl. Acad. Sci. U.S.A.* **46**, 57–64.
Hofer, F. (1977). *FEMS Microbiol. Lett.* **1**, 167–170.
Holloway, B. W., Krishnapillai, V. and Morgan, A. F. (1979). *Microbiol. Rev.* **43**, 73–102.
Hopwood, D. A. (1978). *Annu. Rev. Microbiol.* **32**, 373–392.
Hopwood, D. A. (1981). *Annu. Rev. Microbiol.* **35**, 237–272.
Hopwood, D. A. and Merrick, J. M. (1977). *Bacteriol. Rev.* **41**, 595–635.
Hopwood, D. A., Chater, K. F., Dowding, J. E. and Vivian, A. (1973). *Bacteriol. Rev.* **37**, 371–405.
Ikeda, Y., Iijima, T. and Tajima, K. (1967). *J. Gen. Appl. Microbiol.* **13**, 247–254.
Iordanescu, S. (1977). *J. Bacteriol.* **129**, 71–75.
Iordanescu, S. and Surdeanu, M. (1980). *Plasmid* **4**, 256–260.
Ishiguro, N., Oka, C. and Sato, G. (1978). *Appl. Environ. Microbiol.* **36**, 217–222.

Jacob, A. E., Douglas, G. J. and Hobbs, S. J. (1975). *J. Bacteriol.* **121**, 863–872.
Jacob, A. E., Shapiro, J. A., Yamamoto, L., Smith, D. I., Cohen, S. N. and Berg, D. (1977). *In* "DNA Insertion Elements, Plasmids and Episomes" (A. I. Bukhari, J. A. Shapiro and S. Adhya, Eds), pp. 607–638. Cold Spring Harbor Laboratory, New York.
Jacoby, G. A. (1979). *In* "*Pseudomonas aeruginosa*: Clinical Manifestation of Infections of Current Therapy" (R. G. Dogget, Ed.) pp. 271–309. Academic Press, New York and London.
Jacoby, G. A. and Shapiro, J. A. (1977). *In* "DNA Insertion Elements, Plasmids and Episomes" (A. I. Bukhari, J. A. Shapiro and S. Adhya, Eds), pp. 639–656. Cold Spring Harbor Laboratory, New York.
Johnston, J. H. and Richmond, M. H. (1970). *J. Gen. Microbiol.* **60**, 137–139.
Juni, E. and Janik, A. (1969). *J. Bacteriol.* **98**, 281–288.
Kado, C. I. and Liu, S-T. (1981). *J. Bacteriol.* **145**, 1365–1373.
Kaiser, D. and Manoil, C. (1979). *Annu. Rev. Microbiol.* **33**, 595–639.
Kay, D. (1972). *In* "Methods in Microbiology" (J. R. Norris and D. W. Ribbons, Eds), Vol. 7A, pp. 191–313. Academic Press, London.
Kaulfers, P. M., Laufs, R. and Jahn, G. (1978). *J. Gen. Microbiol.* **105**, 243–252.
Kempler, G. M. and McKay, L. L. (1979). *Appl. Environ. Microbiol.* **37**, 316–323.
Klaenhammer, T. R. and McKay, L. L. (1976). *J. Dairy Sci.* **59**, 396–404.
Klein, D. T. and Klein, R. M. (1956). *J. Bacteriol.* **72**, 308–313.
Kozak, W., Rajchert-Trzpil, M. and Dobrzanski, W. T. (1974). *J. Gen. Microbiol.* **83**, 295–302.
Kondorosi, A. and Johnston, A. W. B. (1981). *In* "Biology of the Rhizobiaceae" (K. L. Giles and A. G. Atherly, Eds), pp. 191–223. *Int. Rev. Cytol.* Suppl. 13.
Lacey, R. W. (1975). *Bacteriol. Rev.* **39**, 1–32.
Lane, H. E. D. (1981). *Plasmid* **5**, 110–126.
Le Hagarat, J. C. and Anaguostopoulous, C. (1977). *Molec. Gen. Genet.* **157**, 167–174.
Lennox, E. S. (1955). *Virology* **1**, 190–206.
Linton, A. H. (1977). *In* "Antibiotics and Antibiosis in Agriculture" (M. Woodbine, Ed.), pp. 315–343. Butterworths, London.
Lomovskaya, N. D., Chater, K. F. and Mkrtumian, N. M. (1980). *Microbiol. Rev.* **44**, 206–229.
Luria, S. E., Adams, J. N. and Ting, R. C. (1960). *Virology* **12**, 348–390.
McHugh, G. L. and Swartz, M. N. (1977). *Antimicrob. Agents Chemother.* **12**, 423–426.
McKay, L. L., Cords, B. R. and Baldwin, K. A. (1973). *J. Bacteriol.* **115**, 801–815.
Matsubara, K. and Otsuji, Y. (1978). *Plasmid* **1**, 284–296.
May, J. W., Houghton, R. H. and Perret, C. J. (1964). *J. Gen. Microbiol.* **37**, 157–169.
Meynell, G. G. (1972). "Bacterial Plasmids". Macmillan, London and New York.
Meynell, G. G. and Meynell, E. (1965). "Theory and Practice in Experimental Bacteriology". Cambridge Univ. Press, London and New York.
Mitsuhashi, S., Harada, K. and Kameda, M. (1961). *Nature (London)* **189**, 947.
Mizuguchi, Y., Fukunaga, M. and Taniguchi, H. (1981). *J. Bacteriol.* **146**, 656–659.
Molnar, J., Beladi, I. and Hollanb, I. B. (1978). *Genet. Res.* **31**, 197–201.
Morgan, A. F. (1979). *J. Bacteriol.* **139**, 137–140.
Moyer, R. W., Fu, A. S. and Szabo, C. (1972). *J. Virol.* **9**, 804–812.
Novick, R. P. and Hoppensteadt, F. C. (1978). *Plasmid* **1**, 421–434.
Novick, R. P., Cohen, S., Yamamoto, L. and Shapiro, J. A. (1977). *In* "DNA Insertion Elements, Plasmids and Episomes" (A. I. Bukhari, J. A. Shapiro and S. Adhya, Eds), pp. 657–662. Cold Spring Harbor Laboratory, New York.

Novick, R. P., Sanchez-Rivas, C., Gruss, A. and Edelman, I. (1980). *Plasmid* **3**, 348–358.

Novick, R. P., Iordanescu, S., Surdeanu, M. and Edelman, I. (1981). *Plasmid* **6**, 159–172.

O'Connor, M., Wopat, A. and Hanson, R. S. (1977). *J. Gen. Microbiol.* **98**, 265–272.

Oliver, D. R., Brown, B. L. and Clewell, D. B. (1977). *J. Bacteriol.* **130**, 759–765.

Ørskov, I. and Ørskov, F. (1973). *J. Gen. Microbiol.* **77**, 487–499.

Ozeki, H. and Ikeda, H. (1968). *Annu. Rev. Genet.* **2**, 245–278.

Page, W. J. and Sadoff, H. L. (1976). *J. Bacteriol.* **125**, 1080–1087.

Palomares, J. C. and Perea, E. J. (1980). *Plasmid* **4**, 352–353.

Poindexter, S. J. (1981). *Microbiol. Rev.* **45**, 123–179.

Privitera, G., Sebald, M. and Fayolle, F. (1979). *Nature (London)* **278**, 657–659.

Raj, C. V. S. and Ramakrishnan, T. (1970). *Nature (London)* **228**, 280–281.

Razin, S. (1978). *Microbiol. Rev.* **42**, 414–470.

Reanney, D. C. and Ackermann, H-W. (1981). *Intervirology* **15**, 190–197.

Reaston, J., Van Den Hondel., C. A. M. J. J., Van Arkel, G. A. and Stewart, W. D. P. (1982). *Plasmid* **7**, 101–104.

Romero, E., Perduca, M. and Pagani, L. (1979). *Microbiologica* **2**, 421–424.

Rood, J. I., Scott, V. N. and Duncan, C. L. (1978). *Plasmid* **1**, 563–570.

Sadowski, P. D. and Kerr, C. (1970). *J. Virol.* **6**, 149–155.

Sasakawa, C., Takamatsu, N., Danbara, H. and Yoshikawa, M. (1980). *Plasmid* **3**, 116–127.

Saunders, V. A. (1978). *Microbiol. Rev.* **42**, 357–384.

Schiller, J., Groman, N. and Coyle, M. (1980). *Antimicrob. Agents Chemother.* **18**, 814–821.

Schmieger, H. and Buch, U. (1975). *Mol. Gen. Genet.* **140**, 111–122.

Schmitt-Slomska, J., Caravano, R. and El-Solh, N. (1979). *Ann. Microbiol. (Paris)* **130A**, 23–27.

Shalita, Z., Hertman, I. and Sarid, S. (1977). *J. Bacteriol.* **129**, 317–325.

Shalita, Z., Murphy, E. and Novick, R. P. (1980). *Plasmid* **3**, 291–311.

Silver, R. P., Leming, B., Garon, C. F. and Hjerpe, C. A. (1979). *Plasmid* **2**, 493–497.

Silver, S., Budd, K., Leahy, K. M., Shaw, W. V., Hammond, D., Novick, R. P., Willsky, G. R., Malamy, M. H. and Rosenberg, H. (1981). *J. Bacteriol.* **146**, 983–996.

Sizemore, R. K. and Colwell, R. R. (1977). *Antimicrob. Agents Chemother.* **12**, 373–382.

Skjold, S. A., Malke, H. and Wannamaker, L. K. (1979). *In* "Pathogenic Streptococci" (M. T. Parker, Ed.), pp. 274–275. Reedbooks, Chertsey.

Smith, H. W. (1977). *In* "Antibiotics and Antibiosis in Agriculture" (M. Woodbine, Ed.), pp. 344–357. Butterworths, London.

Smith, H. O., Danner, D. B. and Deich, R. A. (1981). *Annu. Rev. Biochem.* **50**, 41–68.

Smith, H. W. and Parsell, Z. (1975). *J. Gen. Microbiol.* **87**, 129–140.

Smith, H. W., Parsell, Z. and Green, P. (1978). *J. Gen. Microbiol.* **109**, 305–311.

Smith-Keary, P. F. (1960). *Heredity* **14**, 61–71.

So, M., Heffron, F. and McCarthy, B. J. (1979). *Nature (London)* **277**, 453–456.

Sox, T. E., Mohammed, W., Blackman, E., Biswas, G. and Sparling, P. F. (1978). *J. Bacteriol.* **134**, 278–286.

Stanier, R. Y., Palleroni, N. J. and Doudoroff, M. (1966). *J. Gen. Microbiol.* **43**, 159–273.

Stanisich, V. A. (1982). *In* "Microbial Physiology and Genetics of Industrial

Processes" (N. F. Millis and A. J. Pittard, Eds), pp. 169–211. Ivory City Press, Melbourne, Australia (in press).

Stanisich, V. A. and Richmond, M. H. (1975). *In* "Genetics and Biochemistry of *Pseudomonas*" (P. H. Clarke and M. H. Richmond, Eds), pp. 163–190. Wiley, London.

Stanisich, V. A., Bennett, P. M. and Ortiz, J. M. (1976). *Mol. Gen. Genet.* **143**, 333–337.

Starlinger, P. (1977). *Annu. Rev. Genet.* **11**, 103–126.

Sternberg, N. and Weisberg, R. (1975). *Nature (London)* **256**, 97–103.

Stiffler, P. W., Sweeney, H. M. and Cohen, S. (1974). *J. Bacteriol.* **120**, 934–944.

Summers, A. O. and Silver, S. (1978). *Annu. Rev. Microbiol.* **32**, 637–672.

Tagg, J. R., Dajani, A. S. and Wannamaker, L. W. (1976). *Bacteriol. Rev.* **40**, 722–756.

Talbot, H. W., Yamamoto, D. K., Smith, M. W. and Seidler, R. J. (1980). *Appl. Environ. Microbiol.* **39**, 97–104.

Taylor, D. E. and Summers, A. O. (1979). *J. Bacteriol.* **137**, 1430–1433.

Taylor, D. E., De Grandis, S. A., Karmali, M. A. and Fleming, P. C. (1981). *Antimicrob. Agents Chemother.* **19**, 831–835.

Thomas, C. M. (1981). *Plasmid* **5**, 10–19.

Tirgari, S. and Moseley, B. E. B. (1980). *J. Gen. Microbiol.* **119**, 287–296.

Tomoeda, M., Inuzuka, M., Kubo, N. and Nakamura, S. (1968). *J. Bacteriol.* **95**, 1078–1089.

Tomoeda, M., Kokubu, M., Nabata, H. and Minamikawa, S. (1970). *J. Bacteriol.* **104**, 864–870.

Trehan, K. and Sinha, U. (1981). *J. Gen. Microbiol.* **124**, 349–352.

Tyeryar, F. J. and Lawton, W. D. (1969). *J. Bacteriol.* **110**, 1112–1113.

van den Hondel, C. A. M. J. J., Keegstra, W., Borrias, W. E. and Van Arkel, G. A. (1979). *Plasmid* **2**, 323–333.

Warren, R., Rogolsky, M., Wiley, B. B. and Glasgow, L. A. (1975). *J. Bacteriol.* **122**, 99–105.

Weidinger, G., Klotz, G. and Goebel, W. (1979). *Plasmid* **2**, 377–386.

Whellis, M. L. (1975). *Annu. Rev. Microbiol.* **29**, 505–524.

Wilke, D. (1980). *J. Gen. Microbiol.* **117**, 431–436.

Wilke, D. and Schlegel, H. G. (1979). *J. Gen. Microbiol.* **115**, 403–410.

Willetts, N. S. (1967). *Biochem. Biophys. Res. Commun.* **27**, 112–117.

Willetts, N. S. (1977). *In* "R-factor: Drug Resistance Plasmid" (S. Mitsuhashi, Ed.), pp. 87–107. University of Tokyo Press, Tokyo.

Willetts, N. S. and Skurray, R. (1980). *Annu. Rev. Genet.* **14**, 41–76.

Williams, S. E. and Bainbridge, B. W. (1971). *J. Appl. Bacteriol.* **34**, 683–687.

Wohlhieter, J. A., Lazere, J. R., Snellings, N. J., Johnson, E. M., Synenki, R. M. and Baron, L. (1975). *J. Bacteriol.* **122**, 401–406.

Wright, L. F. and Hopwood, D. A. (1976). *J. Gen. Microbiol.* **95**, 96–106.

Yasbin, R. E. and Young, F. E. (1974). *J. Virol.* **14**, 1343–1348.

Yoshikawa, M. and Sevag, M. G. (1967). *J. Bacteriol.* **93**, 245–253.

3

Conjugation

N. WILLETTS*

Department of Molecular Biology, University of Edinburgh, Edinburgh, Scotland

*Present address: Biotechnology Australia Pty. Ltd., P.O. Box 20, Roseville, NSW 2069, Australia.

METHODS IN MICROBIOLOGY
VOLUME 17   ISBN 0-12-521517-7

I. General introduction

Conjugation is the process whereby DNA is transferred from one bacterial cell to another by a mechanism that requires cell-to-cell contact. Requirement for the physical presence of the donor organism, together with insensitivity to deoxyribonuclease (DNAase), allow conjugation to be readily distinguished from transduction or transformation. Conjugation is determined almost invariably by plasmids and not by bacterial chromosomes, and gives the subset of gene types usually located on plasmids an evolutionary advantage. Firstly, since conjugation is essentially a replication process, it allows plasmids to replicate more frequently than chromosomal genes, and secondly, it enables them to transfer to alternative bacterial hosts. It is therefore not surprising that a large proportion of plasmids of various types, isolated from many different bacterial genera, are conjugative. Even small naturally occurring non-conjugative plasmids frequently possess an origin of conjugal transfer (oriT) and "mobilization" genes that allow them to utilize the conjugation system of a coexisting conjugative plasmid. The only major exceptions are the many staphylococcal plasmids, since conjugation by these has not so far been demonstrated (Lacey, 1975).

The specification of a conjugation system requires a relatively large amount of DNA, and typically takes up about one-third of the plasmid genome (Fig. 1). In the case of the plasmid F this is equivalent to 33 kilobases (kb), and this large input of genetic information can perhaps be correlated with the efficiency of conjugal transfer which can be 100%, even in short-term matings. Genetic analysis of conjugation by F (briefly described in Section VIII) shows that 25 or more genes are involved. Both for F, and for other plasmids where more rudimentary investigations have been carried out, conjugation can be divided on both physiological and genetic bases into two parts: the recognition of recipient cells by donor cells that leads to mating pair formation, and the subsequent physical transfer of plasmid DNA (Fig. 2). In addition, plasmids usually specify a surface (or entry) exclusion system that prevents the unproductive transfer of the plasmid to a cell that already possesses a copy.

Despite these overall similarities, numerous genetically distinct and non-interacting conjugation systems have been identified. Plasmids can therefore be classified on this basis, and there is a notable correlation between the incompatibility group (Chapter 2) and conjugation group: plasmids with a given conjugation system usually belong to a single incompatibility group, or to a small number of such groups (e.g. the IncFI, IncFII, etc. complex). This relationship probably indicates co-evolution of incompatibility and conjugation systems, since these function entirely independently of each other.

II. The conjugation pilus

Conjugative plasmids from Gram-negative (but not Gram-positive, Section VII) bacteria synthesize an extracellular organelle called a pilus that is essential for recognition of recipient cells and formation of mating pairs with them. In addition, pili provide the sites for adsorption of certain bacteriophages, which can therefore be described as plasmid- or pilus-specific (Fig. 3). Since pili, and the pilus-specific phages to which they are sensitive, vary between different conjugation systems, determination of precisely which of these phages will infect a plasmid-containing cell provides a relatively simple method for the preliminary identification of the conjugation system (Table I).

Pili can also be differentiated by their morphology as visualized under the electron microscope, and the three major morphological groups (Fig. 4) can be further subdivided by serological comparisons (Bradley, 1980); however, these techniques are beyond the scope of this chapter.

TABLE I
Pilus types and pilus-specific phages[a]

Plasmid Inc group	Representative plasmid	Pilus type	Ratio of plate to broth transfer frequencies	Phages[b] Isometric RNA	Filamentous single-stranded DNA	Double-stranded DNA[c]
IncI complex	R64-11	Thin flexible	0.9	φIα	If1	—
IncF complex	R100-1	Thick flexible	0.7	f2	f1	—
—	EDP208	Thick flexible	0.9	UA6	f1	—
J[c]	R391	Thick flexible	0.9	—	—	φJ[d,e]
C[c]	RA1	Thick flexible	45	φC-1	φC-2	φJ
P-9	TOL	Thick flexible	18	—	—	PR4[c]
T	Rts1	Thick flexible	260	φt	—	—
X	R6K	Thick flexible	250	—	φX[f]	—
N	N3	Rigid	1×10^4	—	Ike,(φX)	PR4
P	RP1	Rigid	2×10^3	PRR1	Pf3	PR4
P-10	R91-5	Rigid	47	—	—	PR4
W	Sa	Rigid	4×10^4	—	(φX)	PR4

[a] Data are taken from Bradley (1981) and D. E. Bradley (personal communication).

[b] Other related phages are as follows: If1, If2; f2, R17, M12, MS2, Qβ; f1, fd, M13; UA6, φF$_0$lac; PR4, PRD1. Parentheses indicate that a positive titre-increase, but not spot test, was obtained.

[c] The pili of IncJ and IncC plasmids are serologically related: other pili in table I are not.

[d] φJ also infects cells carrying IncD plasmids, and φX infects cells carrying IncM and IncU plasmids.

[e] φJ is similar in morphology to T3, whereas PR4 is a lipid-containing phage with head and tail structures.

[f] φX is unrelated to φX174.

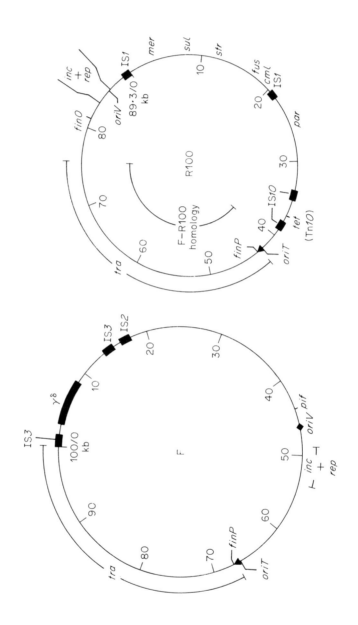

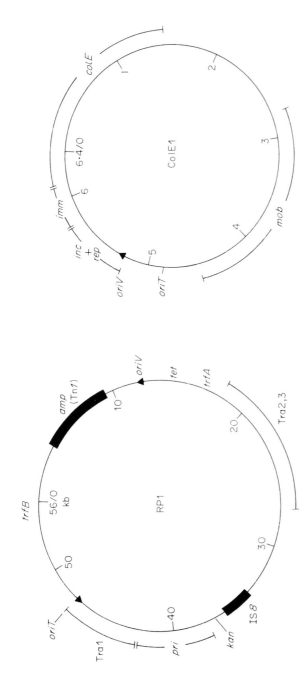

Fig. 1. Genetic and physical maps of four plasmids. Kilobase coordinates are shown inside the circles, and genetic markers and insertion sequences outside. Genetic nomenclature is as follows: *inc*, incompatibility; *rep*, replication; *tra* and Tra, transfer region; *finO*, fertility inhibition; *pif*, phage inhibition; resistances to mercuric ions (*mer*), sulphonamides (*sul*), streptomycin (*str*), fusidic acid (*fus*), chloramphenicol (*cml*), tetracycline (*tet*), ampicillin (*amp*), kanamycin (*kan*); *pri*, DNA primase; *trfA,B* replication functions; *colE*, colicin E; *imm*, immunity to colicin E; *mob*, mobilization; *oriT*, origin of transfer replication; *oriV*, origin of plasmid replication.

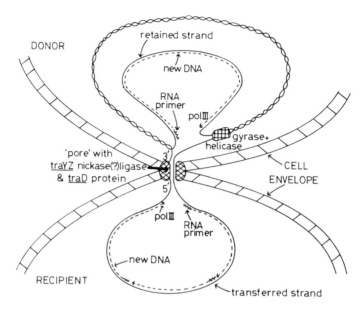

Fig. 2. A model for DNA transfer during conjugation (from Willetts, 1981, with permission).

A. Preparation of phage lysates

Add about 10^6 plaque-forming units (p.f.u.) and 0.1 ml of an overnight L broth (10 g Difco tryptone, 5 g yeast extract, 10 g NaCl per litre, pH 6.8) culture of a sensitive bacterial strain to 2.5 ml molten (46°C) LC top agar (L broth plus 7 g per litre of Difco agar plus 5 mM $CaCl_2$, which is necessary for infection by these phages), and pour onto a nutrient plate. Incubate at 37°C overnight. Scrape off the top agar layer, and emulsify with 5 ml of broth. Centrifuge, remove the supernatant and sterilize this by adding a few drops of chloroform or by membrane filtration. The latter technique must be used for lipid-containing phages, such as PR4, and for filamentous single-strand DNA phages. Phage lysates for IncP-specific RNA phages (e.g. PRR1) or filamentous phages (e.g. Pf3) are best grown in *Pseudomonas aeruginosa* rather than *Escherichia coli.*

B. Titring the lysates

Mix 0.1-ml aliquots of appropriate dilutions in phage dilution buffer (3 g KH_2PO_4, 7 g Na_2HPO_4, 5 g NaCl per litre, plus 1 mM $MgSO_4$, 0.1 mM $CaCl_2$, 0.001% gelatin) and 0.1 ml of an overnight L broth culture of the host strain

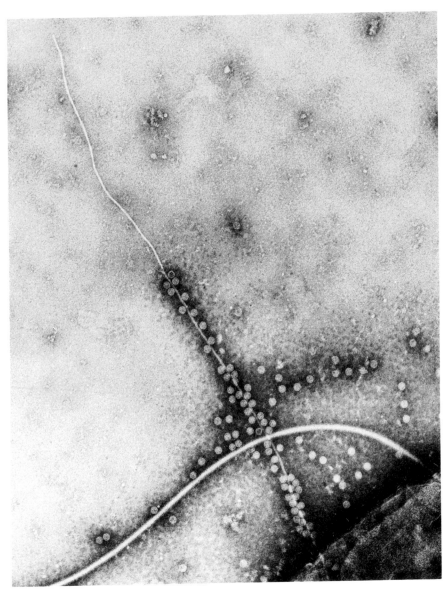

Fig. 3. Adsorption of F-specific phages MS2 and f1 to the sides and tip of an F pilus on an *Escherichia coli* K12 cell. The thicker organelle is a flagellum (courtesy of E. Boy de la Tour and L. Caro, previously published by Broda, 1979).

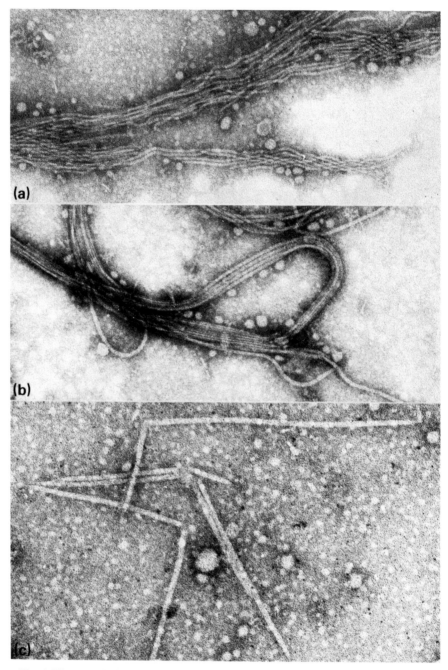

Fig. 4. Pilus morphology (magnification × 140 000). The three panels illustrate (a) thin flexible (of R64-11; 6 nm diameter), (b) thick flexible (of the unclassified plasmid pIN32; 9 nm diameter) and (c) rigid (of N3; 9.5 nm diameter, though rigid pili vary from 8 to 12 nm depending upon the plasmid) pili (courtesy of D. E. Bradley).

with 2.5 ml of molten LC top agar and pour onto a nutrient plate. After overnight incubation, count the plaques.

C. Sensitivity by spot test

This is the simplest qualitative test for phage sensitivity. Add 0.1 ml of an overnight culture of the bacterial strain to 2.5 ml of molten LC top agar and pour onto a nutrient plate. After the top agar has set, mark the bottom of the plate and place 10 μl spots of the phage lysates, diluted to 10^5-10^6 p.f.u. per millilitre, on the surface. Four to eight spots can be accommodated on a single plate. Let the spots dry in, and then incubate the plate at 37 C overnight. Record the turbidity of the spot with respect to a control (a standard plasmid-containing phage-sensitive bacterial host), as this can give some idea of the level of sensitivity. It is also wise to include a plasmid-free strain as a negative control.

It should be noted that apparently unrelated plasmids in the same cell can sometimes inhibit pilus formation and transfer by a coexisting conjugative plasmid. For example, IncN plasmids reduce IncP plasmid transfer by about 10^4-fold (Brown, 1981). It is therefore preferable to test strains which carry only a single plasmid. The nature of the bacterial host can also markedly affect the response to these spot tests (Bradley *et al.*, 1981). For example, when enterobacterial hosts are tested using IncP-specific phages grown in *P. aeruginosa*, it is necessary to use an increased phage inoculum (e.g. 10^5 for PRR1 and 10^8 for Pf3).

D. Efficiency of plating

This parameter is sometimes worth measuring since it can vary from plasmid to plasmid: for example, amongst IncF plasmids, the efficiency of plating (e.o.p.) of RNA phages varies over a more than 100-fold range (Alfaro and Willetts, 1972).

Mix about 2×10^2 p.f.u. of the phage with 0.1 ml of an overnight broth culture of the test strain and pour onto a nutrient plate to determine the titre as described in Section II.B. Simultaneously, repeat this titre using the standard plasmid-containing host. The ratio of the two titres gives the e.o.p.

E. Measurement of titre increase

The conjugation systems of many naturally occurring plasmids are repressed (Section VI), and resistance to a pilus-specific phage may simply be due to this. In general terms, this is true for IncF and IncI plasmids, but not for IncN, IncP or IncW plasmids. In order to test the phage sensitivities of plasmids that transfer at low frequencies (<0.1) and so might be repressed, a titre increase assay can be carried out on a transiently derepressed culture prepared as described in Section VI. 10^4 p.f.u. of the phage are added to 1 ml of the culture, and shaken in a test-tube for 2 h. After chloroforming, the phage titre is measured as described in Section II.B. The ratio of this titre to the phage inoculum titre gives the titre increase. This typically ranges from 10^3 to 10^5 for RNA phage infection of transiently derepressed cultures containing IncF plasmids (Meynell and Datta, 1966).

An alternative approach is to determine the sensitivity by spot test of a genetically derepressed plasmid mutant, obtained as described in Section VI.

III. Conjugative plasmid transfer

Detection or measurement of plasmid transfer is straightforward when the plasmid carries a selectable marker such as antibiotic resistance. Of the commonly used antibiotics, care should be taken with chloramphenicol and β-lactams such as ampicillin, since these become ineffective if too many cells (10^6–10^8) are plated; in addition, ampicillin is unstable both in solution and in plates. Trimethoprim is inactivated in many nutrient media, and minimal medium is preferable for this antibiotic and also for sulphonamides. Dilute solutions and plates containing mercuric ions are notoriously unstable. Note, furthermore, that a high level of antibiotic resistance can sometimes be determined by chromosomal markers, for example in *Pseudomonas* strains (Holloway *et al.*, 1979).

In essence, a conjugation experiment is carried out by mixing broth cultures of the donor and recipient strains under appropriate conditions, and selecting plasmid-containing transconjugants of the recipient strain. Selection against the donor strain is often achieved by using a recipient strain resistant to an antibiotic such as streptomycin, spectinomycin, nalidixic acid or rifamycin to which the donor is sensitive. Alternatively, a (multi)auxotrophic donor strain can be crossed with a prototrophic (or differently auxotrophic) recipient strain, and transconjugants selected on the appropriate minimal medium.

The following notes apply to all quantitative matings. Cultures of donor and recipient strains (obtained by diluting overnight cultures 1:20 with fresh L broth) should be grown separately, with shaking, to 2×10^8 cells per millilitre. These cultures can then be stored on ice (for up to 1 h) until required. Culture density is most easily measured during growth by using side-arm flasks as the culture vessels, and a Klett–Summerson colorimeter with a red filter, into which the side-arms can be placed. Alternatively, absorption at 620 nm can be followed. Whenever culture dilutions are made in saline or phosphate buffer rather than broth, and plating is on minimal medium, 0.1 ml broth per plate should be included to prevent step-down conditions that can lead to a five-fold reduction in transconjugant recovery. Usually a 0.1 ml sample of an appropriate dilution is plated. Plating can be done either by a top layer overlay technique, mixing the sample with 2.5 ml molten water agar (0.7% Difco agar), or by spreading the sample with an alcohol-sterilized glass rod spreader. Incubate plates at 37 C for one (nutrient medium) or two (minimal medium) days, or as otherwise appropriate. The efficiency of transfer can then be calculated as the number of transconjugants per donor cell. Plasmids differ in their transfer frequencies over a wide range (10^{-8}–1) so that some preliminary experiments may be necessary to establish the appropriate dilutions for selecting transconjugants of a new plasmid. It may also be worthwhile to test fresh overnight cultures instead of exponential ones, since for many plasmids these give almost equally efficient transfer. It is wise to check about 25 colonies from the donor viable count plates for continued presence of the plasmid, by a patching (see below) and replica-plate technique, since some plasmids are unstable.

Plasmids synthesizing rigid pili and some synthesizing thick flexible pili, transfer efficiently only when the mating cells are supported on a solid surface, while plasmids that determine thin flexible pili also transfer efficiently in broth matings (Table I; Bradley et al., 1980). For an unknown plasmid, then, it is best to choose a surface mating technique (Section III.A or III.B), or to compare the two methods.

A. Membrane filter matings

This is perhaps the most efficient technique, although it is tedious if a large number of matings has to be carried out. Mix 0.2 ml of the donor culture and 1.8 ml of the recipient culture and filter through a 2.5-cm diameter 0.45-μm pore-size filter. A Millipore Swinnex assembly and disposable syringe provides the simplest means for this. Place the filter (using sterile forceps) on a pre-warmed nutrient agar plate, cells uppermost, and incubate at 37 C for $\frac{1}{2}$ to 1 h or longer if required. Then immerse the filter in 2 ml of broth, resuspend the cells by vortexing and plate appropriate dilutions on selective plates. Because of the variable efficiency of resuspension, it is best to measure the donor viable count at this stage by plating dilutions on plates selective for the donor strain.

B. Plate mating

This technique is simpler, but may be up to ten times less efficient than membrane filter mating. Spread 0.1 ml of an appropriate dilution (found in a preliminary experiment) of an exponential broth culture of the donor strain with 0.1 ml of an exponential (or overnight) culture of the recipient strain together on a selective plate, and incubate at 37°C for one to two days. Other steps are as described in Section III.A, except that the donor culture viable count can be determined on nutrient medium.

In these plate matings, the contraselective marker should be Str^r or Spc^r, not Nal^r since nalidixic acid inhibits conjugation (Barbour, 1967). If nalidixic acid *must* be used, or if a delay prior to selection is necessary to allow expression of the plasmid marker in the recipient cells, then the mating should be carried out for the desired time on a nutrient plate, before resuspending the cells in 1 ml of broth and plating dilutions on selective plates.

C. Broth mating

Mix 0.2 ml of the donor strain culture with 1.8 ml of the recipient strain culture in a large (18 mm × 150 mm) test-tube. This ensures adequate aeration without shaking, which might disrupt mating pairs. Incubate at 37°C for 30 min (or longer if required), and in the meantime plate dilutions to measure the viable count of the donor culture. Stop the mating by placing the tubes in ice, and plate dilutions on selective plates as described.

D. Transfer of plasmids without selectable markers

Transfer of such plasmids can only be measured if it is relatively frequent, such that when a reasonable number (10–1000) of exconjugant recipient colonies are screened, a proportion carrying the plasmid will be found. After mating as described in Section III.A, III.B or III.C (but using a 1:1 donor to recipient ratio), dilutions of the mating mix are plated on medium selective for the recipient cells only. Individual colonies are then "patched" in a geometric array of up to 100 areas per nutrient plate, using flat-ended sterile toothpicks. After growing up, the colonies can be replica-plated onto whatever medium is appropriate for detecting plasmid-containing cells. If the plasmid has no detectable marker, colonies can be screened using a small-scale technique (Chapter 9) for the physical presence of the plasmid: however, it is probably simpler to construct a transposon-carrying derivative in such cases (Chapters 10 and 11).

To measure transfer of Col (colicin-producing) plasmids (to a colicin-resistant recipient strain), the mating mixture is plated on recipient-selective nutrient medium using a top agar overlay technique, this layer when set being overlayed with a further 2.5 ml of agar to prevent the colonies from growing through the agar. After incubation overnight, the transconjugant colonies are killed by brief exposure to chloroform vapour (introduced on a piece of filter paper on the lid of the inverted plate) and a third overlay applied, containing 0.1 ml of an overnight culture of a colicin-sensitive strain able to grow on the recipient-selective nutrient medium. After further overnight growth, clear areas (lacunae) will be observed around Col^+ colonies (Monk and Clowes, 1964).

E. Qualitative transfer techniques

These are useful for screening for transfer ability, or for constructing plasmid-containing strains. 10^2–10^3 colonies are most easily screened by patching them in a geometric array on nutrient agar plates (50–100 patches per plate). After incubation at 37 C for about 6 h, to give exponentially growing cells, this array is replica-plated onto a selective plate that has been spread with 0.1 ml of an overnight culture of the recipient strain concentrated ten times in buffer. After one to two days incubation, transconjugant patches will appear where the donor colonies carried a conjugation-proficient plasmid.

One to ten colonies can be tested for transfer by a cross-streak mating, which has the advantage that it includes control areas showing that neither donor nor recipient strain alone will grow on the selective plate. Streak two loopfuls of an overnight broth culture of the recipient strain across the centre of a selective plate, and allow to dry in. Then streak loopfuls of broth cultures of the donor strains perpendicularly across this in marked positions. After incubation, transconjugant growth beyond where the donor and recipient streaks cross identifies transfer-proficient donor cells.

To construct plasmid-containing derivatives, perhaps the simplest and most rapid technique is to mix loopfuls of the donor and recipient cultures in a small area on a selective plate. After incubation for 1–2 h, cells can be streaked out from this area, and further incubation will give single transconjugant colonies, ready for a second round of purification on nutrient plates.

F. Measurement of surface exclusion

The presence of a plasmid commonly reduces the ability of a cell to function as a recipient in matings with donor cells containing the same or a related plasmid. The quantitative level of this property can be measured by comparing the frequency of transconjugant formation by plasmid-free and plasmid-containing cells, and the ratio is called the surface exclusion index. Any of the mating techniques described in Section III.A, III.B or III.C can be used for the measurement. The donor plasmid must carry an extra selectable marker and if necessary this is most easily achieved by constructing a transposon derivative, or by deleting a marker from the plasmid in the recipient.

Surface exclusion indices usually range from 100 to 1000, and surface exclusion systems are highly specific; for example, four different ones have been detected amongst IncF plasmids (Willetts and Maule, 1974).

IV. Mobilization of non-conjugative plasmids

Many naturally occurring plasmids are non-conjugative, but nonetheless have an *oriT* site and genes that allow their transfer, or mobilization, when present in the same cell as a conjugative plasmid (Willetts, 1981). Non-conjugative plasmids are occasionally large, and may then be transfer-deficient mutants of conjugative plasmids. The most common non-conjugative plasmids are relatively small (2–10 kb), but many, if not all of these, are efficiently mobilized if the appropriate conjugation system is provided by a coexisting conjugative plasmid. Examples of such plasmids are listed in Table II, together with their frequencies of mobilization by some conjugative plasmids. All these plasmids have mobilization genes that probably initiate transfer from their *oriT* sites, and substitute for similar functions encoded by the conjugative plasmid that are specific for its own *oriT*. However, only some conjugative plasmids will mobilize a given non-conjugative plasmid. In a practical sense, this means that several different conjugative plasmids must be tested for their abilities to mobilize any new non-conjugative plasmid. Experience suggests that these should include (derepressed) IncP, IncI and IncF plasmids; if all give negative results, a wider search is necessary.

TABLE II
Mobilization of non-conjugative plasmids[a]

Conjugative plasmid	Incompatibility group	Transfer (fraction of conjugative)			
		ColE1	ColE2	pSC101	RSF1010
R64-11	Iα	0.7	0.8	5×10^{-3}	0.06
F*lac*	FI	1	$< 10^{-4}$	10^{-7}	10^{-5}
R100-1	FII	10^{-3}	$< 10^{-4}$	5×10^{-5}	10^{-5}
R91-5	P-10	—	—	—	0.6
R6K	X	5×10^{-4}	—	10^{-3}	0.1
RP1	P	0.5	—	0.13	1
R46	N	10^{-6}	—	$< 10^{-5}$	10^{-7}
R388	W	10^{-2}	—	$< 4 \times 10^{-7}$	10^{-4}

[a] Data are taken from Willetts (1981), and the unpublished data of K. Derbyshire and N. S. Willetts.

A. Mobilization from double-plasmid strains

The simplest technique is to transfer various conjugative plasmids into the strain carrying the non-conjugative plasmid, as described in Section III.E, and then to use these strains as donors with a suitable recipient strain. Use of a

RecA⁻ host will prevent mobilization via possible homologous recombination with the conjugative plasmid.

A low frequency of mobilization may indicate not that this is taking place via an *oriT* site on the non-conjugative plasmid, but rather that one of the two plasmids carries a transposable DNA sequence that allows cointegrate formation, and hence mobilization (even in a RecA⁻ host). This is in fact a simple method for the detection of such a sequence, in systems where *oriT* mobilization does not occur (Chapters 10 and 11).

B. Triparental matings

This technique is not so sensitive nor is it quantitative, but it avoids strain construction when many pairs of plasmids have to be tested, and will give transient double-plasmid cells (Section VIII) even when the plasmids are incompatible. The simplest variation is to mix 0.05 ml spots of overnight broth cultures of the donor strain carrying the conjugative plasmid and the intermediate strain carrying the non-conjugative plasmid on an appropriate selective plate that has been spread with 0.1 ml of an overnight culture of a recipient strain resistant to some antibiotic contraselective to both donor and intermediate strains. If necessary, this technique can be modified by using exponential cultures, membrane filter or broth matings, or by carrying out the donor and intermediate, and intermediate and recipient matings separately.

V. Mobilization of the bacterial chromosome

An important use of conjugative plasmids is for transfer, by conjugation, of segments of the host bacterial chromosome, thus providing a genetic system for its analysis. Such transfer is achieved by covalently linking the chromosome to the origin of transfer sequence of a conjugative plasmid, so that it is transferred as an "extension" of the plasmid DNA. This covalent linkage can be established by a variety of recombinational mechanisms, and may be transient or reversible rather than essentially permanent as in the classical system for transfer of the *E. coli* K12 chromosome by integration of F to give Hfr strains (Hayes, 1953; Davidson *et al.*, 1975).

A further important feature of mobilization of the bacterial chromosome by its covalent linkage to a conjugative plasmid is that by a further recombination event between sites different from those used for plasmid integration, plasmid primes can be formed. These carry a segment of the chromosome integrated into the plasmid genome in a relatively stable fashion (although it is often preferable to use RecA⁻ hosts to prevent or reduce their breakdown). Plasmid primes are useful for constructing cells that are diploid for that region of the chromosome or as a source of that segment of chromosomal DNA.

The review by Bachmann (1983) gives the most up-to-date linkage map of *E. coli*, and that of Bachmann and Low (1980) is an excellent source of information about Hfr and F prime strains, and genetic techniques useful for mapping in this organism. Given below are details of techniques for measuring the frequency of transfer of chromosomal markers and for the classical interrupted mating experiment, and brief descriptions of the various methods for mobilizing the bacterial chromosome and for constructing plasmid primes.

A. Measurement of chromosome transfer

The techniques are similar to those given in Section III, except that mating should be carried out for 2 h to allow transfer of long DNA segments. Recipient strains are usually (multi)auxotrophic or unable to ferment one or more sugars, so that selection for inheritance of the wild type allele can be performed on the appropriate minimal selective medium. Depending upon the nature of the donor strain, markers may be transferred at frequencies varying from 10^{-8} to 10^{-1}. The recipient strain is also usually resistant to an antibiotic to allow contraselection of the donor strain. Care should be taken that the antibiotic-sensitive allele is not transferred as an early marker by the donor strain, especially if it is dominant (e.g. str^s, spc^s, rif^s). Antibiotic resistances can be introduced at alternative chromosomal locations if required, by inserting a transposon. Note also that strains containing an R plasmid with an Sm^r/Sp^r marker give rise, at a relatively high frequency (about 10^{-5}), to moderate to high level Sm^r mutants (Pearce and Meynell, 1968) so that such strains should be contraselected with a high level (1–2 mg ml^{-1}) of streptomycin, or with some other antibiotic.

B. The interrupted mating experiment

The following technique is one variant for carrying out an interrupted broth mating between an *E. coli* K12 Hfr strain and a multiauxotrophic recipient strain. It can be improved by taking more samples (every 15 s) at critical periods if an efficient interrupting device (Low and Wood, 1965) is available, or if mating is interrupted by treating the samples for 10 min with a concentrated T6 lysate (using a T6^s donor and T6^r recipient). It is also possible to carry out an interrupted plate mating by using Nal^s donor and Nal^r recipient strains, and adding nalidixic acid (which prevents further DNA transfer) at various intervals (Haas and Holloway, 1978).

   Mix 1 ml of an exponential broth culture of the Hfr strain with 9 ml of a similar culture of the recipient strain in a 100-ml conical flask, and incubate in a water bath at 37°C without agitation. Leaving the flask in the bath, remove 0.5 ml samples to test-tubes containing 4.5 ml of phosphate buffer or saline at 0, 5, 10, 15, 20, 25, 30, 40, 50, 60, 75 and 90 min. Vortex for 1 min to disrupt mating pairs and plate appropriate dilutions (found by trial and error) on plates selective for each marker in turn. Count the colonies after incubation at 37°C for two days, and plot on semi-logarithmic graph paper (Fig. 5). The curves obtained demonstrate the differing times of entry (obtained by extrapolation to the abscissa) of different chromosomal markers, and that late

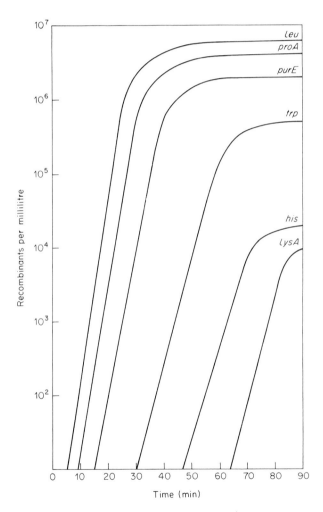

Fig. 5. The interrupted mating experiment. Data are taken from a mating between Hfr Hayes and a (multi)auxotrophic recipient strain.

markers are transferred less frequently than early ones because of spontaneous chromosome breakage.

C. Chromosome transfer by autonomous plasmids

Some conjugative plasmids transfer the chromosome because they carry regions of homology that allow the plasmid and chromosome to recombine, using the host's homologous recombination system. Examples include F, which, like the E. coli K12 chromosome, carries copies of IS2, IS3 and $\gamma\delta$, and F primes (or other plasmid primes) carrying segments of the chromosome. Alternatively, homology can be provided at the desired location by introducing into the chromosome a copy of a transposon already carried by the plasmid (Kleckner et al., 1977). The frequency of mobilization varies with the extent of homology being, for example, quite high for F primes (10^{-2}) but low for F itself (10^{-5}). Chromosome transfer begins within the region of homology.

Other conjugative plasmids mobilize the chromosome because they carry a transposable DNA sequence, since a cointegrate between the two is formed as an intermediate in the transposition of this sequence to the chromosome (Chapters 10 and 11). Mobilization by R68.45 (Haas and Holloway, 1978) [which carries the highly transposable IS21 (Willetts et al., 1981)] and by plasmids with an inserted Mu (Faelen and Toussaint, 1976; Denarié et al., 1977) or mini-Mu (Toussaint et al., 1981; Van Gijsegem and Toussaint, 1982) prophage is by this mechanism; these plasmids are of particular value since they have a broad host range and will mobilize the chromosomes of a variety of Gram-negative genera (Holloway, 1979). The frequency of chromosome transfer is relatively low (10^{-4}–10^{-8}) and is initiated at a large number of chromosome sites owing to the lack of specificity of the transposition process.

Finally, yet other plasmids mobilize the chromosome by mechanisms that have not been determined. These include the FP plasmids in *Pseudomonas* (Holloway, 1979) and *Streptococcus* plasmids (Franke et al., 1978).

D. Chromosome transfer by integrated plasmids

To study chromosomal genetics by conjugation, it is clearly advantageous to construct an Hfr strain with a conjugative plasmid stably integrated into the chromosome, since transfer then occurs at a high frequency from a defined point. F-derived E. coli K12 Hfr strains can be isolated, and are relatively stable, because the bacterial homologous recombination system is inefficient in carrying out recombination between the short IS regions of homology. For the same reason, Hfr strains arise at low frequencies (10^{-6}) in F^+ cells, and the frequency may be even lower for other plasmids with perhaps even shorter regions of homology or yet more inefficient plasmid–chromosome recombination. However, it is possible to select for such integration events if the plasmid carries a suitable marker and its replication (or that of the chromosome, for *E. coli* K12 *dnaA* hosts) is temperature-sensitive; temperature-resistant survivors carrying the marker frequently have the plasmid integrated into the chromosome, allowing both molecules to replicate (Broda and Meacock, 1971; Tresguerres *et al.*, 1975; Harayama *et al.*, 1980).

An alternative technique for constructing enterobacterial F-derived Hfr strains is to transpose Tn*2301*, a transposon construct in which the entire F transfer region (without the replication and incompatibility genes) has been cloned into an ampicillin-resistance transposon, from a plasmid to the bacterial chromosome (Johnson and Willetts, 1980).

E. Construction of plasmid primes

There are two general techniques available for plasmid prime construction, both of which depend upon preventing transferred chromosome segments from recombining into the recipient chromosome. One technique uses a recombination deficient (*recA*) recipient (Low, 1973), whereas the other uses a heterospecific recipient in which the donor genes are expressed, but DNA homology is not sufficient for recombination (Van Gijsegem and Toussaint, 1982; Morgan, 1982). Any of the donor strains transferring the bacterial chromosome and described in Section V.C or V.D can be used, and the rare transconjugants that arise in such matings include a proportion that are plasmid prime partial diploids. These can be identified in further qualitative matings as described in Section III.E.

VI. Regulation of conjugation

Expression of many plasmid conjugation systems is subject to control by fertility inhibition (*fin*) genes also present on the plasmid. For example, most IncF plasmids have two genes, *finO* and *finP*, the products of which act in concert to prevent transcription of *traJ*, a positive control gene necessary for transcription of all the other transfer genes (Finnegan and Willetts, 1973; Willetts, 1977). Consequently, established cells carrying wild type IncF plasmids transfer these at about 0.1% of maximal frequency, and are resistant to pilus-specific phages (Meynell *et al.*, 1968). Fertility inhibition can also be caused by a coexisting conjugative plasmid of quite different type: for example, the IncI plasmid R62 reduces F transfer by about 100-fold (Meynell, 1973) and IncN plasmids reduce transfer of IncP plasmids by 10^4-fold (Brown, 1981). The transfer frequency of a new plasmid should therefore be measured using cells containing only this plasmid, and if it is low, this might be due to the presence of *fin* genes, rather than to an inefficient conjugation system.

A. Recognition of Fi^+ (F) plasmids

F is an atypical IncF plasmid in that it carries no *finO* gene, and therefore expresses its conjugation system constitutively. However, the *finO* product can be provided in *trans* by other IncF plasmids, reducing F transfer by 100- to 1000-fold and making the cells resistant to F-specific phages. Such plasmids are denoted Fi^+(F) and this usually (but not always) indicates that they are themselves IncF plasmids compatible with F. The classification Fi^-(F) has essentially no meaning since it includes all other plasmids.

To test for the Fi^+(F) phenotype, the plasmid is transferred as described in Section III.E into cells carrying a convenient F prime such as F*lac*. The sensitivity of the resultant strain to F-specific phages (Section II.C) or the transfer frequency of the F prime (Section III.C) is then determined.

The Fi^+ phenotype of one conjugative plasmid towards a second can be recognized in similar experiments.

B. Preparation of transiently derepressed cultures

In a manner analogous to zygotic induction of a lambdoid prophage or of the *lacZ* gene, cells that have just received a repressed conjugative plasmid lack the *fin* gene products, and after $\frac{1}{2}$- to 1-h delay (for expression of the transfer genes), will retransfer the plasmid at the derepressed frequency. If there is an excess of recipient cells in the culture, repeated retransfer ultimately results in the infectious spread of the plasmid through the population to give a transiently derepressed or high frequency of transfer (HFT) culture (Watanabe, 1963). Such cultures can be used to identify pilus-specific phages by titre increase experiments (Section II.E). Repression is ultimately re-established after about 6 h for IncF plasmids (Willetts, 1974).

Add 10^4 cells from an overnight broth culture of the donor strain and 4×10^5 cells from a similar culture of the plasmid-free recipient strain to 1 ml of fresh broth. Incubate overnight. Next day, dilute 1:20 with fresh broth and grow to exponential phase, to give the HFT culture.

C. Isolation of transfer-derepressed mutants

If transiently derepressed cultures can be prepared, it should also be possible to isolate transfer-derepressed mutants. Such mutants are useful for recognition of the pilus-specific phage group by spot tests (Section II.C) and for measurement of the full transfer potential of the plasmid. They are easily selected by carrying out sequential matings beginning with a mutagenized culture of a strain carrying the repressed plasmid.

Mix 0.5 ml of such a culture grown to exponential phase with 0.5 ml of a (say) Sm^r recipient strain and mate for 1 h in broth or on a membrane filter as appropriate (Section III). Select transconjugants in liquid by adding to 10 ml of broth containing the plasmid-selecting antibiotic plus streptomycin, and incubating overnight at $37°C$. This also allows re-establishment of repression in transiently derepressed transconjugant cells. Dilute 1 ml of the culture to 10 ml with fresh broth, and grow to exponential phase. Mate as above with a Sm^r-Nal^r recipient strain, and this time plate out dilutions on selective medium to obtain single transconjugant colonies. Patch these, and screen them for mutants transferring at high frequency by replica-plate mating with an appropriate (Sp^r) recipient strain as described in Section III.E.

VII. Conjugation in Gram-positive organisms

The majority of conjugative plasmids have been found in Gram-negative bacteria, and previous sections have been concerned solely with these. However, conjugative plasmids have more recently been identified in Gram-positive organisms, most notably in various species of *Streptococcus* (Clewell, 1981). Conjugation in the actinomycetes has also been described, and in a *Streptomyces coelicolor* strain has been shown to be due to a conjugative plasmid (Hopwood and Merrick, 1977). In addition, conjugative plasmids have been found in the anaerobic organisms *Clostridium perfringens* (Rood et al., 1978) and *Bacteroides fragilis* (Welch et al., 1979; Privitera et al., 1979). It seems likely that conjugation systems in other genera will be discovered as investigations broaden.

Conjugative streptococcal plasmids differ from enterobacterial plasmids in that mating pair formation does not involve a pilus. In fact there are two basic types of such streptococcal plasmids: those that can transfer efficiently in broth matings, and those that transfer only in long-term membrane filter matings (Clewell, 1981). The mating pair formation systems of the latter plasmids have not been identified, although these plasmids are of some interest because their host range includes *Staphylococcus aureus* as well as a variety of *Streptococcus* species. Plasmids transferring efficiently in broth do so because potential recipient cells excrete sex pheromones, heat-stable polypeptides that induce the donor cells to become adherent. The donor cells synthesize a new protein which apparently covers the entire cell surface, and causes them to aggregate both with each other and with recipient cells to form mating aggregates. Since cell-free filtrates of recipient strains induce self-aggregation of donor cells, sex pheromones are sometimes referred to as clumping inducing agents (CIAs). Several CIAs with different plasmid specificities have been identified, and recipient strains can produce several of these, although their levels or efficiencies in inducing mating by different plasmids vary from strain to strain. Synthesis or function of the corresponding CIA (but not of any others) is inhibited in cells carrying a conjugative plasmid.

Streptococcus also harbours many non-conjugative plasmids, and as in Gram-negative bacteria, these can be mobilized by a coexisting conjugative plasmid; as yet, the mechanisms have not been investigated. One phenomenon peculiar to *Streptococcus* is that of conjugative transposons (Clewell, 1981). These are antibiotic-resistance determinants integrated into the bacterial chromosome, but apparently capable of accurately excising from it, transferring by conjugation to a recipient strain, and there re-integrating into the chromosome.

A. Broth matings in *S. faecalis*

Given the mechanism of mating pair formation described above, there are two ways to carry out matings between a plasmid-carrying donor strain and a recipient strain producing the appropriate CIA: by simply incubating the cultures together for an extended period or by pre-inducing the donor cells with the CIA and mating for a much shorter period. The protocols given below were taken from Dunny and Clewell (1975) and Dunny et al. (1979).

For the first, mix 0.05 ml of an overnight broth culture of the donor strain with 0.5 ml of a similar culture of the recipient, and 4.5 ml fresh broth (Oxoid No. 2). Agitate gently at $37°C$ for 2 h. Vortex to break up clumps, and plate out dilutions on selective plates. A recipient strain producing the appropriate CIA must be chosen, and can be made resistant to streptomycin, rifamycin or fusidic acid to provide the necessary contraselective marker.

For the second, a cell-free CIA preparation must first be made. Grow CIA-producing recipient cells to late exponential phase (5×10^8 cells per millilitre), pellet the cells by centrifugation, and filter the supernatant through a Millipore filter (0.22-μm pore size). Store the CIA filtrate at $4°C$, preferably after autoclaving. Grow donor and recipient cultures separately to late exponential phase, and dilute the former 1:10 into 2 ml of a 1:1 mixture of CIA filtrate and fresh broth. Dilute the recipient culture similarly, but into broth. Incubate with shaking at $37°C$ for 45 min. Mix 0.2 ml of the donor culture with 1.8 ml of the recipient culture, and shake at $37°C$ for a further 10 or 20 min. Vortex and plate out as above.

B. Membrane filter matings in *S. faecalis*

A method similar to that for enterobacterial plasmids (Section III.A; Franke *et al.*, 1978) can be used for conjugative streptococcal plasmids unable to transfer in broth matings.

VIII. Genetic analysis of conjugation

A full discussion of the genetic analysis of conjugation is beyond the scope of this chapter, and the interested reader is referred to other publications describing the conjugation systems of IncF (Fig. 6; Willetts and Skurray, 1980), IncP (Barth *et al.*, 1978; Stokes *et al.*, 1981) and IncP-10 (Carrigan and Krishnapillai, 1979; Moore and Krishnapillai, 1982) plasmids. However, such analysis is essentially similar to the analysis of any other complex biological function. Some of the important specialized techniques required are briefly described below.

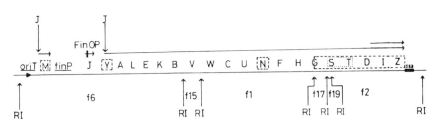

Fig. 6. A genetic map (not to scale) of the F conjugation region. Letters indicate *tra* genes. Those not required for pilus formation are boxed and the surface exclusion genes are double-boxed. The various *tra* operons and their transcriptional regulatory systems are indicated, as are the *Eco*RI sites and fragment numbers (from Willetts, 1981, with permission).

A. Isolation of *tra* point mutants

Tra⁻ mutants are best isolated by screening colonies derived from a mutagenized cell population for transfer ability. It is necessary to test about 10^5 colonies, given a mutation frequency of 10^{-3}, to obtain the hundred or so necessary mutants. Immediately after treatment with mutagens such as ethylmethanesulphonate or nitrosoguanidine, the culture is diluted with broth and divided into many small cultures for overnight incubation. Micro-titre plates are convenient for this. Ultimately, only one mutant is chosen from each culture, to avoid siblings. Alternatively, isolated plasmid DNA or transducing phages can be treated directly with hydroxylamine; an advantage of this technique is that the plasmid transformants or transductants then obtained are not siblings (Carrigan et al., 1978; Stokes et al., 1981).

Overnight cultures are diluted and plated on nutrient plates to obtain 100–150 colonies per plate. Five to ten plates are prepared per culture. These colonies can then be directly replica-plate mated with an appropriate recipient strain as described in Section III.E. Putative Tra⁻ clones are identified by comparing the master and replica plates, patched onto a further nutrient plate and retested by replica-plate mating before purification. It is worth carrying out these experiments in non-suppressing hosts at 42°C, so that screening for suppressible and temperature-sensitive mutations can be carried out later.

It is possible to select pilus-specific phage-resistant mutants directly (Ohtsubo et al., 1970; Carrigan et al., 1978), but since phage-sensitive Tra⁻ mutants would be missed, it is preferable to isolate mutants by screening, and then test them for phage sensitivity.

Ultimately, the Tra⁻ plasmid mutants should be tested in a different host strain to ensure that the transfer deficiency is not due to a chromosomal mutation similar, for example, to those that lead to a reduction in F transfer (Beutin et al., 1981).

B. Isolation of polar *tra* mutants

These mutants are necessary for the identification of *tra* operons. They can be obtained by using standard techniques to insert Mu (Faelen and Toussaint, 1976), lambda (Dempsey and Willetts, 1976) or a transposon (Chapters 10 and 11) into the transfer genes creating *tra* mutations identified as above. Mu is probably the best insertion element, because of its lack of site specificity (compared to lambda) and because of the reliance that can be placed on the mutations being strongly polar (compared to transposons, where some insertions are non-polar or only weakly polar).

C. Isolation of *tra* deletion mutants

Deletion mutants can be constructed by first inserting Mu*cts* or λ*cts* into or nearby the transfer region and then selecting deletion mutants from the resultant lysogens as temperature-resistant survivors after growth at 42°C (Dempsey and Willetts, 1976).

Alternatively, deletions can be made by linearizing the plasmid molecule at a convenient (unique) restriction endonuclease site, and either transforming cells directly with the linear DNA (Thompson and Achtman, 1979), or first treating this with the progressive exonuclease BAL-31 (Lau and Gray, 1979) followed by blunt-end ligation (Chapter 9). Transfer regions often have relatively few cleavage sites for restriction endonucleases, but it may be necessary to delete sites elsewhere on the plasmid, or to clone the transfer region, before this technique can be used.

D. Cloning the transfer region

This plays a central role in facilitating the genetic analysis of conjugation, since such clones allow construction of stable heterozygotes for complementation tests, as well as aiding the genetic and physical mapping of *tra* genes. The precise details of the vector and cloning enzyme depends upon the array of restriction endonuclease sites; if necessary, these can be supplemented by transposon insertion (Kleckner *et al.*, 1977). Cleavage sites should be chosen that allow the transfer region to be cloned separately from the incompatibility region either as a whole or as a collection of segments.

If plasmid derivatives with *λcts* inserted into or near to the transfer region are available, *λtra* transducing phages can be obtained by induction. These provide a second method for cloning not dependent upon *in vitro* techniques (Willetts and McIntire, 1978).

E. Complementation analysis of *tra* mutants

If the plasmid transfers at a high frequency (>0.1) in short-term broth matings and suppressible mutants are available, it is feasible to utilize a technique for complementation in transient heterozygous cells, where the transfer proficiency of the cell carrying two incompatible *tra* mutants is tested immediately after its construction (Achtman *et al.*, 1972). Otherwise, a set of *tra* mutants of a compatible *in vitro* recombinant plasmid carrying all or part of the transfer region must be constructed, either by mutagenesis or homozygote formation, to allow strains carrying two *tra* mutations to be tested for complementation.

Complementation is carried out, firstly, between point mutants to identify the *tra* genes, second, between representative point mutants and deletion mutants to map the order of the *tra* genes (and the *oriT* site) and third, between the representative point mutants and polar insertion mutants to recognize any operons.

Acknowledgements

I am grateful to Lucien Caro for Fig. 3, to David Bradley for Fig. 4 and for information given in Table I, and to Don Clewell and Alan Jacob for advice concerning streptococcal plasmid conjugation.

References

Achtman, M., Willetts, N. and Clark A. J. (1972). *J. Bacteriol.* **110**, 831–842.
Alfaro, G. and Willetts, N. S. (1972). *Genet. Res.* **20**, 279–289.
Bachmann, B. J. and Low, K. B. (1980). *Microbiol. Rev.* **44**, 1–56.
Bachmann, B. J. (1983). *Microbiol. Rev.* **47**, 180–230.
Barbour, S. D. (1967). *J. Mol. Biol.* **28**, 373–376.
Barth, P. T., Grinter, N. J. and Bradley, D. E. (1978). *J. Bacteriol.* **133**, 43–52.
Beutin, L., Manning, P. A., Achtman, M. and Willetts, N. S. (1981). *J. Bacteriol.* **145**, 840–844.
Bradley, D. E. (1980). *Plasmid* **4**, 155–169.
Bradley, D. E. (1981). *In* "Molecular Biology, Pathogenicity and Ecology of Bacterial Plasmids" (S. Levy, R. C. Clowes, and E. Koenig, Eds), pp. 217–226. Plenum, New York.
Bradley, D. E., Taylor, D. E. and Cohen, D. R. (1980). *J. Bacteriol.* **143**, 1466–1470.
Bradley, D. E., Coetzee, J. N., Bothma, T. and Hedges, R. W. (1981). *J. Gen. Microbiol.* **126**, 389–396 *et seq.*
Broda, P. (1979). *In* "Plasmids", Chapter 5. Freeman, San Francisco, California.
Broda, P. and Meacock, P. (1971). *Mol. Gen. Genet.* **113**, 166–173.
Brown, A. M. C. (1981). Ph.D. thesis, University of Edinburgh.
Carrigan, J. M. and Krishnapillai, V. (1979). *J. Bacteriol.* **140**, 809–816.
Carrigan, J. M., Helman, Z. M. and Krishnapillai, V. (1978). *J. Bacteriol.* **135**, 911–919.
Clewell, D. B. (1981). *Microbiol. Rev.* **45**, 409–436.
Davidson, N., Deonier, R. C., Hu, S. and Ohtsubo, E. (1975). *Microbiology — 1974* 56–65.
Dempsey, W. B. and Willetts, N. S. (1976). *J. Bacteriol.* **126**, 166–176.
Denarié, J., Rosenberg, C., Bergeron, B., Boucher, C., Michel, M. and de Bertalmio, M. (1977). *In* "DNA Insertion Elements, Plasmids, and Episomes" (A. Bukhari, J. Shapiro and S. Adhya, Eds), pp. 507–520. Cold Spring Harbor, New York.
Dunny, G. and Clewell, D. B. (1975). *J. Bacteriol.* **124**, 784–790.
Dunny, G., Craig, R., Carron, R. and Clewell, D. B. (1979). *Plasmid* **2**, 454–465.
Faelen, M. and Toussaint, A. (1976). *J. Mol. Biol.* **104**, 525–539.
Finnegan, D. J. and Willetts, N. S. (1973). *Mol. Gen. Genet.* **127**, 307–316.
Franke, A. E., Dunny, G. H., Brown, B. L., An, F., Oliver, D. R., Damle, S. P. and Clewell, D. B. (1978). *Microbiology — 1978* 45–47.
Haas, D. and Holloway, B. W. (1978). *Mol. Gen. Genet.* **158**, 229–237.
Harayama, S., Tsuda, M. and Iino, T. (1980). *Mol. Gen. Genet.* **180**, 47–56.
Hayes, W. (1953). *J. Gen. Microbiol.* **8**, 72–88.
Holloway, B. W. (1979). *Plasmid* **2**, 1–19.
Holloway, B. W., Krishnapillai, V. and Morgan, A. F. (1979). *Microbiol. Rev.* **43**, 73–102.
Hopwood, D. A. and Merrick, M. J. (1977). *Bacteriol. Rev.* **41**, 595–635.
Johnson, D. A. and Willetts, N. S. (1980). *J. Bacteriol.* **143**, 1171–1178.
Kleckner, N., Roth, J. and Botstein, D. (1977). *J. Mol. Biol.* **116**, 125–159.
Lacey, R. W. (1975). *Bacteriol. Rev.* **39**, 1–32.
Lau, P. P. and Gray, H. B. (1979). *Nucleic Acids Res.* **6**, 331–357.
Low, B. and Wood, T. H. (1965). *Genet. Res.* **6**, 300–303.
Low, K. B. (1973). *Bacteriol. Rev.* **36**, 587–607.

Meynell, E. (1973). *J. Bacteriol.* **113**, 502–503.

Meynell, E. and Datta, N. (1966). *Genet. Res.* **7**, 134–140.

Meynell, E., Meynell, G. G. and Datta, N. (1968). *Bacteriol. Rev.* **32**, 55–83.

Monk, M. and Clowes, R. C. (1964). *J. Gen. Microbiol.* **36**, 365–384.

Moore, R. and Krishnapillai, V. (1982). *J. Bacteriol.* **149**, 276–293.

Morgan, T. (1982). *J. Bacteriol.* **149**, 654–661.

Ohtsubo, E., Nishimura, Y. and Hirota, Y. (1970). *Genetics* **64**, 173–188.

Pearce, L. E. and Meynell, E. (1968). *J. Gen. Microbiol.* **50**, 173–175.

Privitera, G., Sebald, M. and Fayolle, F. (1979). *Nature (London)* **278**, 657–659.

Rood, J. I., Scott, V. N. and Duncan, C. L. (1978). *Plasmid* **1**, 563–570.

Stokes, H. W., Moore, R. J. and Krishnapillai, V. (1981). *Plasmid* **5**, 202–212.

Thompson, R. and Achtman, M. (1979). *Mol. Gen. Genet.* **169**, 49–57.

Toussaint, A., Faelen, M. and Resibois, A. (1981). *Gene* **14**, 115–119.

Tresguerres, E. F., Nandasa, H. G. and Pritchard, R. H. (1975). *J. Bacteriol.* **121**, 554–561.

Van Gijsegem, F. and Toussaint, A. (1982). *Plasmid* **7**, 30–44.

Watanabe, T. (1963). *J. Bacteriol.* **85**, 788–794.

Welch, R. A., Jones, K. R. and Macrina, F. L. (1979) *Plasmid* **2**, 261–268.

Willetts, N. S. (1974) *Mol. Gen. Genet.* **129**, 123–130.

Willetts, N. S. (1977). *J. Mol. Biol.* **112**, 141–148.

Willetts, N. S. (1981) *In* "Molecular Biology, Pathogenicity and Ecology of Bacterial Plasmids" (S. Levy, R. C. Clowes and E. Koenig, Eds), pp. 207–215. Plenum, New York.

Willetts, N. S. and Maule, J. (1974). *Genet. Res.* **24**, 81–89.

Willetts, N. S. and McIntire, S. (1978). *J. Mol. Biol.* **126**, 525–549.

Willetts, N. S. and Skurray, R. (1980). *Annu. Rev. Genet.* **14**, 41–76.

Willetts, N. S., Crowther, C. and Holloway, B. W. (1981). *Plasmid* **6**, 30–52.

4

Transformation of Bacteria by Plasmid DNA

J. R. SAUNDERS*, A. DOCHERTY‡,[1] AND G. O. HUMPHREYS*,[1]

* *Department of Microbiology, University of Liverpool, Liverpool, UK*

‡ *Department of Microbiology, University of Bristol, Bristol, UK*

I. General introduction

The ability to introduce purified DNA into bacteria has been of vital importance in the development of microbial genetics. Most of our understanding of the mechanisms of transformation has come from studies on the uptake and incorporation of chromosomal DNA by *Bacillus subtilis*, *Haemophilus influenzae* and *Streptococcus pneumoniae* (Lacks, 1977; Venema, 1979). Recent interest in plasmids has led to the development of a variety of methods for introducing plasmid DNA into many different bacterial species.

---

[1] *Present address:* Celltech Ltd, 250 Bath Road, Slough, UK.

METHODS IN MICROBIOLOGY
VOLUME 17   ISBN 0-12-521517-7

This chapter describes techniques currently available for transforming bacteria with plasmid DNA. Methods for introducing purified plasmid DNA into intact bacteria, bacterial protoplasts and spheroplasts will be considered. We have avoided the term transfection (Benzinger, 1978) when referring to the uptake of plasmid DNA, preferring to reserve this term for instances involving uptake and infection by bacteriophage DNA.

Bacterial transformation systems can be divided into two categories, natural (physiological) and artificial (Low and Porter, 1978). In naturally transformable species the cells become competent (able to take up DNA into a deoxyribonuclease-resistant form) at particular stages in the growth cycle or after shifts in nutritional status of cultures (Lacks, 1977). In some cases (e.g. *S. pneumoniae*), competence is dependent on diffusible competence factors (Tomasz, 1969). In others, competence depends on the presence of components of the cell envelope such as membrane proteins (Zoon and Scocca, 1975), autolysins (Seto and Tomasz, 1975) or pili (Sox *et al.*, 1979). However, many bacterial species do not become naturally competent under normal culture conditions and must be rendered permeable to DNA artificially. This may involve treating whole cells with high concentrations of divalent cations (Cohen *et al.*, 1972; Cosloy and Oishi, 1973). Alternatively, all or part of the cell envelope exterior to the cytoplasmic membrane may be removed to form protoplasts or spheroplasts, which can then be induced to take up DNA by divalent cations or by polyethylene glycol (PEG) (Hopwood, 1981).

In general, bacteria that can be transformed by chromosomal DNA can also be transformed by plasmid DNA. There are, however, notable differences in the efficiency with which plasmid and chromosomal markers will transform competent cells, due largely to differential processing of the various topological forms of DNA.

Transformation can be divided broadly into three stages: binding of DNA to the outside of the cell, transport of DNA across the cell envelope and establishment of the transforming DNA either as a replicon itself, or by recombination with a resident replicon. Transformation systems generally can be saturated by high concentrations of DNA. Hence, a characteristic dose–response curve is observed when a fixed number of competent cells (or protoplasts) is exposed to increasing amounts of transforming DNA (Fig. 1). At non-saturating DNA concentrations the slope of the dose–response curve provides information about the number of DNA molecules required to produce a single transformant. Typically, for single or closely linked genetic markers this slope $= 1$ and for two markers it is 2 (Goodgal, 1961; Trautner and Spatz, 1973; Weston *et al.*, 1979). If the slope $= 1$ with a homogeneous population of plasmid DNA molecules, it can be concluded that a single molecule is sufficient to produce a transformant. If, on the other hand, the dose response is > 1, then a number of plasmid molecules must react co-operatively

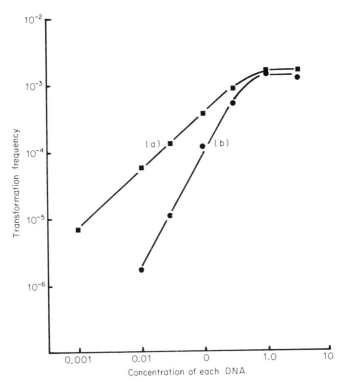

Fig. 1. Typical dose response curves for plasmid transformation. Approximately 5×10^8 *Escherichia coli* cells were transformed with various amounts of plasmid DNA according to the protocol described in the text. (a) Transformation by DNA of plasmid NTPI encoding Ap^r (mol. wt 5.6×10^6). The curve has a slope of 1 below saturation. (b) Simultaneous transformation by DNA of the compatible plasmids NTP 1 and NTP 11, which encodes Km^r (mol. wt 5.9×10^6). Selection was for both plasmids (ampicillin + kanamycin) and the curve has a slope of 2 below saturation.

to produce a single transformant (Saunders and Guild, 1981a; Weston *et al.*, 1981).

The efficiency of plasmid transformation can be expressed either as transformants per viable cell (with saturating DNA concentrations this will be a measure of the total number of transformable bacteria in a population), or as transformants per μg of DNA. In the latter case measurements must be made at subsaturating concentrations of DNA or the frequency per μg will be artificially depressed.

II. Mechanisms of transformation

A. Physiologically competent bacteria

1. Gram-positive systems

Streptococcus sanguis, *S. pneumoniae* and *B. subtilis* become competent under natural physiological conditions. There is no DNA specificity for transformation; these bacteria will take up DNA from their own species (homospecific) as well as that from unrelated species (heterospecific) (Lacks, 1977; Notani and Setlow, 1974). Uptake of DNA involves the activity of surface-bound nucleases which degrade one strand of double-stranded DNA (Lacks, 1977). Models for the uptake of linear chromosomal (Lacks, 1977) and circular phage DNA (Lacks, 1979) explain the role of surface nucleases in transformation of these bacteria.

Until recently a lack of suitable plasmids has limited studies of plasmid transformation to a small number of physiologically competent bacteria (Table I). Ehrlich (1977) and Gryczan *et al.* (1978) demonstrated that resistance plasmids derived from *Staphylococcus aureus* could be used to transform *B. subtilis*. Covalently closed circular (CCC) but not open circular (OC) or linear plasmid DNA was capable of transforming *B. subtilis*. However, the process was inefficient (10^{-3}–10^{-4} transformants per molecule bound) (Contente and Dubnau, 1979a). The competence of *B. subtilis* for transformation by either chromosomal or plasmid DNA develops at the same growth phase in batch culture (Contente and Dubnau, 1979a; Fig. 4).

TABLE I
Plasmid transformation systems involving natural competence

Bacillus subtilis	Canosi *et al.* (1978)
	Ehrlich (1977)
	Gryczan *et al.* (1978)
	Lovett *et al.* (1976)
Streptococcus pneumoniae	Barany and Tomasz (1980)
	Saunders and Guild (1980)
Streptococcus sanguis	LeBlanc and Hasell (1976)
	Macrina *et al.* (1981)
Anacystis nidulans	van den Hondel (1980)
Haemophilus influenzae	Albritton *et al.* (1978)
Haemophilus parainfluenzae	Gromkova and Goodgal (1981)
Neisseria gonorrhoeae	Sox *et al.* (1979)
Rhodopseudomonas sphaeroides	Tucker and Pemberton (1980)

Monomeric forms of plasmids were shown by Canosi *et al.* (1978) to be inactive in transforming intact cells of *B. subtilis*. In contrast, plasmid oligomers transform with high specific activity (Mottes *et al.*, 1979). A single oligomeric plasmid DNA molecule is apparently sufficient to produce a transformant (Contente and Dubnau, 1979a; de Vos *et al.*, 1981). Monomeric plasmid DNA can, however, transform *B. subtilis* protoplasts (de Vos and Venema, 1981; Mottes *et al.*, 1979). Genetic markers on monomeric plasmid DNA species can also be rescued by a *rec E*-dependent process in competent *B. subtilis* strains already carrying an homologous plasmid (Contente and Dubnau, 1979b; Docherty *et al.*, 1981; Gryczan *et al.*, 1980). Monomeric CCC forms of plasmid DNA carrying inserts of *B. subtilis* chromosomal DNA are also active in transformation (Canosi *et al.*, 1981; Duncan *et al.*, 1978) as are monomers containing ϕ105 DNA in transforming ϕ105 lysogens (Bensi *et al.*, 1981). Homology between the chromosome and plasmid-borne chromosomal fragments can lead to the integration of such plasmids into the recipient chromosome (Duncan *et al.*, 1978; Young, 1980). Transformation by monomers of plasmid pBC1, which carries a fragment of the *B. subtilis* chromosome, was found by Canosi *et al.* (1981) to be *recE*-dependent. However, oligomers of the plasmid showed progressively less dependence on *recE* with increasing size. These findings suggest that plasmid DNA is processed extensively, presumably by surface nucleases, during uptake. Accordingly, only single-stranded plasmid DNA is found in *B. subtilis* immediately after exposure to monomers but fully and partially double-stranded DNA can also be found if oligomers are used (de Vos *et al.*, 1981). Models, based on the reannealing of partially homologous single strands taken up from surface-bound oligomers, have been proposed by Canosi *et al.* (1981) and de Vos *et al.* (1981) to account for plasmid transformation in *B. subtilis*.

LeBlanc and Hassell (1976) showed that *S. sanguis* Challis could be transformed at low frequency (10^{-6}–10^{-7} transformants per cell) with plasmids from *Streptococcus faecalis*. In *S. sanguis* (Macrina *et al.*, 1981) and *S. pneumoniae* (Barany and Tomasz, 1980; Saunders and Guild, 1980, 1981a) CCC plasmid oligomers transform efficiently with single-hit kinetics. However, in contrast to *Bacillus*, CCC monomers are active in transformation of both *S. pneumoniae* (Saunders and Guild, 1981a) and *S. sanguis* (Macrina *et al.*, 1981) but with two-hit kinetics. Corresponding results have been obtained with open circular and linear forms of oligomers and monomers but efficiencies are at least 35-fold lower than with CCC DNA (Saunders and Guild, 1981b). Plasmid molecules linearized at a unique site are inactive in transformation of *S. pneumoniae*, but mixtures of molecules linearized at different sites are active (Saunders and Guild, 1981b). Thus it seems likely that two monomeric plasmid molecules damaged during uptake can co-operate, presumably by reannealment of overlapping single strands, to produce a functional replicon in streptococci.

Plasmid transformation in streptococci shows similar low efficiency (10^{-3}–10^{-4} transformants per viable cell at saturation) to *B. subtilis* (Barany and Tomasz, 1980; Contente and Dubnau, 1979a; Ehrlich, 1977). However, about 10–50 times more plasmid DNA is required to saturate competent *B. subtilis* than streptococci (Barany and Tomasz, 1980; Macrina *et al.*, 1981). Also, linearization of plasmid DNA causes a 1000-fold reduction in transformation frequency in *B. subtilis* (Contente and Dubnau, 1979b; Ehrlich, 1977) but only a 10- to 100-fold reduction in *S. pneumoniae* (Barany and Tomasz, 1980; Saunders and Guild, 1981b).

2. Gram-negative bacteria

A number of Gram-negative bacteria are naturally transformable by plasmid DNA (Table I). In most transformation systems competent bacteria will take up heterospecific as well as homospecific DNA. In contrast, *H. influenzae* (Scocca *et al.*, 1974), *Neisseria meningitidis* (Jyssum *et al.*, 1971) and *Neisseria gonorrhoeae* (Dougherty *et al.*, 1979) can discriminate against heterospecific DNA and will only take up DNA of the same or closely related species. DNA uptake by competent cells of *H. influenzae* requires the presence of a specific base sequence (uptake site) on double-stranded DNA. Thus, pBR322 DNA is not taken up by *H. influenzae*. However, *H. influenzae* (Chung and Goodgal, 1979) or *H. parainfluenzae* chromosomal DNA (Sisco and Smith, 1979) cloned on pBR322 in *Escherichia coli* is taken up. The uptake site necessary for transformation in *H. influenzae* has the sequence 5′-AAGTGCGGTCA-3′ (Danner *et al.*, 1980). The genomes of *H. influenzae* and *H. parainfluenzae* contain about 600 copies of this sequence, amounting to about one site per 4 kilobases (kb) of DNA (Sisco and Smith, 1979). This sequence also occurs in heterologous DNA, but only approximately once per 300 kb, thus substantially reducing the chances of successful transformation. The sequence is probably recognized by cell-surface receptors on competent *Haemophilus* (Danner *et al.*, 1980; Deich and Smith, 1980). Deich and Smith (1980) have estimated that each competent cell has only four to eight such receptors and that each receptor can be used only for the transport of a single DNA molecule. It is possible, however, to circumvent uptake specificity by transforming *Haemophilus* cells that have been made artificially competent by $CaCl_2$ treatment (Elwell *et al.*, 1977; Gromkova and Goodgal, 1981).

Certain conjugative plasmids (e.g. pUB701) that are found in *H. influenzae* will not transform the organism (Elwell *et al.*, 1977). Albritton *et al.* (1981) have demonstrated that transformation frequencies with such plasmids are dramatically enhanced in *H. influenzae* Rd recipients that already carry homologous plasmids either in a chromosomally integrated form (Stuy, 1980) or extrachromosomally. These results presumably reflect a requirement for recombinational rescue of plasmid molecules that have become damaged during uptake.

Frequencies of transformation by plasmid DNA in *H. parainfluenzae* (Gromkova and Goodgal, 1977) and *H. influenzae* (Notani *et al.*, 1981) are generally lower by several orders of magnitude than those obtained with chromosomal DNA. Gromkova and Goodgal (1979) have shown that piliated *H. parainfluenzae* are transformed by chromosomal or plasmid markers at frequencies that are 20 and 100 times greater, respectively, compared with non-piliated cells. Furthermore, plasmid, but not chromosomal transformation can be further stimulated 50-fold by the addition of 10 mM $CaCl_2$ and/or 20 mM $MgCl_2$ (Gromkova and Goodgal, 1977). Stimulation of plasmid transformation by divalent cations occurs whether the plasmid is circular or linear. This suggests that there may be differences in the uptake and/or processing of plasmid and chromosomal DNA in *H. parainfluenzae*. Interestingly, Ca^{2+}-stimulated transformation occurs with heterologous as well as homologous DNA. Ca^{2+} stimulation of *H. parainfluenzae* transformation differs from that observed in *E. coli* because it occurs only in cells that are already competent for transformation by chromosomal DNA (Gromkova and Goodgal, 1981).

In *N. gonorrhoeae*, cells are highly competent for transformation by homologous chromosomal DNA at all stages of growth (Sparling, 1977; Dougherty *et al.*, 1979). The specificity for uptake does not seem to be so stringent as in *Haemophilus* (Dougherty *et al.*, 1979), and recent evidence suggests that a different uptake sequence is required (Graves *et al.*, 1981). A practical problem is encountered with the transformation of *N. gonorrhoeae* because only piliated cells are competent and the ability of gonococci to produce pili is lost readily on subculturing the organism on solid media (Sparling, 1977). Piliated forms can be identified by microscopic examination of colonial morphology (Kellogg *et al.*, 1963; Swanson, 1978). Norlander *et al.* (1979) have shown that the presence of 24.5-megadalton gonococcal conjugative plasmids in *N. gonorrhoeae* confers low levels of transformability on otherwise non-transformable non-piliated cells. These plasmids might therefore be used to facilitate transformation of gonococci. β-Lactamase plasmids isolated from *N. gonorrhoeae* transform piliated (Kellogg colony types T1 and T2) but not non-piliated (colony types T3 and T4) cells of *N. gonorrhoeae*. However, transformation frequencies are about 1000-fold lower than those achieved with most chromosomal markers (Eisenstein *et al.*, 1977; Sox *et al.*, 1979). Norlander and Normark (1980) found that T1 cells took up four times more plasmid DNA into a DNAase-resistant form than T4 cells, and that DNA was more extensively degraded in T4 cells. Even in piliated cells, approximately 25% of the transformants obtained with the gonococcal β-lactamase plasmid pFA3 were found to contain deleted plasmids (Sox *et al.,*) 1979). The findings suggest that some processing of plasmid DNA occurs as a consequence of transformation in *N. gonorrhoeae*.

Frequencies of transformation by β-lactamase plasmids are disappointingly low (approximately 1–5 transformants per μg of plasmid DNA) in *N. gonorrhoeae*. However, recombinants formed naturally between these plasmids and the 2.6-megadalton cryptic plasmid of *N. gonorrhoeae* transform at 10^3- to 10^4-fold higher frequencies (Sparling *et al.*, 1980). This suggests that the 2.6-megadalton plasmid in these hybrids provides a gonococcal uptake sequence (analogous to that of *Haemophilus*) and/or sequence homology with the resident 2.6-megadalton plasmid in the recipient, allowing recombinational rescue of transformation-damaged DNA molecules. [It should be noted that the 2.6-megadalton plasmid is present in >95% of all gonococcal strains (Roberts *et al.*, 1979).]

In addition to the well-characterized transformation systems of *Haemophilus* and *Neisseria*, certain photosynthetic procaryotes can be transformed by circular DNA. van den Hondel *et al.* (1980) have transformed the cyanobacterium *Anacystis nidulans* with cloning vectors derived from the insertion of Tn901 into an indigenous plasmid. The photosynthetic bacterium *Rhodopseudomonas sphaeroides* has also been transformed by the DNA of Rϕ6P, a temperate bacteriophage with a circular genome which encodes β-lactamase production (Tucker and Pemberton, 1980). In this case, competence is dependent on concomitant infection of recipients by a helper phage, Rϕ9.

B. Artificial competence in intact cells

1. Calcium-induced competence

Mandel and Higa (1970) found that high concentrations of $CaCl_2$ permitted the transfection of intact *E. coli* by phage λ DNA. Subsequently, $CaCl_2$ treatment has been used for transfection of *E. coli* by other phages (Benzinger, 1978) and for transformation by chromosomal DNA (Cosloy and Oishi, 1973; Wackernagel, 1973). Cohen *et al.* (1972) first used such treatment to render *E. coli* transformable with plasmid DNA. Subsequently this method has been modified and applied to other bacteria, most of which are Gram-negative (Table II). However, the Gram-positive bacterium *S. aureus* has been transformed by plasmid DNA in the presence of 100 mM $CaCl_2$ and a helper bacteriophage (Rudin *et al.*, 1974). The mechanism of Ca^{2+}-mediated DNA uptake in *S. aureus* and the precise role of the helper have not yet been resolved.

TABLE II
Plasmid transformation systems involving calcium shock

Organism	Reference
Alcaligenes eutrophus	J. R. Saunders (unpublished data)
Citrobacter intermedius	Prieto *et al.* (1979)
Erwinia herbicola	Lacy and Sparks (1979)
Escherichia coli	Brown *et al.* (1979)
	Cohen *et al.* (1972)
	Kushner (1978)
Proteus vulgaris	Gnedoi *et al.* (1977)
Salmonella typhimurium	Lederberg and Cohen (1974)
Serratia marcescens	Reid *et al.* (1982)
Flavobacterium sp. K172	Negoro *et al.* (1980)
Haemophilus influenzae	Elwell *et al.* (1977)
Pseudomonas aeruginosa	Bagdasarian and Timmis (1981)
	Haque (1979)
	Sano and Kageyama (1977)
	Sinclair and Morgan (1978)
Pseudomonas phaseolicola	Gantotti *et al.* (1979)
Pseudomonas putida	Chakrabarty *et al.* (1975)
Pseudomonas savastanoi	Comai and Kosuge (1980)
Azotobacter vinelandii	David *et al.* (1981)
Staphylococcus aureus[a]	Rudin *et al.* (1974)

[a] Requires helper phage.

The basic procedure required to produce competent *E. coli* is outlined in Fig. 2. The minimum length of time required for full expression of transformed markers varies with strain, plasmid and marker. In particular, resistances to aminoglycoside antibiotics require at least 1 h for complete expression (Cohen *et al.*, 1972). Variables affecting the transformation procedure, such as optimum times of exposure to Ca^{2+} and DNA and the duration of heat pulse, have been examined in different strains of *E. coli* (Bergmans *et al.*, 1981; Brown *et al.*, 1979; Cohen *et al.*, 1972; Humphreys *et al.*, 1979; Norgaard *et al.*, 1978).

Transformation of *E. coli* is dependent on the presence of divalent cations; the efficiency of transformation varies with the cation present— $Ca^{2+} \gg Ba^{2+} > Sr^{2+} > Mg^{2+}$ (Weston *et al.*, 1981). The $CaCl_2$–heat shock procedure causes large and variable (10–50%) losses in cell viability. Increasing the concentration of $CaCl_2$ generally increases the transformation frequency (transformants per viable cell at saturating DNA concentrations), but at high concentrations, gains due to increased numbers of transformants are outweighed by losses in viability (Humphreys *et al.*, 1979; Weston *et al.*,

Subculture an overnight broth culture
Grow on with aeration
↓
Harvest in early exponential phase
(A_{600} ≤0.2)
wash by centrifugation in
10 mM $CaCl_2$ or NaCl
↓
Resuspend in 75 mM $CaCl_2$
↓
Add DNA to cells in 75 mM $CaCl_2$
Incubate at 0°C, 45 min
↓
Heat pulse at 42°C for 1–10 min
↓
Cool, add medium and incubate at
37°C to allow expression
↓
Score transformants and viable
cells on appropriate plates.

Fig. 2. Outline of the basic $CaCl_2$ technique for *E. coli* transformation (Cohen *et al.*, 1972; Humphreys *et al.*, 1979).

1981). The optimum concentrations of divalent cations necessary to produce maximum yields of transformants in *E. coli* C600 vary. Ca^{2+} and Sr^{2+} produce optimal effects at 75 mM, Ba^{2+} at 50 mM and Mg^{2+} at 120 mM (Brown, 1980). Preferences for divalent cations and optimal concentrations vary for other strains and species due presumably to differences in the precise architecture of the cell envelope. Higher transformation frequencies have been obtained by using combinations of $CaCl_2$ (30 mM) and $MgCl_2$ (26 mM) in *E. coli* (Bergmans *et al.*, 1980). Prewashing bacteria with $MgCl_2$ before $CaCl_2$ treatment results in improved transformation frequencies in *Salmonella typhimurium* (Lederberg and Cohen, 1974) and *Pseudomonas aeruginosa* (Sano and Kageyama, 1977; Sinclair and Morgan, 1978). Mercer and Loutit (1979) have shown that $MgCl_2$ (150 mM) is considerably superior to $CaCl_2$ in promoting transformation of *P. aeruginosa* with RP1-DNA. Kushner (1978) obtained increased frequencies with ColE1-derived plasmids by transforming *E. coli* that had been washed with RbCl prior to $CaCl_2$ treatment. Bagdasarian and Timmis (1981) included 10 mM RbCl in 100 mM $MgCl_2$ prewash and 100 mM $CaCl_2$ suspension fluids to obtain efficient transformation of *P. aeruginosa*. Treatment of *Flavobacterium* sp. with protease, α-amylase and other enzymes has permitted transformation with plasmid DNA in the presence of 50 mM $CaCl_2$ (Negoro *et al.*, 1980).

Marginal improvements in transformation frequencies can be made by ensuring that the pH of the divalent cation solutions employed is within the optimum range (pH 6.0–7.5 for *E. coli* C600), buffering where necessary with 10 mм 3-(N-Morpholino) propane-sulphonic acid (MOPS), pH 6.5 (Bagdasarian and Timmis, 1981; Humphreys *et al.*, 1979) or 12 mм N-2-hydroxyethylpiperazine-N'-ethanesulphonic acid (HEPES) pH 6.0 (Bergmans *et al.*, 1981). Addition of glucose (0.5% w/v) to competent cells in 75 mм $CaCl_2$ improves frequencies two- to four-fold in *E. coli* (Brown, 1980; Humphreys *et al.*, 1979).

The state of growth of recipient cultures has a dramatic effect on transformation frequencies of $CaCl_2$-treated *E. coli*. The transformation frequency varies over a 100-fold range during batch growth of *E. coli* C600 (Brown *et al.*, 1979). Transformation frequencies (1–7% of cells transformed with pBR322 DNA giving 10^6–10^7 transformants per μg) rise to a maximum in early exponential phase ($A_{660} = 0.15$ to 0.2) and decline thereafter (Brown *et al.*, 1979; Humphreys *et al.*, 1981; Fig. 3). The larger the dilution of inoculum used the greater the magnitude and duration of maximal competence obtained. There is no evidence for either a diffusible competence factor or inhibitor of transformation (Brown *et al.*, 1979). However, maximum competence is associated with a time in a batch culture when the mean cell volume of the culture is at its greatest (Humphreys *et al.*, 1981) and the cells are most susceptible to killing by the $CaCl_2$ treatment (Brown *et al.*, 1979). Repeated two-fold dilution of cultures at the time of maximal transformability leads to maintenance of both transformability and mean cell volume (Brown *et al.*, 1979; M. G. M. Brown, unpublished data). Jones *et al.* (1981) have demonstrated that *E. coli* exhibits maximum transformability (equivalent to the highest achieved in batch culture) in carbon-, nitrogen- or phosphate-limited chemostat cultures growing at maximum dilution rate. The relationship between cell volume and transformability is not yet clear although larger cells have increased surface area for binding DNA and may have stressed cell envelopes.

Dagert and Ehrlich (1979) have claimed that prolonged incubation in $CaCl_2$ at 0°C improves the competence of *E. coli* by as much as ten-fold but their results have been difficult to reproduce. Interestingly, Sabelnikov and Domaradsky (1981) have found that cells incubated overnight at 0°C in Ca^{2+} adsorb ten times more radiolabelled plasmid DNA in a given time than those incubated at 0°C for only 20 min. It is possible to maintain competent $CaCl_2$-treated *E. coli* (and presumably other species) by rapidly freezing the cells in $CaCl_2$ containing 15% w/v glycerol and storing them at −70°C (Morrison, 1977). These cells retain transformability and viability for a year or more and provide a means of maintaining a constant population of competent bacteria that can be thawed and used as desired.

Covalently closed circular and open circular plasmid DNA species are

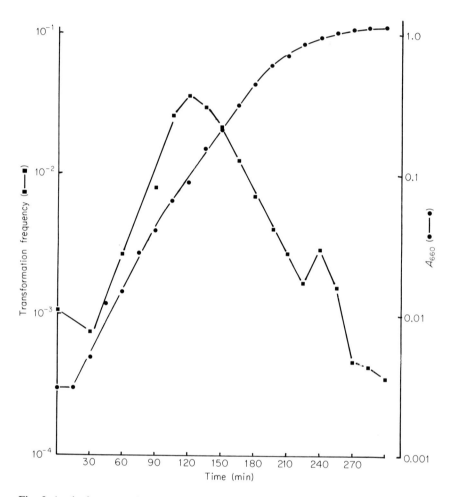

Fig. 3. 1 ml of an overnight static culture of *E. coli* C600 grown at 37°C in nutrient broth was inoculated into 500 ml of prewarmed nutrient broth and incubation continued with vigorous aeration at 37°C. At the times indicated, samples (4–80 ml as appropriate) were removed, harvested by centrifugation, washed in 10 mM $CaCl_2$ and concentrated to a constant cell density of about 10^9 bacteria per millilitre in 75 mM $CaCl_2$. 5×10^8 cells were then mixed with saturating amounts (3 µg) of pBR322 DNA and transformed as described in the text ●, A_{660}; ■, transformants per viable cell.

taken up equally well by *E. coli* (Cohen *et al.*, 1972), but variations in transformation ability occur between different preparations of the same plasmid DNA. Double-stranded circular DNA is taken up by Ca^{2+} treated *E. coli* without conversion to the single-stranded form (Strike *et al.*, 1979). There appears to be no specificity for homologous DNA uptake (Brown *et al.*, 1981).

Furthermore, monomeric plasmid DNA molecules are active in transformation with single-hit kinetics (Mottes *et al.*, 1979). DNA seems to be taken up in the form in which it is presented whether as single-stranded circular, CCC, OC or double-stranded linear (Cohen *et al.*, 1972; Strike *et al.*, 1979). Transformation of wild type *E. coli* with linearized plasmid DNA occurs with frequencies that are about 100-fold lower than with CCC or OC DNA (Bergmans *et al.*, 1980; Cohen *et al.*, 1972). Most of the damage to linear DNA is attributable to the *recBC* product (exonuclease V) which normally severely inhibits transformation of *E. coli* with chromosomal DNA (Cosloy and Oishi, 1973; Hoekstra *et al.*, 1980; Wackernagel, 1973). However, it is possible to transform *recB*, *recC*, *sbcB* (or *sbcA*) strains of *E. coli* with linear chromosomal fragments at high frequency due to the absence of exonuclease V and the presence of a functional *recF* pathway (Cosloy and Oishi, 1973). Unfortunately some plasmid replicons, notably ColEl and its derivatives, are not stably maintained in *recB,C sbcB* backgrounds (Vapnek *et al.*, 1976).

Kushner (1978) found that one strain of *E. coli*, SK1590, was more transformable than other commonly used strains such as C600. By contrast, Dagert and Ehrlich (1979) found only marginal differences in frequency between these strains. However, it is difficult to compare individual strains of *E. coli* for efficiency of transformation unless all have been harvested under growth conditions permitting maximal competence (Brown *et al.*, 1979).

Attempts to resolve the precise mechanisms involved in Ca^{2+}-mediated transformation have been hampered by the relatively low efficiency of the process. At best, using a small plasmid such as pBR322, only about 5% of bacteria in an *E. coli* population can be transformed (Humphreys *et al.*, 1981; Kushner, 1978). Transformation frequencies with larger plasmids (> 15 kb) are dramatically reduced (Humphreys *et al.*, 1979) due presumably to the damage incurred during uptake and establishment. Dose–response experiments suggest that a single (monomeric) plasmid DNA molecule is sufficient to produce one transformant (Mottes *et al.*, 1979; Weston *et al.*, 1979, 1981). However, considerably more plasmid DNA molecules bind tightly to the outside of the competent cells than get in, as judged by resistance of transforming DNA molecules to deoxyribonuclease or by the number of transformants obtained (Sabelnikov and Domaradsky, 1981; Weston *et al.*, 1981). Even under optimum conditions, only about 10^{-3}–10^{-4} of the plasmid DNA molecules in a transformation mixture will give rise to transformants. Experiments using pairs of plasmid DNA species to transform *E. coli* have suggested that the capacity of the competent subfraction to be transformed by more than one plasmid molecule is limited; estimates are that > 80% of competent cells can take up and establish only one molecule, < 20% two and < 1% three or more (Weston *et al.*, 1979, 1981). These results presumably reflect the low efficiency with which externally bound plasmid DNA molecules are transported across the cell envelope to the cytoplasm where they become established.

The precise role of Ca^{2+} in promoting DNA uptake is not yet clear. Divalent cations might be required for a number of processes that act either alone or in concert to mediate transformation. Such ions are probably required to promote DNA binding (presumably by neutralization of negative charges) to the outer and inner membranes as a prelude to DNA transport. Weston *et al.* (1981) have demonstrated that divalent cations are essential for binding of radiolabelled plasmid DNA to isolated inner and outer membranes. Furthermore, considerable amounts of DNA remain firmly attached to both membranes after transformation (Sabelnikov *et al.*, 1975; Weston *et al.*, 1981). Ca^{2+} also causes dramatic rearrangements of the lipopolysaccharide and protein of the outer membrane of Gram-negative bacteria (van Alphen *et al.*, 1978), which might allow the binding and/or inward transport of DNA molecules. Treatment of isolated outer membranes with trypsin dramatically reduces Ca^{2+}-promoted binding of plasmid DNA (Weston *et al.*, 1981). In addition, proteases reduce transformation frequencies in intact Ca^{2+}-treated *E. coli* (Brown, 1980). This suggests that binding of DNA to protein exposed by Ca^{2+} may be a prerequisite for DNA transport to the cytoplasm. The combination of low temperature and Ca^{2+} also causes freezing of membrane lipids (Overath *et al.*, 1975; Sabelnikov and Domaradsky, 1979). Subsequent heating of cells during the heat pulse would cause unfreezing of the lipids and possible ingestion of DNA molecules which might have bound to the outside of the inner membrane. A further role of Ca^{2+} in transformation has been suggested by Grinius (1980) whereby Ca^{2+}–DNA complexes would be transported down a Ca^{2+} gradient extending across the inner membrane to the interior of the cell. Whether Ca^{2+} contributes directly to generate electrochemical gradients across the inner membrane or whether it merely brings DNA into contact with inner membrane transporters is not clear. The role of the electrochemical proton gradient in transformation is in any case the subject of current debate. Santos and Kaback (1981) conclude that the proton gradient and, in particular, the membrane potential, plays a critical role in Ca^{2+}-mediated transformation of *E. coli* by plasmid DNA. The opposite conclusion, namely that proton motive force does not play any significant role in uptake of plasmid DNA, has been reached by Sabelnikov and Domaradsky (1979, 1981). The precise role of energetic processes in Ca^{2+}-mediated transformation therefore awaits elucidation. It is clear, however, that the heat pulse is essential for efficient transformation. Weston *et al.* (1981) showed that plasmid DNA responsible for the production of transformants did not get into the cells until the heat pulse. Bergmans *et al.* (1981) have demonstrated that a heat pulse carried out in the absence of DNA renders cells transformable by chromosomal DNA and suggest that induction of competence is separable from DNA uptake per se.

2. Transformation with liposome-entrapped plasmid DNA

It is possible to entrap biologically active plasmid DNA in liposomes (Dimitriadis, 1979; Fraley et al., 1979). Liposome-entrapped pBR322 DNA transforms Ca^{2+}-treated E. coli at frequencies about 1% of those achieved with free pBR322 DNA (Fraley et al., 1979). Such transformation is resistant to DNAase. This system has little advantage in E. coli but may well be useful for bacterial species that are normally not transformable because of, for example, a lack of competence or the production of extracellular nucleases.

3. Transformation of frozen and thawed bacteria

Dityatkin and Iliyashenko (1979) showed that E. coli HB101 could be transformed in the absence of added Ca^{2+} by freezing cells with pMB9 DNA at $-70°C$ or $-196°C$ and then thawing at $42°C$. Optimal yields of transformants were obtained with $1–5 \times 10^9$ cells per millilitre and 0.05–0.5 µg per millilitre of plasmid DNA in reaction mixtures containing 0.5–1% (w/v) bactopeptone at pH 7.5. The freeze–thaw procedure presumably produces sufficient stress on the cell envelope to allow penetration of DNA. In E. coli, transformation frequencies are substantially lower than with $CaCl_2$–heat shock techniques, but freeze–thaw may be useful in organisms that cannot be transformed by other methods, such as Agrobacterium tumefaciens (Holsters et al., 1978) and Rhizobium meliloti (Selvaraj and Iyer, 1981).

4. Transformation of spheroplasts

Spheroplasts of E. coli and other Gram-negative bacteria can be readily transfected in the presence of low concentrations of divalent cations (Benzinger, 1978). Unfortunately, spheroplasts generated by lysozyme treatment do not regenerate and cannot be used as recipients for transformation by chromosomal or plasmid DNA. Suzuki and Szalay (1979) have isolated mutants with temperature-sensitive defects in peptidoglycan biosynthesis which produce spheroplasts which will regenerate. Spheroplast formation is controlled by shifting the temperature of cultures maintained in 0.25M sucrose. Such spheroplasts of E. coli can be transformed with efficiencies that are similar to those obtained with Ca^{2+} treatment. The method is applicable to the transformation of Micrococcus luteus, H. influenzae, H. parainfluenzae, Providencia stuartii, S. typhimurium, Aerobacter aerogenes and Klebsiella pneumoniae (Suzuki and Szalay, 1979).

5. Transformation of protoplasts

The ability of PEG to promote the uptake of plasmid DNA into bacterial protoplasts was first described in *Streptomyces coelicolor* and *Streptomyces parvulus* (Bibb *et al.*, 1978; Hopwood, 1981). Chang and Cohen (1979) have demonstrated PEG–protoplast transformation of *B. subtilis*. Their procedure has subsequently been utilized to introduce plasmid DNA into *Bacillus megaterium* (Brown and Carlton, 1980; Vorobjeva *et al.*, 1981) and *Bacillus stearothermophilus* (Imanaka *et al.*, 1982).

Protoplasts are normally prepared by enzymic degradation of the cell wall in an osmotically buffered medium. They are then exposed to DNA in the presence of PEG. (The optimum chain length and concentration of PEG varies between systems.) The PEG is then washed out. Protoplasts are incubated to allow expression of transformed markers and subsequently plated on a complex medium which favours cell wall regeneration. [For details of methods used in various bacterial species see Hopwood (1981) and Chater *et al.* (1982).] Regeneration of *B. subtilis* protoplasts has been carried out on plates containing sodium succinate, but difficulties have been experienced with the expression of some antibiotic (particularly neomycin) resistance phenotypes (Chang and Cohen, 1979). These problems can be overcome by replacing the succinate with sorbitol (A. J. P. Docherty, unpublished data) or mannitol (Gray and Chang, 1981) in the regeneration medium. Protoplasts of *B. subtilis* strain BD 170 (Gryczan *et al.*, 1978) can be regenerated on a suitably supplemented minimal regeneration medium, but frequencies are about ten-fold lower (A. J. P. Docherty, unpublished data).

Bacillus subtilis protoplasts (and probably those of other species) are transformed at the same efficiency by plasmid monomers as by dimers or higher oligomers (de Vos and Venema, 1981; Mottes *et al.*, 1979). Linear monomers, open circular and non-supercoiled DNA molecules (constructed by *in vitro* litigation) all give rise to transformants but at frequencies between one and three orders of magnitude lower than those observed with native plasmid preparations (Chang and Cohen, 1979; Gryczan *et al.*, 1980). Plasmid DNA enters *B. subtilis* protoplasts in a double-stranded and predominantly CCC form, with each plasmid molecule that enters being sufficient to produce a transformant (de Vos and Venema, 1981). The high efficiency of protoplast transformation in *B. subtilis* (up to 80%) and lack of requirement for oligomeric DNA makes this method an alternative (for CCC DNA) to transforming intact competent cells.

The development of PEG–protoplast systems has permitted the efficient transformation of bacteria that cannot be made competent by other means. In addition, protoplast fusions can be used to transfer non-conjugative plasmids between cells of *E. coli* (Vorobjeva and Khmel, 1979) or between *Bacillus* species (Dancer, 1980). Plasmids can also be transferred from bacteria to eucaryotes by fusion of *E. coli* spheroplasts or protoplasts with yeast protoplasts (Broach *et al.*, 1979; Kingsman *et al.*, 1979) or mammalian cells

(Schaffner, 1980). It should be noted that the act of protoplasting itself may lead to curing of resident plasmids in *S. aureus* (Novick *et al.*, 1980) and *Streptomyces* species (Hopwood, 1981) (Chapter 5).

III. Applications of plasmid transformation

A. Gene transfer

Plasmid transformation is a useful method of genetic exchange, especially where phage vectors for transduction or conjugative plasmids for mobilization are not available. A limitation of the process is that transformation frequencies tend to decrease with increasing plasmid size. Thus, with plasmids of >75 kb frequencies may be prohibitively low. Transformation is an efficient method for transferring small non-mobilizable derivatives of non-conjugative plasmids. For example, Warren and Sherratt (1978) have determined incompatibility hierarchies among ColEl-derived replicons by transforming cell lines already carrying homologous plasmids. In such instances transformation has the advantage of permitting the introduction of limited numbers (usually one) of plasmid DNA molecules into bacteria.

B. Identification of plasmid function

Transformation provides a means of reintroducing chemically pure plasmid DNA into bacteria and can be used as a direct assay of biological activity of plasmid DNA preparations (Roberts and Strike, 1981). Phenotypes specified by plasmids can be identified by separation of individual DNA species (e.g. by agarose gel electrophoresis) which can then be used to transform standard recipients. This may be of value in analysing wild type isolates harbouring a number of plasmids with unassigned functions.

C. Selection of cryptic plasmids by cotransformation

Cotransformation (Congression) is a valuable technique for the indirect selection of plasmids lacking easily identifiable selectable phenotypes. Kretschmer *et al.* (1975) transformed Ca^{2+}-treated *E. coli* cells with a mixture of a small amount of the DNA of an indicator plasmid pSC201 (which specifies resistance to kanamycin and tetracycline and is temperature-sensitive for replication) and an excess (10^3- to 10^5-fold) of the DNA of a second plasmid which did not have an identifiable marker. Between 50 and 85% of cells that had been selected on the basis of acquisition of pSC201 were found also to have acquired the unmarked plasmid. Cell lines carrying this plasmid alone could then be isolated simply by growing the transformants at 42°C and eliminating pSC201 by segregation. This method has been applied to the transformation of *E. coli* with enterotoxin plasmids (Penaranda *et al.*, 1980). As an alternative to an indicator plasmid, Bergmans *et al.* (1980) have used *E. coli* chromosomal DNA as an indicator in conjunction with a genetically marked hypertransformable strain of *E. coli* as recipient. Selection for a particular chromosomal marker after transformation with chromosomal DNA in the presence of a 10- to 20-fold excess of unmarked plasmid DNA leads to a high frequency (5–10%) of coinheritance of the plasmid. The advantage of this method is that there is no need to remove an indicator plasmid from the cotransformed strain.

Although both these methods were devised for Ca^{2+}-treated *E. coli*, there is no reason, in principle, why they might not be adapted to any other organism where suitable indicator plasmid or chromosomal systems are available.

D. Formation of *in vivo* deletions

The formation of deletions is a valuable tool for analysing the genetic structure of plasmids or any cloned inserts they might carry. For example, about 25% of plasmid transformants of *N. gonorrhoeae* contain deleted plasmids of various molecular weights (Sox *et al.*, 1979). However, deletion of circular transforming DNA does not occur in *E. coli*. To obtain deletants in *E. coli* it is first necessary to linearize the plasmid DNA by random mechanical shearing or by specific cleavage with restriction endonucleases. Processing of linear DNA in the recipient, presumably involving exonucleolytic cleavage, prior to circularization and repliconation then leads to the generation of *in vivo* deletants in about 1–20% of transformants (Thompson and Achtman, 1979). Alternatively, it is possible to truncate the DNA *in vitro* by exonucleolytic digestion of the terminal sequences before transformation (Timmis, 1981).

E. Introduction of recombinant DNA into bacteria

Transformation is the main method by which plasmid cloning vectors containing DNA inserted *in vitro* may be reintroduced into bacteria. The development of plasmid transformation regimes is thus an important prerequisite for the extension of recombinant DNA technology to previously unexplored bacteria. Transformation systems are, however, limited both by the low efficiency of the process and by the maximum length of plasmid DNA that can be successfully taken up by recipient cells, and plasmid chimeras containing large DNA inserts may be positively discriminated against. This may hinder the formation of gene banks where large random fragments must be cloned to ensure that an entire genomic sequence has been included. These problems can be overcome by using cosmids, vectors which are derived from plasmids but which possess the *cos* (cohesive ends) site of bacteriophage λ (Collins and Hohn, 1978). The *cos* site on the plasmid vector enables *in vitro* packaging of DNA by lysates of λ-infected cells. The headful limitation on DNA packaging means that 30–45 kb of DNA can be incorporated and introduced with high efficiency into *E. coli* by phage infection (Collins and Hohn, 1978; Ish-Horowicz and Burke, 1981). Cosmids thus combine a large and uniform size of DNA transferred with the ability to infect recipient cells with much higher efficiency than is possible with plasmid transformation.

IV. Transformation methods

A. Media

1. Spizizen salts (1 × SS)

K_2HPO_4	14 g
KH_2PO_4	6 g
$Na_3C_6H_5O_7.2H_2O$	1 g
$(NH_4)_2 SO_4$	2 g
$MgSO_4.7H_2O$	0.2 g

Distilled water to 1000 ml
Autoclave at 115 C for 20 min

2. L-Broth

Difco Tryptone	10 g
Difco Yeast Extract	5 g
NaCl	0.5 g
1 M NaOH	2 ml

Distilled water to 1000 ml
Adjust pH to 7.0 with 1 M NaOH
Autoclave at 115 C for 20 min
Add 10 ml of sterile glucose (20% w/v)

3. Nutrient Broth

Lab M (or Oxoid) Nutrient Broth No. 2.	25 g

Distilled water to 1000 ml
Autoclave at 121 C for 15 min

4. Nutrient Agar

Lab M (or Oxoid) Nutrient Broth No. 2.   25 g
Davis New Zealand Agar   10 g
Autoclave at 121°C for 15 min
When cooled to about 50°C, antibiotics are added where appropriate. Selective
concentrations for *E. coli* are ampicillin (20 μg ml^{-1}), chloramphenicol (20 μg ml^{-1}),
kanamycin (30 μg ml^{-1}), streptomycin (40 μg ml^{-1}), tetracycline (10 μg ml^{-1}). Plates
are dried at 37°C for 1 h before use.

5. Phosphate-buffered minimal salts

KH_2PO_4 6 g
K_2HPO_4 6 g
NH_4Cl 2 g
$Mg \cdot SO_4 \cdot 7H_2O$ 50 mg
$FeSO_4 \cdot H_2O$ 5 mg
Distilled water to 1000 ml
Autoclave at 115°C for 30 min
Then add sterile glucose solution to 0.2% (w/v)

6. MOPS—buffered minimal salts

As phosphate-buffered minimal salts but containing 120 mM MOPS (pH 7.0) and
100 μM phosphate

7. Minimal Salts Agar

As for phosphate-buffered minimal salts but containing 120 mM Tris-HCl (pH 7.0)
100 μM phosphate and 1% (w/v) Davis New Zealand Agar

8. PP broth

Difco Protease Peptone No. 3.   15 g
NaCl   5 g
K_2HPO_4 4 g
$KH_2PO_4 \cdot 2H_2O$ 1 g
Soluble starch   1 g
Distilled water to 1000 ml
Autoclave at 115°C for 30 min
Then add 1% v/v sterile GC supplement

9. GC supplement

Glucose   40 g
L-Glutamine   0.5 g
Ferric nitrate   50 mg
Thiamine pyrophosphate   2 mg
Distilled water to 1000 ml
pH adjusted to 7.2 after filter sterilization

10. PP agar

As for PP broth but containing 10 g l⁻¹ Davis New Zealand Agar

11. Penassay Broth

Lab Lemco	1.5 g
Difco Yeast Extract	1.5 g
Difco Bacto Peptone	5 g
Glucose	1 g
NaCl	3.5 g
K_2HPO_4	3.68 g
KH_2PO_4	1.32 g
Distilled water to 1000 ml	
pH adjusted to 7.0 and autoclave at 115 C for 20 min.	

12. 2 × SMM

Sucrose	342.3 g
Maleic acid	4.64 g
$MgCl_2 \cdot 6H_2O$	8.13 g
Oxoid gelatin	10 g
Distilled water to 1000 ml	
pH adjusted to 6.5 and autoclave at 115 C for 30 min	

13. Protoplast Maintenance Buffer (PMB)

4 × strength Penassay broth	50 ml
2 × SMM	50 ml

14. Protoplast Regeneration Agar (PRI)

Difco Technical Casamino acids	15 g
Difco Yeast Extract	15 g
Difco Bacto Agar	34 g
Distilled water to 1000 ml	
Autoclave at 115 C for 20 min	

15. Protoplast Regeneration Sorbitol (PRII)

Sorbitol (Sigma)	182 g
Oxoid Gelatin	40 g
Distilled water to 1000 ml	
pH adjusted to 8.0 and autoclave at 115 C for 30 min	

16. Regeneration plates

Molten PRI	150 ml
Molten PRII	250 ml
5 × SS	100 ml
Glucose (10% w/v)	10 ml

Plus, where appropriate, selective concentrations of either chloramphenicol (5 μg ml^{-1}) or neomycin (7.5 μg ml^{-1})

Plates should be dried at 37°C for 1 h before use

17. *Streptomyces growth medium (YEME)*

Difco Yeast Extract	3 g
Difco Peptone	5 g
Oxoid Malt Extract	3 g
Glucose	10 g

Distilled water to 1000 ml
Autoclave at 115°C for 20 min

18. *P medium*

Sucrose	10.3 g
K_2SO_4	0.025 g
$MgCl_2 \cdot 6H_2O$	0.203 g
*trace element solution	0.2 ml
distilled water	80 ml

Autoclave at 115°C for 20 min
Then add sequentially, sterile solutions of

KH_2PO_4 (0.5% w/v)	1 ml
$CaCl_2 \cdot 2H_2O$ (3.68% w/v)	10 ml
Tris-HCl 10 mM, EDTA 1 mM, NaCl 0.25 M, pH 7.2	10 ml

*Trace element solution is

$ZnCl_2$	40 mg
$FeCl_3 \cdot 6H_2O$	200 mg
$CuCl_2 \cdot 2H_2O$	10 mg
$MnCl_2 \cdot 4H_2O$	10 mg
$Na_2B_4O_7 \cdot 10H_2O$	10 mg
$(NH_4)_6Mo_7O_{24} \cdot 4H_2O$	10 mg

Distilled water to 1000 ml
Autoclave at 115°C for 20 min

19. *R2YE plates*

Sucrose	10.3 g
K_2SO_4	0.025 g
$MgCl_2 \cdot 6H_2O$	1.012 g
Difco Casamino acids	0.01 g
Difco Agar	2.2 g
Distilled water	80 ml

Autoclave at 115°C for 20 min
Then add sequentially, sterile solutions of

Trace element solution (Section IV.A.18)	0.2 ml
KH_2PO_4 (0.5% w/v)	1.0 ml
$CaCl_2 \cdot 2H_2O$ (3.68% w/v)	8.02 ml
L-Proline (20% w/v)	1.5 ml
Tris-HCl 10 mM, EDTA 1 mM, NaCl 0.25 M, pH 7.2	10 ml
1 M NaOH	0.5 ml
Yeast Extract (10% w/v)	5 ml

B. Isolation of transforming DNA

Plasmid DNA isolated by any of the methods outlined in Chapter 6 can be used for transformation. For routine preparation of large amounts of plasmid DNA of high specific activity for transformation it is best to use a method employing purification by ethidium bromide–CsCl gradient centrifugation (e.g. by the method of Humphreys *et al.*, 1975). Plasmid DNA preparations should be dialysed exhaustively against distilled water or buffers (pH 7.0–8.0) containing 1 mM EDTA and preserved at $-70°C$. Repeated freezing and thawing of plasmid DNA preparations should be avoided as this may lead to nicking of CCC DNA molecules.

C. Transformation protocols

1. Plasmid transformation of competent Bacillus subtilis *cells (A. J. P. Docherty unpublished data)*

(a) *Preparation of competent cells.* A single colony of the strain to be transformed is used to inoculate a 250-ml conical flask containing a 100 ml of double-strength L-Broth. After incubation at 37°C overnight with gentle shaking, the culture should have an A_{575} of 1.5–1.7. 5 ml of this culture are used to inoculate a further flask containing 100 ml of prewarmed $1 \times SS$ supplemented with glucose (0.5% w/v) and the amino acids and vitamins (each at $50 \mu g \, ml^{-1}$) required by the strain. (If competent cells are to be prepared of a strain harbouring a resident plasmid the medium should also contain selective concentrations of the relevant antibiotics.) The culture is then shaken vigorously at 37°C. Exponential growth continues from $A_{575} = 0.1$ for nearly 3 h until the stationary phase is reached at $A_{575} = 1.0$ (Fig. 4). Maximal competence occurs 2.5 h after the cessation of exponential growth. For example, Fig. 4 shows the development of competence for transformation of *B. subtilis* IG20 by pUB110 DNA. The precise time of maximal competence for individual strains should be determined by removing 0.2-ml samples of the culture and transforming with plasmid DNA as described below.

Cells are harvested at the time of maximal competence by centrifugation at 4 C and concentrated ten-fold by resuspension in 10 ml of culture supernatant containing glycerol (10% v/v). Cell suspensions are then either used directly or divided into 0.5-ml samples and shell-frozen with ethanol dry ice. Frozen competent cells kept at -60 to $-80°C$ remain viable for at least nine months.

(b) *Transformation.* 0.2 ml of fresh or frozen cells thawed slowly on ice and then washed to remove glycerol is mixed with plasmid DNA (1–5 μg in 5–50 μl) and incubated at 37°C for 30 min with gentle shaking. 0.8 ml of double-strength L-Broth is added and incubation continued at 37°C for 90 min. Transformants are scored by plating dilutions of the transformation mixture on appropriate selective media.

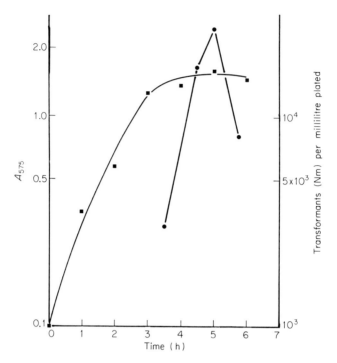

Fig. 4. Development of competence in *Bacillus subtilis* strain IG20. 5 ml of an overnight culture of *B. subtilis* IG20 were inoculated into 100 ml 1 × SS supplemented with tryptophan (50 μg ml^{-1}) and glucose (0.5% w/v). The A_{575} of the culture (■) was recorded at intervals thereafter. Samples (0.2-ml) were taken at the times indicated and transformed with pUB110 DNA (0.5 μg in 5 μl of 10 mM Tris-HCl pH 7.5, 0.1 mM EDTA). After dilution and a suitable period of expression the number of transformants per mililitre (●) was obtained by plating on nutrient agar plates containing neomycin (10 μg ml^{-1}).

2. *Standard procedure for transforming* Escherichia coli *cells by calcium shock treatment (modified from Humphreys* et al., *1979)*

(a) *Preparation of fresh competent cells.* 100 ml of prewarmed nutrient broth in a 250 ml conical flask are inoculated with 1 ml of a culture of *E. coli* grown statically for 18 h at 37°C in nutrient broth. Incubation is continued at 37°C with aeration (gyratory shaker at 160 r/min) until $A_{660} = 0.15$–0.2. The culture is then chilled on ice and the cells are harvested by centrifugation (12 000 × g for 5 min at 4°C). The pellet is resuspended in 25 ml of 10 mM $CaCl_2$ and washed by centrifugation. The final cell pellet is resuspended in 5 ml of 75 mM $CaCl_2$ (optionally containing 0.5% w/v glucose, 10 mM MOPS, pH 6.5). This produces a suspension of competent cells ($2.5–5.0 \times 10^9$ per millilitre) which can be kept at 0 to 4°C for up to 48 h without significant loss of viability.

(b) *Transformation.* 0.2 ml of competent cells is mixed in sterile glass or polypropylene tubes with plasmid DNA (0.01–10 μg) and made to 0.5 ml with 75 mM $CaCl_2$, plus 0.5% (w/v) glucose, 10 mM MOPS at pH 6.5 if required. (Note that this system is saturated with 0.5–1μg DNA per $5 \times 10^8 – 1 \times 10^9$ viable cells.) The transformation mixture is kept on ice for 45 min and then the tubes are transferred to a 42°C water bath for 10 min. 0.5 ml of nutrient broth is then added and incubation continued at 37°C for 2 h with shaking to allow expression. Plate appropriate dilutions of transformation mixtures on nutrient agar plus an appropriate agent to select for plasmid transformants and on nutrient agar alone to quantify the number of viable cells surviving the procedure.

3. Cryogenic preservation of competent Escherichia coli *cells (modified from Morrison, 1977)*

100 ml of *E. coli* cells are grown in the manner described for fresh competent cells. The cells are harvested, washed successively by centrifugation ($12\,000 \times \mathbf{g}$ for 5 min at 4°C) in 25 ml of 0.1 M $MgCl_2$ and then in 25 ml of 10 mM $CaCl_2$. The pellet is finally resuspended in 4.25 ml of 75 mM $CaCl_2$ and 0.75 ml of sterile glycerol. 0.2-ml amounts of the cell suspension are dispensed into sterile polypropylene micro-centrifuge tubes and frozen in a methanol/dry ice bath. Frozen cells are then stored at -70°C until required. (Note that MOPS buffer should not be used for freezing competent cells as it affects viability under these conditions.) When required, cells should be thawed by immersion in iced water.

4. Transformation of Salmonella typhimurium *(Lederberg and Cohen, 1974)*

(a) *Preparation of competent cells.* 50 ml of prewarmed L-Broth in a 250-ml conical flask are inoculated with 0.5 ml of a culture of *S. typhimurium* grown statically at 37°C overnight. Incubation is continued at 37°C with aeration until $A_{600} = 0.6$. The culture is then chilled and the cells harvested by centrifugation ($12\,000 \times \mathbf{g}$ for 5 min at 4°C). The pellet is resuspended and washed by centrifugation in 50 ml of ice-cold 100 mM $MgCl_2$ and then in 25 ml of 100 mM $CaCl_2$. The cell suspension is held on ice for 20 min and then harvested and resuspended in 2.5 ml of 100 mM $CaCl_2$.

(b) *Transformation.* 0.1 ml of plasmid DNA (0.01–10μg) in distilled water or TEN buffer [0.02 M Tris (hydroxymethyl) aminomethane, 1 mM ethylenediaminetetraacetic acid, 0.02 M NaCl, pH 8.0] is mixed with 0.2 ml of competent cells. The mixture is incubated on ice for 30 min and then subjected to a 42°C heat pulse of 2 min to allow uptake of DNA. After chilling on ice, the mixture is diluted ten-fold with prewarmed L-Broth and incubated at 37°C for 2 h to allow expression of transformed DNA. Dilutions are then plated on appropriate media to select for transformants and to estimate viable cells.

5. *Transformation of* Pseudomonas aeruginosa *(essentially the modification of Bagdasarian and Timmis (1981) of Kushner's (1978) method for* E. coli*)*

(a) *Preparation of competent cells.*   Cultures of *P. aeruginosa* are grown in L-Broth to early exponential phase (approximately 2×10^8 cells per millilitre), chilled and harvested by centrifugation at 0°C. Cells are washed by resuspension and centrifugation in an equal volume of cold 10 mM MOPS pH 7.0, 10 mM RbCl, 100 mM $MgCl_2$. The cell pellet is then resuspended in an equal volume of cold 100 mM MOPS pH 6.5, 10 mM RbCl, 100 mM $CaCl_2$ and kept at 0°C for 30 min. The cells are then harvested by centrifugation and resuspended in 1/10 volume of the $CaCl_2$ buffer at 0°C.

(b) *Transformation.*   0.2-ml portions of this suspension are mixed with plasmid DNA (0.2–1.0 µg), incubated at 0°C for 45 min and then at 42°C for 1 min. The transformation mixture is diluted with 3 ml of L-Broth and incubated at 30°C with aeration for 90 min to allow expression before plating on selective media.

6. *Selection of cryptic plasmids by cotransformation of* Escherichia coli

(a) *Using a competing plasmid (based on the method of Kretschmer et al. 1975).*   1 µg of the non-selected (cryptic) plasmid is mixed with 0.5 ng of pSC201 indicator DNA (or DNA of any suitable plasmid that is temperature-sensitive for replication or which can be removed from transformants as required) in a total of 0.3 ml of 75 mM $CaCl_2$. 0.2 ml of competent cells of *E. coli* K12, prepared as outlined above, is then added and transformation carried out as described above except that expression must be at 32°C. At the end of the expression period selection is made for a genetic marker on the indicator plasmid. Transformants can then be examined directly, e.g. by agarose gel electrophoresis, for the coinheritance of the unmarked plasmid (normally 50–80%). The indicator plasmid can be removed from appropriate transformant clones by subculturing into liquid media and incubating at 42°C for sufficient time to allow segregation (at least ten generations). Loss of the indicator and retention of the cryptic plasmid is confirmed by agarose gel electrophoresis.

(b) *Using competing chromosomal DNA (Bergmans et al., 1980).* *E. coli* strains AM1268, a Rec⁺Sbc⁺ derivative of the transformable strain AM1095 (*recB21, recC22, sbc15, leu*), is grown in phosphate-buffered minimal salts medium until early exponential phase. Cells are chilled, harvested by centrifugation, washed once with 10 mM NaCl and resuspended in 0.05 original culture volume of 20 mM HEPES buffer pH 6.0. 0.3 ml of the cell suspension is then mixed with chromosomal DNA from a prototroph (3.2 μg ml^{-1}) and cryptic plasmid DNA (50 μg ml^{-1}) and with CaCl$_2$ and MgCl$_2$ to a final concentration of 30 mM and 26 mM, respectively, in a final volume of 0.5 ml. The mixture is incubated at 0°C for 10 min, heated to 42°C for 6 min, chilled and incubated at 0°C for a further 30 min. It is then diluted 1:10 in supplemented minimal salts medium buffered with 120 mM MOPS pH 7.0 and incubated at 37°C with aeration for 90 min to allow expression. Leu⁺ transformants are selected on minimal agar lacking leucine. After incubation, Leu⁺ transformants are screened for the presence of plasmid DNA. Approximately 5–10% are cotransformed with the plasmid.

7. Plasmid transformation of Neisseria gonorrhoeae *(based on the method of Sox et al., 1979)*

(a) *Preparation of competent cells.* Piliated (Kellogg type 1 or 2) colonial forms of *N. gonorrhoeae* are grown at 37°C for 18 h, in the presence of 5–10% (v/v) CO$_2$, on the surface of PP agar plates. Colonies growing on the surface of the plates are resuspended to a density of between 5×10^7 and 1×10^8 colony forming units (c.f.u.) in PP broth containing 10 mM MgCl$_2$. (Note that cell densities of $> 10^8$ c.f.u. per millilitre lead to reduced frequencies because of competition with DNA from lysing cells.)

(b) *Transformation.* 0.1–5 μg of plasmid DNA are added to 1 ml of competent cell suspension and incubation continued at 37°C for 30 min. The transformation is then terminated by adding DNAase I (25 μg ml). The suspension is diluted 1:10 with PP broth and incubation continued with shaking at 37°C in 5–10% (v/v) CO$_2$ for 3–6 h. Dilutions are then spread on PP agar plates containing the selective agent (normally benzyl penicillin at 0.2 μg ml^{-1} for β-lactamase plasmids). Alternatively, the transformed culture can be incorporated in soft agar overlayers. Transformant colonies normally appear within 48 h on incubation at 37°C in 5–10% (v/v) CO$_2$.

8. Transformation of Bacillus subtilis *protoplasts (based on Chang and Cohen, 1979)*

(a) *Preparation of protoplasts.* Cultures of *B. subtilis* strains are grown at

37 C in 50 ml of Penassay Broth to $A_{575} = 0.7–1.0$. The cells are then harvested by centrifugation and resuspended in 4 ml of PMB. 1 ml of filter-sterilized lysozyme solution (10 mg ml^{-1} in PMB) is added. After gentle shaking at 37 C for 120 min, essentially 100% of cells should have been converted to protoplasts (as monitored by phase-contrast microscopy). 5 ml of PMB are added and the protoplasts harvested by centrifugation at approximately $2500 \times g$ for 10 min at room temperature. The protoplasts are resuspended in fresh PMB and the washing procedure repeated twice in order to remove any residual lysozyme. [Note that this may be important since biological inactivation of DNA by lysozyme has been reported (Wilson and Bott, 1970).] The washed protoplasts are finally resuspended in 2 ml of PMB.

(b) *Transformation.* Plasmid DNA ($\sim$ 5 μg) in 5–50 μl of 10 mM Tris-HCl 0.1 mM EDTA, pH 7.5 is added to 0.5 ml of protoplast suspension. PEG 1500 (1.5 ml of 40% w/v in 1 × SMM) is then added with thorough mixing. PEG 1500 is less viscous than PEG 6000 and allows easier mixing without reducing transformation frequencies. After 2 min, 5 ml of PMB are added and mixed thoroughly. The protoplasts are harvested as described above, resuspended in 1 ml of fresh PMB and incubated at 37°C with gentle shaking for 90 min. 0.1-ml dilutions in PMB are then plated on regeneration media to assay for transformants. Dilutions may also be plated on ordinary nutrient agar in order to determine the number of osmotically stable non-protoplasted cells in the preparations. On sorbitol-containing regeneration plates colonies appear after overnight incubation at 37°C. Typically, from each protoplast suspension 5×10^7 colonies can be regenerated, of which less than 0.001% grow on nutrient agar. When plasmids such as pUB110 or pBD64 (Gryczan *et al.*, 1980) are used in this procedure, between 0.1 and 10% of regenerated protoplasts give rise after direct selection to neomycin- (7.5 μg ml^{-1}) or chloramphenicol- (5 μg ml^{-1}) resistant transformants. (Note that disposable plastic pipettes should be used when handling protoplasts to prevent problems arising from traces of detergent in washed glass pipettes.)

9. Transformation of Streptomyces *protoplasts* (method of Chater *et al.*, 1982).

The protocols are for *Streptomyces lividans* but with modification they should be applicable to other *Streptomyces* species.

(a) *Preparation of protoplasts.* 25-ml cultures (30–36 h) of *S. lividans* are grown with aeration in medium containing 25 ml of YEME, 34% (w/v) sucrose, 0.005 M MgCl$_2$ and 0.5% (w/v) glycine. The cells are washed twice by resuspension in 10.3% (w/v) sucrose and centrifugation. The mycelium is then resuspended in 4 ml of lysozyme solution (1 mg ml^{-1}) in P medium, with

$CaCl_2$ and $MgCl_2$ concentrations reduced to 0.0025 M and incubated at 30°C for 15–60 min. The solution is then mixed by pipetting three times in a 5 ml pipette and incubation continued for a further 15 min. 5 ml of P medium are added and the solution again mixed by pipetting. The solution is filtered through cotton wool and the protoplasts sedimented gently (7 min at 800 × **g**) at room temperature. The protoplasts are resuspended in 4 ml of P medium and recentrifuged. Repeat this wash and finally suspend the protoplasts in the drop of P medium remaining after decanting the supernatant. For storage, add 2 ml of P medium to the suspended pellet. Protoplasts can be used for several days after preparation if stored at 4°C and for many months if stored at −70°C (slow freezing and rapid thawing are best).

Note that the growth stage is important for obtaining high transformation frequencies. Very late logarithmic mycelium is best for *S. lividans* but the optimum growth time should be determined for each species.

(b) *Transformation.* Take the protoplasts (∼ 4 × 10⁹, viability normally 1%), resuspended in the drop of P medium left after decanting the supernatant. Add DNA in ⩽ 20 μl of buffer (10 mM Tris-HCl, 1 mM EDTA, pH 8.0). Immediately add 0.5 ml of PEG 1000 solution [2.5 g of PEG dissolved in 7.5 ml of 2.5% (w/v) sucrose, 0.0014 M K_2SO_4, 0.1 M $CaCl_2$, 0.05 M Tris-maleic acid pH 8.0 plus trace elements] and pipette once to mix. After 1 min add 5 ml of P medium and sediment the protoplasts by gentle centrifugation. Resuspend the pellet in 1 ml of P medium. Plate out 0.1-ml samples on R2YE plates (plates should be dried to 85% of their fresh weight), and incubate at 30°C for one to three days. Transformants are detected either by the formation of "pocks" by plasmid-containing regenerants in a plasmid-free background (Bibb *et al.*, 1977) or by screening for drug resistance markers by overlaying plates with soft agar containing the appropriate drug after a suitable time of growth to allow phenotypic expression.

V. Ground rules for transforming previously untransformed species

Increasing interest in the use of molecular genetic techniques for analysing potentially useful genes in different micro-organisms may create the need to introduce DNA into bacteria that have previously not been transformed. Therefore we have attempted to lay down a series of guidelines for the development of novel transformation systems and the improvement of existing ones. The scheme (Fig. 5) is intended as an outline guide and the protocols and original references should be consulted for details. Table III lists the major factors which should be attended to when devising or improving transformation protocols.

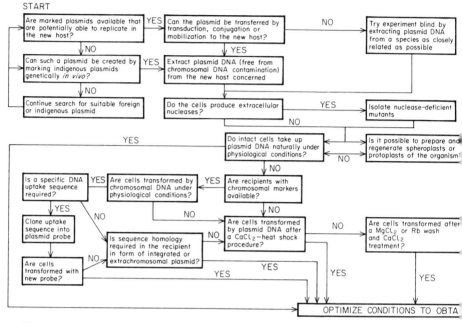

Fig. 5. Flow chart for devising a plasmid transformation protocol in a "new" bacterial species.

TABLE III
Factors affecting plasmid transformation systems

1. The nature of plasmid DNA used as probe
   Small size (ideally < 15 kb)
   Stable replication in new host (wide host range plasmids useful)
   Plasmid DNA preferably already modified for new host
   Purity from chromosomal DNA or RNA
   Topological state (e.g. CCC, OC, linear)
2. The state of recipient cells
   Growth phase
   Nutritional status
   Aeration
   Extracellular nucleases (remove by mutation if present)
   Homologous replicons in recipient for rescue
3. Preparation procedures
   Concentration of divalent and other ions
   Prewashing (e.g. with RbCl or MgCl$_2$).
   Presence of basic proteins (e.g. spermidines)
4. Exposure to DNA
   Concentration relative to saturation
   Duration of exposure to DNA
5. Expression of transformed markers
   Duration of expression period
   Concentrations of selective agents

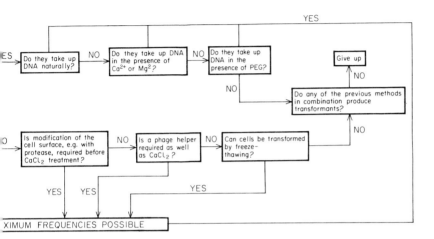

Acknowledgements

We thank D. A. Hopwood and K. N. Timmis for unpublished protocols, and V. A. Saunders for critical reading of the manuscript. The support of grants from the Medical Research Council is gratefully acknowledged.

References

Albritton, W. L., Bendler, J. W. and Setlow, J. K. (1981). *J. Bacteriol.* **145**, 1099–1101.

Alikhanian, S. I., Ryabchenko, N. F., Buckanov, N. O. and Sakanyan, V. A. (1981). *J. Bacteriol.* **146**, 7–9.

Bagdasarian, M. and Timmis, K. N. (1981). *Curr. Top. Microbiol. Immunol.* **96**, 47–67.

Barany, F and Tomasz, A. (1980). *J. Bacteriol.* **144**, 698–709.

Bensi, G., Iglesias, A., Canosi, U. and Trautner, T. A. (1981). *Mol. Gen. Genet.* **184**, 400–404.

Benzinger, R. (1978). *Microbiol. Rev.* **42**, 194–236.

Bergmans, H. E. N., Kooijman, D. H. and Hoekstra, W. P. M. (1980). *FEMS Microbiol. Lett.* **9**, 211–214

Bergmans, H. E. N., van Die, I. M. and Hoekstra, W. P. M. (1981). *J. Bacteriol.* **146**, 564–570.

Bibb, M. J., Ward, J. M. and Hopwood, D. A. (1977). *Mol. Gen. Genet.* **154**, 155–156.

Bibb, M. J., Ward, J. M. and Hopwood, D. A. (1978). *Nature (London)* **274**, 398–400.

Broach, J. R., Stathem, J. and Hicks, J. B. (1979). *Gene* **8**, 121–123.

Brown, B. J. and Carlton, B. C. (1980). *J. Bacteriol.* **142**, 508–512.
Brown, M. G. M. (1980). Ph.D. thesis, University of Liverpool.
Brown, M. G. M., Weston, A., Saunders, J. R. and Humphreys, G. O. (1979). *FEMS Microbiol. Lett.* **5**, 219–222.
Brown, M. G. M., Saunders, J. R. and Humphreys, G. O. (1981). *FEMS Microbiol. Lett.* **11**, 97–100.
Canosi, U., Morelli, G. and Trautner, T. A. (1978). *Mol. Gen. Genet.* **166**, 259–268.
Canosi, U., Iglesias, A. and Trautner, T. A. (1981). *Mol. Gen. Genet.* **181**, 434–440.
Chakrabarty, A. M., Mylroie, J. R., Friello, D. A. and Vacca, J. G. (1975). *Proc. Natl. Acad. Sci. U.S.A.* **72**, 3647–3651.
Chang, S. and Cohen, S. N. (1979). *Mol. Gen. Genet.* **168**, 111–115.
Chater, K. F., Hopwood, D. A., Keiser, T. and Thompson, C. J. (1982). *Curr. Top. Microbiol. Immunol.* **96**, 69–95.
Chung, B. and Goodgal, S. H. (1979). *Biochem. Biophys. Res. Commun.* **88**, 208–214.
Cohen, S. N., Chang, A. C. Y. and Hsu, L. (1972). *Proc. Natl. Acad. Sci. U.S.A.* **69**, 2110–2114.
Collins, J. and Hohn, B. (1978). *Proc. Natl. Acad. Sci. U.S.A.* **75**, 4242–4246.
Comai, L. and Kosuge, T. (1980). *J. Bacteriol.* **143**, 950–957.
Contente, S. and Dubnau, D. (1979a) *Mol. Gen. Genet.* **167**, 251–258.
Contente, S. and Dubnau, D. (1979b). *Plasmid* **2**, 555–571.
Cosloy, and Oishi, M. (1973). *Proc. Natl. Acad. Sci. U.S.A.* **70**, 84–87.
Dagert, M. and Ehrlich, S. D. (1979). *Gene* **6**, 23–28.
Dancer, B. N. (1980). *J. Gen. Microbiol.* **121**, 263–266.
Danner, D. B., Deich, R. A., Sisco, K. L. and Smith, H. O. (1980). *Gene* **11**, 311–318.
David, M., Tranchet, M. and Denairie, J. (1981). *J. Bacteriol.* **146**, 1154–1157.
Deich, R. A. and Smith, H. O. (1980). *Mol. Gen. Genet.* **177**, 369–374.
de Vos, W. and Venema, G. (1981). *Mol. Gen. Genet.* **182**, 39–43.
de Vos, W. M., Venema, G., Canosi, H. and Trautner, T. A. (1981). *Mol. Gen. Genet.* **181**, 424–433.
Dimitriadis, G. J. (1979). *Nucleic Acids Res.* **6**, 2697–2708.
Dityatkin, S. Y. A. and Ilyashenko, B. N. (1979). *Genetika* **15**, 220–225.
Docherty, A. J. P., Grandi, G., Grandi, R., Gryczan, T. J., Shivakumar, A. G. and Dubnau, D. (1981). *J. Bacteriol.* **145**, 129–137.
Dougherty, T. J., Asmus, A. and Tomasz, A. (1979). *Biochem. Biophys. Res. Commun.* **86**, 97–104.
Duncan, C. H., Wilson, G. A. and Young, F. E. (1978). *Proc. Natl. Acad. Sci. U.S.A.* **75**, 3664–3668.
Ehrlich, S. D. (1977). *Proc. Natl. Acad. Sci. U.S.A.* **74**, 1680–1682.
Eisenstein, B. I., Sox, T., Biswas, G., Blackman, E. and Sparling, P. F. (1977). *Science* **195**, 998–1000.
Elwell, L. P., Saunders, J. R., Richmond, M. H. and Falkow, S. (1977). *J. Bacteriol.* **131**, 356–362.
Fraley, R. T., Fornari, C. S. and Kaplan, S. (1979). *Proc. Natl. Acad. Sci. U.S.A.* **76**, 3348–3352
Gantotti, B. V., Patil, S. S. and Mandel, M. (1979). *Mol. Gen. Genet.* **174**, 101–103.
Gnedoi, S. N., Babushkina, L. M., Frolov, V. N. and Levashev, U. S. (1977). *ZH. Mikrobiol. Epidemiol. Immunobiol.* **1**, 99–104.
Goodgal, S. H. (1961). *J. Gen. Physiol.* **45**, 205–228.
Graves, J. F., Biswas, G. D., Blackman, E. Y. and Sparling, P. F. (1981). "Abstracts of the 25th Wind River Conference on Genetic Exchange", p. 17.
Gray, O. and Chang, S. (1981). *J. Bacteriol.* **145**, 422–428.

Grinius, L. (1980). *FEBS Lett.* **113**, 1–10.
Gromkova, R. and Goodgal, S. H. (1977). *In* "Modern Trends in Bacterial Transformation" (A. Portoles, R. Lopez and M. Espinosa, Eds), pp. 299–306. North-Holland Publ., Amsterdam.
Gromkova, R and Goodgal, S. (1979). *Biochem. Biophys. Res. Commun.* **88**, 1428–1434.
Gromkova, R. and Goodgal, S. (1981). *J. Bacteriol.* **146**, 79–84.
Gryczan, T. J., Contente, S. and Dubnau, D. (1978). *J. Bacteriol.* **134**, 318–329.
Gryczan, T., Contente, S. and Dubnau, D. (1980). *Mol. Gen. Genet.* **177**, 459–467.
Haque, H. (1979). *Mol. Gen. Genet.* **171**, 107–109.
Hoekstra, W. P. M., Bergmans, J. E. N. and Zuidweg, E. M. (1980). *J. Bacteriol.* **143**, 1031–1032.
Holsters, M., De Waele, D., Messens, E., van Montagu, M. and Schell, J. (1978). *Mol. Gen. Genet.* **163**, 181–187.
Hopwood, D. (1981). *Annu. Rev. Microbiol.* **35**, 237–272.
Humphreys, G. O., Willshaw, G. A. and Anderson, E. S. (1975). *Biochim. Biophys. Acta* **383**, 457–463.
Humphreys, G. O., Weston, A., Brown, M. G. M. and Saunders, J. R. (1979). *In* "Transformation 1978" (S. W. Glover and L. O. Butler, Eds), pp. 254–279. Cotswold Press, Oxford.
Humphreys, G. O., Saunders, J. R., Brown, M. G. M. and Royle P. M. (1981). *In* "Transformation 1980" (M. Polsinelli and G. Mazza, Eds), pp. 307–312. Cotswold Press, Oxford.
Ish-Horowicz, D. and Burke, J. F. (1981). *Nucleic Acids Res.* **9**, 2989–2998.
Jones, I., Primrose, S. B., Robinson, A. and Elwood, D. C. (1981). *J. Bacteriol.* **146**, 841–846.
Jyssum, K., Jyssum, S. and Gundersen, W. B. (1971). *Acta Pathol. Microbiol. Scand. Sect. B* **79**, 563–571.
Kellogg, D. S., Peacock, W. L., Deacon, W. E., Brown, L. and Pirkle, C. I. (1963). *J. Bacteriol.* **85**, 1274–1279.
Kingsman, A., Clarke, L., Mortimer, R. K. and Carbon, J. (1979). *Gene* **7**, 141–152.
Kretschmer, P. J., Chang, A. C. Y. and Cohen, S. N. (1975). *J. Bacteriol.* **124**, 225–231.
Kushner, S. R. (1978). *In* "Genetic Engineering" (H. B. Boyer and S. Nicosa, Eds), pp. 17–23. Elsevier, Amsterdam.
Lacks, S. A. (1977). *In* "Receptors and Recognition, Series B" (J. L. Reissig, Ed.), Vol. 3, Microbiol Interactions, pp. 177–232. Chapman & Hall, London.
Lacks, S. (1979). *J. Bacteriol.* **138**, 404–409.
Lacy, G. H. and Sparks, R. B. (1979). *Phytopathology* **69**, 1293–1297.
Le Blanc, D. J. and Hassell, F. P. (1976). *J. Bacteriol.* **128**, 347–355.
Lederberg, E. M. and Cohen, S. N. (1974). *J. Bacteriol.* **119**, 1072–1074.
Lovett, P. S., Duvall, E. J. and Keggins, K. M. (1976). *J. Bacteriol.* **127**, 817–828.
Low, K. B. and Porter, D. D. (1978). *Annu. Rev. Genet.* **12**, 249–287.
Macrina, F. L., Jones, K. R. and Welch, R. A. (1981). *J. Bacteriol.* **146**, 826–830.
Mandel, M. and Higa, A. (1970). *J. Mol. Biol.* **53**, 157–162.
Martin, P. A. W., Lohr, J. R. and Dean, D. H. (1981). *J. Bacteriol.* **145**, 980–983.
Mercer, A. A. and Loutit, J. S. (1979). *J. Bacteriol.* **140**, 37–42.
Morrison, D. A. (1977). *J. Bacteriol.* **132**, 349–351.
Mottes, M., Grandi, G., Sgaramella, V., Canosi, U., Morelli, G. and Trautner, T. A. (1979). *Mol. Gen. Genet.* **174**, 281–286.
Negoro, S., Shinagawa, H., Nagata, A., Kinoshita, S., Hatozaki, T. and Okada, H. (1980). *J. Bacteriol.* **143**, 248–245.

Norgaard, M. V., Keem, K. and Monahan, J. J. (1978). *Gene* **3**, 279–292.
Norlander, L. and Normark, S. (1980). *In* "Genetics and Immunobiology of Pathogenic *Neisseria*" (S. Normark and D. Danielsson, Eds), pp. 173–175. University of Umea.
Norlander, L., Davies, J. and Normark, S. (1979). *J. Bacteriol.* **138**, 756–761.
Notani, N. K. and Setlow, J. K. (1974). *Prog. Nucleic Acid Res. Mol. Biol.* **14**, 39–100.
Notani, N. K., Setlow, J. K., McCarthy, D. and Clayton, N-L. (1981). *J. Bacteriol.* **148**, 812–816.
Novick, R. P., Sanchez-Ruras, C., Gruso, A. and Edelman, R. (1980). *Plasmid* **3**, 348–358.
Overath, P., Brenner, M., Gulik-Krzywicki, T., Sheckter, E. and Letellier, L. (1975). *Biochim. Biophys. Acta* **389**, 358–369.
Penaranda, M. E., Mann, M. B., Evans, D. G. and Evans, D. J. (1980). *FEMS Microbiol. Lett.* **8**, 251–254.
Prieto, M. J., Jofre, J., Tomas, J. and Pares, R. (1979). *In* "Transformation 1978" (S. W. Glover and L. O. Butler, Eds), pp. 339–348. Cotswold Press, Oxford.
Reid, J. D., Stoufer, S. D. and Ogrydziak, D. M. (1982). *Gene* **17**, 107–112.
Roberts, M., Piot, P. and Falkow, S. (1979). *J. Gen. Microbiol.* **114**, 491–494.
Roberts, R. J. and Strike, P. (1981). *Plasmid* **5**, 213–220.
Rudin, L., Sjöström, J. E., Lindberg, M. and Philipson, L. (1974). *J. Bacteriol.* **118**, 155–164.
Sabelnikov, A. G. and Domaradsky, I. V. (1979). *Mol. Gen. Genet.* **172**, 313–318.
Sabelnikov, A. G. and Domaradsky, I. V. (1981). *J. Bacteriol.* **146**, 435–443.
Sabelnikov, A. G., Avdeeva, A. V. and Ilyashenko, N. N. (1975). *Mol. Gen. Genet.* **138**, 351–358.
Sano, Y. and Kageyama, M. (1977). *J. Gen. Appl. Microbiol.* **23**, 183–186.
Santos, E. and Kaback, R. H. (1981). *Biochem. Biophys. Res. Commun.* **99**, 1153–1160.
Saunders, C. W. and Guild, W. R. (1980). *Mol. Gen. Genet.* **180**, 573–578.
Saunders, C. W. and Guild, W. R. (1981a). *Mol. Gen. Genet.* **181**, 57–62.
Saunders, C. W. and Guild, W. R. (1981b) *J. Bacteriol.* **146**, 517–526.
Schaffner, W. (1980). *Proc. Natl. Acad. Sci. U.S.A.* **77**, 2163–2167.
Scocca, J. J., Poland, R. L. and Zoon, K. C. (1974). *J. Bacteriol.* **118**, 369–373.
Selvaraj, G. and Iyer, V. N. (1981). *Gene* **15**, 279–283.
Seto, H. and Tomasz, A. (1975). *J. Bacteriol.* **121**, 344–353.
Sinclair, M. I. and Morgan, A. F. (1978). *Aust. J. Biol. Sci.* **31**, 679–688.
Sisco, K. L. and Smith, H. O. (1979). *Proc. Natl. Acad. Sci. U.S.A.* **76**, 972–976.
Sparling, P. F. (1977). *In* "The Gonococcus" (R. Roberts, Ed.), pp. 111–135. Wiley, New York.
Sparling, P. F., Biswas, G., Graves, J. and Blackman, E. (1980). *In* "Genetics and Immunobiology of Pathogenic *Neisseria*" (S. Normark and D. Danielsson, Eds), pp. 123–125. University of Umea.
Sox, T. E., Mohammed, W. and Sparling, P. F. (1979). *J. Bacteriol.* **138**, 510–518.
Strike, P., Humphreys, G. O. and Roberts, R. J. (1979). *J. Bacteriol.* **138**, 1033–1035.
Stuy, J. (1980). *J. Bacteriol.* **142**, 925–930.
Suzuki, M. and Szalay, A. A. (1979). *In* "Methods in Enzymology" (R. Wu, Ed.), Vol. 68, Recombinant DNA, pp. 331–342. Academic Press, New York and London.
Swanson, J. (1978). *Infect. Immun.* **19**, 320–331.
Timmis, K. N. (1981). *In* "Genetics as a Tool in Microbiology" (S. W. Glover and D. A. Hopwood, Eds), pp. 49–109. Cambridge University Press, London and New York.

Tomasz, A. (1969). *Annu. Rev. Genet.* **3**, 217–232.

Thompson, R. and Achtman, M. (1979). *Mol. Gen. Genet.* **169**, 49–57.

Trautner, T. A. and Spatz, H. C. (1973). *Curr. Top. Microbiol. Immunol.* **62**, 61–88.

Tucker, W. T. and Pemberton, J. M. (1980). *J. Bacteriol.* **143**, 43–49.

van Alphen, L., Verkleij, A., Leunissen-Bijvelt, J. and Lugtenberg, B. (1978). *J. Bacteriol.* **134**, 1089–1098.

van den Hondel, C. A. M. J. J., Verbeek, S., van der Ende, A., Weisbeek, P. J., Borrias, W. E. and van Arkel, G. A. (1980). *Proc. Natl. Acad. Sci. U.S.A.* **77**, 1570–1574.

Vapnek, D., Alton, N. K., Bassett, C. L. and Kushner, S. R. (1976). *Proc. Natl. Acad. Sci. U.S.A.* **73**, 3492–3496.

Venema, G. (1979). *Adv. Microb. Physiol.* **19**, 245–331.

Vorobjeva, J. P. and Khmel, I. A. (1979). *In* "Advances in Protoplast Research" (L. Ferenczy and G. L. Farkas, Eds), pp. 37–41. Pergamon, Oxford.

Verokjeva, I. P., Khmel, I. A. and Alfoldi, I. (1980). *FEMS Microbiol. Lett.* **7**, 261–264.

Wackernagel, W. (1973). *Biochem. Biophys. Res. Commun.* **51**, 306–311.

Warren, G. and Sherratt, D. (1978). *Mol. Gen. Genet.* **161**, 39–47.

Weston, A., Humphreys, G. O., Brown, M. G. M. and Saunders, J. R. (1979). *Mol. Gen. Genet.* **172**, 113–119.

Weston, A., Brown, M. G. M., Perkins, H. R., Saunders, J. R. and Humphreys, G. O. (1981). *J. Bacteriol.* **145**, 780–787.

Wilson, G. A. and Bott, K. F. (1970). *Biochim. Biophys. Acta* **199**, 464–475.

Young, F. E. (1980). *J. Gen. Microbiol.* **119**, 1–15.

Zoon, K. C. and Scocca, J. J. (1975). *J. Bacteriol.* **123**, 666–677.

5

Study of Plasmid Replication *in vivo*

L. CARO, G. CHURCHWARD AND M. CHANDLER*

University of Geneva, Geneva, Switzerland

I. Introduction

In this chapter we have collected a variety of techniques that are currently employed in the analysis of different aspects of plasmid replication *in vivo*. Section II contains methods that are primarily useful for the measurement of plasmid copy number and for the determination of the rate of plasmid replication. These two types of measurement allow the characterization of plasmid replication under a variety of experimental conditions: for example in different genetic backgrounds or following different treatments of plasmid-containing cells. We emphasize most DNA–DNA hybridization methods since they are not widely used, and yet are straightforward. In principle they are more accurate than other techniques, since they do not require prior separation of bacterial and plasmid DNA. In Section III we describe methods that can be used to cure plasmids, and to measure rates of plasmid segregation. Most of the techniques described are for *Escherichia coli* and its plasmids, but most have been applied or are potentially applicable to other organisms.

*Present address: Institute de Recherche en Biochimie et Genetique Cellulaire de CNRS, 118 Route de Narbonne, 31062 Toulouse CEDEX, France.

METHODS IN MICROBIOLOGY
VOLUME 17   ISBN 0–12–521517–7

II. Measurement of plasmid copy number and the study of plasmid replication

Since the methods described in this section generally require radioactive labelling of DNA we first provide a short description of some of the methods and pitfalls involved in DNA labelling. There follows a detailed description of DNA–DNA hybridization techniques for the determination of plasmid copy number and the rate of plasmid replication. We then describe an alternative method of determining plasmid copy numbers by centrifugation in dye–caesium chloride gradients and list other uses of centrifugation techniques, particularly for the preparation of replicative intermediates. Finally, we outline some useful techniques for the determination of plasmid copy numbers by monitoring plasmid gene expression. These have been particularly useful in the genetic analysis of plasmid replication.

A. Radioactive labelling of DNA

A complete review of the complexities of thymine metabolism in bacteria is beyond the scope of this chapter. The reader is urged to consult the review by O'Donovan (1974). We only summarize a few salient points here.

1. Wild type bacteria

The first step in the incorporation of thymine into DNA is its conversion to thymidine by condensation with deoxyribose-1-phosphate. This reaction is catalysed by thymidine phosphorylase. Exogenous thymine is not normally incorporated by wild type cells, because there is insufficient deoxyribose-1-phosphate. The difficulty can be circumvented by including deoxyguanosine in the medium at a concentration greater than 50 μg ml^{-1}. This provides an intracellular source of deoxyribose-1-phosphate. Though deoxyadenosine may be used, it is toxic for certain strains. Alternatively, thymidine can be used instead of thymine. However, since it is rapidly degraded by thymidine phosphorylase, thymidine is useful only for short pulses. Two methods which overcome this problem are in current use. Long-term labelling with thymidine can be achieved by using a strain lacking thymidine phosphorylase. A more generally applicable technique, however, is based on the observation that uridine, at 50 μg ml^{-1}, is an efficient inhibitor of thymidine phosphorylase. The use of uridine together with thymidine in the growth medium is thus an efficient way in which to label DNA and since thymidine is utilized more efficiently than thymine, it is also useful in switching labels. For example, a long-term ^{14}C-thymine prelabel may be switched to short or long-term ^{3}H-thymidine label simply by adding a mixture of ^{3}H-thymidine and uridine.

Typical concentrations of thymidine which we employ are 0.5 μg ml^{-1} (20 Ci mM^{-1}) for short-term labelling and 0.005 μg ml^{-1} (20 Ci mM^{-1}) for long-term labelling.

2. *Thymine-requiring mutants*

Such mutants, defective in thymidylate synthetase, readily incorporate exogenous thymine into DNA since the defect results in a low pool of dTMP and a high pool of deoxyribose-1-phosphate. These strains are not convenient to use since they usually have a rather high thymine requirement (50 μg ml^{-1}) making labelling expensive. Secondary mutations that block the catabolism of deoxyribose-1-phosphate reduce the level of thymine required in the medium to 2 μg ml^{-1} or less. Many commonly used strains are of this type. Unfortunately, such strains possess a potential disadvantage: the rate of synthesis of DNA at the replication fork is limited by the exogenous concentration of thymine in the medium. This results in an altered cellular physiology particularly in the amount of DNA per cell mass and in the mass per cell or cell size (Pritchard and Zaritsky, 1970; Pritchard, 1974). These effects must be taken into account if one is, for example, measuring plasmid copy number as a percentage of cellular DNA (Section II.C.1). It is possible to avoid this problem by including high concentrations of deoxyguanosine (200 μg ml^{-1}) in the medium (Pritchard, 1974). This type of problem does not, however, affect estimates of copy number per chromosome origin because the number of chromosome origins per cell mass, unlike all other regions of the chromosome, is not altered in these strains (Section II.B).

(a) *Method for isolating thymine auxotrophs.* If no thymine-requiring mutants are available, they can be readily isolated as follows. An exponentially growing culture is diluted to about 5×10^2 cells per millilitre into minimal medium supplemented with required growth factors, thymine (200 μg ml^{-1}) and aminopterin (200 μg ml^{-1}) or trimethoprim (200 μg ml^{-1}) and incubated overnight at 37°C. Cells are plated on nutrient agar supplemented with thymine (200 μg ml^{-1}) and, after growth of the colonies, replica plated onto minimal agar plates without thymine. Colonies which fail to grow are mutant at the *thyA* locus and require relatively high levels of thymine for growth (O'Donovan, 1974). Derivatives also carrying a secondary mutation (*drm* or *dra*) and which require lower levels of thymine for growth can then be selected directly by plating the cells on minimal medium supplemented with 2–5 μg ml^{-1} thymine.

3. Balanced growth

For reproducible measurements of parameters such as plasmid copy numbers it is essential that the cultures are in balanced growth. This means that all measurable properties of the culture increase with the same doubling time. In practice, this situation is achieved by allowing the culture to grow for at least ten cell doublings before measurements are made. Normally, a fresh overnight culture is diluted 1000-fold and grown to a rather low optical density (typically $A_{450} = 0.3$–0.6). The culture should be maintained at this density by periodic dilution into fresh prewarmed medium. This procedure ensures that the growth of the cells never becomes limited by nutrients or aeration, and that DNA is fully labelled.

B. DNA–DNA hybridization

Complementary single strands of DNA can reassociate *in vitro* to form stable double-stranded molecules (Marmur and Lane, 1960: Doty *et al.*, 1960). This specific reaction can be used to measure copy number or replication rates of plasmids.

Two parameters are important: the rate of the reaction and its specificity. Both are dependent on the DNA used and the reaction conditions. In the simple situation of renaturation in liquid of a single species of DNA molecules, the rate of the reaction follows second-order kinetics of the form $-d(C)/dt = KC^2$ where C is the concentration of denatured DNA in bases per millilitre (Wetmur and Davidson, 1968). For a given concentration the rate of the reaction is inversely proportional to the complexity of the DNA, i.e. the total length of the sequence (Wetmur and Davidson, 1968). Thus, if a preparation of phage λ DNA (mol. wt 33 megadaltons) can reach a plateau of renaturation in, say, 5 h, plasmid R100 DNA (mol. wt 63 megadaltons) will take twice as long and *E. coli* chromosomal DNA (mol. wt 3000 megadaltons) 90 times as long (20 days).

In early hybridization experiments the reaction was run at high temperature, close to the melting temperature of the DNA (T_m). Marmur and Doty (1961) determined empirically that the maximum rate of reaction is obtained at approximately 25°C below T_m (Marmur *et al.*, 1963; Wetmur and Davidson, 1968). Prolonged exposure of DNA to high temperatures can, however, damage the molecule by causing strand breaks or depurination. The melting temperature of the DNA can be lowered by adding denaturing agents such as formamide (Bonner *et al.*, 1967; Kourilsky *et al.*, 1971), dimethylsulphoxide (Legault-Démare *et al.*, 1967) or urea (Kourilsky *et al.*, 1968) to the reaction. Thus, McConaughy *et al.* (1969) found that formamide lowers the T_m of *B. subtilis* DNA by 0.72°C per 1% formamide added. Reaction rates and melting temperatures increase with higher salt concentrations (Marmur *et al.*, 1963; Nygaard and Hall, 1964). The reaction rate at the optimum temperature is inversely proportional to solvent viscosity (Wetmur and Davidson, 1968).

For the study of plasmid copy number or of plasmid replication, the most convenient hybridization method is undoubtedly the nitrocellulose technique first described by Gillespie and Spiegelman (1965) for DNA–RNA hybrids and modified by various authors for DNA–DNA hybrids (Denhardt, 1966; Warnaar and Cohen, 1966; Legault-Démare *et al.*, 1967; Kourilsky *et al.*, 1971). In this technique, denatured unlabelled DNA is immobilized on a nitrocellulose filter and is challenged with labelled fragmented probe DNA. A sufficient fraction of the DNA sequences bound to the filter remains available for a specific hybridization reaction. When the reaction is completed, the unbound DNA is washed away and the amount of radioactivity remaining bound to the filter gives a measurement of the hybridization reaction.

The kinetics and the extent of the reaction in filter hybridization are much more complicated than in a liquid reaction and are often not easily predictable. Thus, while in liquid, the reaction rate increases with the size of the DNA fragments (Wetmur and Davidson, 1968) the reverse appears to be true in filter hybridization (Kourilsky *et al.*, 1970). One reason for such complexities is that in filter hybridization, annealing of the probe DNA to the filter-bound species competes with re-annealing of the probe DNA to itself.

For these reasons the absolute number of counts binding to a filter has little meaning. A normalization procedure is essential. In the method for copy number measurements outlined below the plasmid copy number is measured relative to a chromosomal marker of similar dimensions whose amount is itself determined by hybridization in the same reaction. A normalization is obtained by establishing a calibration curve, that is by introducing in the same reaction a series of filters loaded with carefully measured amounts of plasmid or chromosomal marker DNA. Such a reconstruction experiment provides an assurance that the reaction is linear, in other words that the number of specific counts bound is directly proportional to the amount of unlabelled plasmid marker. It also provides a good measurement of background binding, and, when the relative amount of two different markers is being compared, allows accurate corrections for differences in specific activities of the probe DNAs.

The specificity of the hybridization reaction on filters is affected by two types of artefacts: non-specific binding of the probe DNA to the filter and non-specific hybridization of probe DNA to the DNA sequences bound to the filter. Single-stranded DNA binds efficiently to nitrocellulose filters. If this happens during the hybridization reaction it will cause a background that can reach high levels. A number of methods have been devised to reduce this background to an acceptable level. These include an albumin pretreatment of the filters, after loading with the cold DNA (Denhardt, 1966), and an elution of non-hybridized DNA from filters with a buffer of low ionic strength and high pH (Warmaar and Cohen, 1966). Very low non-specific binding can also be achieved when the reaction is carried out in the presence of a denaturing agent such as formamide (Bonner *et al.*, 1967). This particular solution to the non-specific binding problem has additional advantages mentioned above. We describe below hybridization techniques using formamide as the denaturing agent.

In all hybridization experiments the amount of background binding of probe DNA to the filters should be determined and a correction for it made in the final calculations. This amount is higher for unloaded filters than for filters loaded with DNA. The filters used to measure background should therefore be loaded with an amount of calf thymus DNA similar to the amount of DNA loaded on the other filters.

The second type of background, hybridizing of probe DNA to heterologous sequences of the DNA bound to the filter, results from the accidental presence of short homologous sequences on both DNAs for any one of a number of causes (insertion sequences, evolutionary relationship etc.). The conditions of the hybridization reaction will determine how extensive such a spurious homology has to be before it contributes significantly to the background. In choosing these conditions a balance must thus be found between maximum specificity and maximum efficiency. McConaughy *et al.* (1969) have studied the effects of formamide concentration, salt concentration and temperature on both the extent and the specificity of the reaction. It appears from their work that the best compromise between reasonable working conditions and optimum reaction rate and specificity will be found at temperatures from 35 to 45°C, formamide concentrations between 30 and 50% and salt concentrations of 0.3 to 0.9 M.

In each experiment every effort must be made to determine the extent of this non-specific hybridization and correct the final results for it. This is not always easy.

Below, we call "background" the binding of probe DNA to the filter and "non-specific hybridization" its binding to heterologous portions of the DNA loaded on the filter.

1. Plasmid copy number

The "copy number" of a plasmid must be expressed in terms of some other significant cellular parameter. The copy number per cell has little meaning since cell growth and cell division are not always tightly coupled in *E. coli* and other bacteria. The copy number per cell mass is a more meaningful concept, but since cell mass and copy number must be measured by very different techniques a measurement of one relative to the other is subject to potentially large errors. The best reference parameter is the number of chromosomal replication origins, since this provides a direct comparison of plasmid and chromosomal replication and is not subject to the type of variation discussed in Section II.A. The number of chromosomal origins can be measured by hybridization under conditions nearly identical to those of the plasmid copy number and simultaneously with it (Bird *et al.*, 1972; Prentki *et al.*, 1977).

In a variety of experiments in *E. coli* we have used the Mu–1 prophage inserted close to the chromosomal replication origin, *oriC*, as an "origin marker" (Bird *et al.*, 1972; Chandler *et al.*, 1975; Prentki *et al.*, 1977). The advantages of this are that Mu–1 phage DNA can be used as a probe and that the amount of non-specific hybridization of Mu–1 DNA to *E. coli* chromosomal DNA can be readily measured. By using another prophage such as ϕ80 located near the terminus of the replication we can obtain, in one experiment, a complete picture of the state of chromosome replication (origin/terminus ratio), plasmid replication (plasmid/origin ratio) and, if desired, of DNA replication relative to cell mass (total DNA/mass measured by standard techniques) (Churchward *et al.*, 1981; Frey *et al.*, 1981).

If a prophage is not available as a marker for chromosomal origins, a plasmid containing a chromosomal segment located near the origin can be used (Yahara, 1971; Chandler *et al.*, 1976; Lycett *et al.*, 1980). It is not, however, usually possible in such a system to determine the extent of non-specific hybridization of that segment to the rest of the chromosome. To do so would require a strain in which the segment was deleted.

If neither of these methods is available, the amount of cell DNA could be measured directly on each filter, using the diphenylamine reaction (Meijs and Schilperoort, 1971) and the absolute amount of plasmid DNA on the filter determined by hybridization, using the calibration curve described below. One could thus obtain a copy number of plasmid per chromosome equivalent. The error could, however, be fairly large.

To illustrate the measurement of copy number of a plasmid relative to a chomosomal marker we will describe below the measurement of Pl prophage copy number (i.e. Pl established in plasmid form) (Prentki *et al.*, 1977).

(a) *Strains and DNA.* The strains used are LC537, a strain of *E. coli* carrying the prophages Plkc and Mu–1, the latter being inserted into *ilv*, very close to the origin of chromosome replication (Bachmann and Low, 1980), and its prophageless parental strain LC0129.

1. Grow a 500-ml culture of LC537 in the desired medium, monitoring the absorption at 450 nm to control growth. At $A_{450} = 0.3$ remove a 100-ml sample from the culture and pour onto 30 ml of crushed frozen growth medium containing 10% pyridine. Dilute the remaining culture 1:1 with fresh prewarmed medium, grow back to $A_{450} = 0.3$ and repeat the procedure twice more. (This

protocol provides a control for balanced growth and measures growth rate; the three growth curves between $A_{450} = 0.15$ and $A_{450} = 0.30$ should be parallel.)

2. Sample the remaining culture, plate for single colonies (if genetic tests are needed) and test for free Pl and Mu–1 phage. A free phage level of less than 10^{-3} per cell is essential.

3. Prepare a 300-ml culture of the control strain (LC0129). Since it will be used only for a measurement of non-specific hybridization the requirement for balanced growth is less critical and a single culture will be used. Grow it to $A_{450} = 0.3$ and treat the same as the first experimental culture.

4. Extract and purify the total DNA from the three samples of LC537 and the culture of LC0129, using the following method: centrifuge the cells and resuspend in 10 ml of DNA buffer (10 mM Tris-HCl, 50 mM EDTA pH 8.0). Centrifuge again and resuspend in 1 ml of DNA buffer. Add 100 μl of lysozyme (10 mg ml^{-1}) and incubate at 37°C for 15 min. Add 10μl of 10% Sarkosyl and 100 μl of RNAase (1 mg ml^{-1}) and incubate at 37°C. After 1 h add 100 μl of Proteinase K (20 mg ml^{-1}) and continue the incubation for a further 2 h. Adjust volume of the lysate to 1.6 ml and add 3.4 ml of CsCl solution (refractive index 1.4120). Layer this solution over 5.0 ml of CsCl (refractive index 1.4120) and centrifuge at 40 000 r/min for 16 h in a Beckman 50 Ti rotor. The DNA is collected by piercing the bottom of the tube. Usually it is not necessary to collect fractions as the presence of DNA is obvious with a marked increase in viscosity in the middle of the gradient. The DNA is dialysed against 10 mM Tris-HCl, 1 mM EDTA pH 8.0 and the concentration determined by the diphenylamine reaction (Burton, 1956).

(b) *Materials needed for hybridization*

1. Nitrocellulose membrane filters, 25-mm diameter, Sartorius SM113 (Millipore DA or HA, and Schleicher and Schuell B-6 filters have also been used).

2. 20 × SSC solution (3 M NaCl, 0.3 M sodium citrate adjusted to pH 7.0). This is diluted as needed.

3. Formamide: Merck, analytical grade. A good grade of formamide should be used. Various criteria of purity have been proposed: McConaughy *et al.* (1969) suggest that the optical density at 270 μm, 1 cm path length, of 100% formamide should not exceed 0.15; Brack (1981) asks that a 10% solution should have a conductivity less than ten times that of deionized water. If necessary, formamide can be purified by recrystallization (Robberson *et al.*, 1971) or passage on ion-exchange resins (Maniatis *et al.*, 1975).

4. A multiple unit filtering apparatus such as the New Brunswick DNA-40 or DNA-10, or Millipore 1225. Ten to twenty filters can be conveniently handled in one operation. A larger unit would not improve speed significantly.

5. An 80°C vacuum oven. If not available, a simple oven at 60°C can be used.

6. A vacuum desiccator.

7. A Branson Sonifier with microprobe.

8. Tweezers, pencil.

(c) *Preparing filters*

1. Write filter identification number with a soft pencil, near the edge, on the side to

be loaded with DNA. Do not at any time touch filters with fingers. Use tweezers and gloves throughout.
2. Soak filters for at least 30 min in 6 × SSC. Reject filters that do not wet properly. In our experience, long-term exposure of the filters to air results in poor wetting.

(d) *Preparing denatured DNA*

For the experiment described here, the following amounts of DNA should be available: 8 μg of calf thymus DNA (Sigma), 8 μg of DNA from each of the three cultures of the plasmid containing strain LC537, 48 μg of DNA from the plasmid-free strain LC0129, 4 μg of phage P1 DNA and 4 μg of phage Mu–1 DNA. Each point is in triplicate.

The filters used for copy number measurement are loaded each with 2 μg of DNA from the exponential cultures of LC537 (nine filters).

Filters loaded with 2 μg of calf thymus DNA are used for measuring background. A series of filters loaded each with a mixture of 2 μg of *E. coli* (LC0129) DNA and 0, 0.2, 0.4, 0.6, 0.8 or 1.0 μg each of unlabelled P1 and Mu-1 DNA are used to establish calibration curves.

1. Prior to denaturation, the DNA must be cut into fragments small enough so that all covalently closed circular plasmid molecules have been disrupted. They otherwise quickly renature. Treat each batch of DNA in a Branson Sonifier, using the microprobe, at maximum power for 1 min, in a 15-ml Corex tube. Although sonication for 1 min is sufficient for large plasmids such as P1 (90 kilobases), under our conditions 3 min are necessary for pBR322 (4.36 kilobases). An alternative technique (see below) is to boil the DNA in NaOH. Then, for each sample:
2. Prepare, in a 25-ml Erlenmeyer, 3 ml of 0.1 × SSC containing 8 μg of LC537 DNA, or for the calibration curve filters, 8 μg of *E. coli* DNA and 0, 0.8, 1.6, 2.4, 3.2 or 4 μg of each of the phage DNA. Place on ice.
3. Add 0.45 ml of 1 N NaOH. Stir occasionally for 10 min.
4. Add 0.45 ml of 1 N HCl and 1.40 ml of 20 × SSC. Control pH with pH paper and adjust to approximately 7.0.
5. Add 14.70 ml of 6 × SSC. Keep on ice until filtration, which should be carried out as soon as practical.

(e) *Loading filters*

1. Soak filters briefly in 6 × SSC, then place them on the multiple filtration unit. Wet with 5 ml of 6 × SSC, adjust vacuum on filtration unit for a slow drip (2–3 min for 5 ml).
2. Filter 5 ml of appropriate DNA solution. Rinse twice with 25 ml of 6 × SSC at low flow rate.
3. Drain filters on paper towel. Dry overnight under vacuum at room temperature in open large Petri dishes.
4. Bake for 2 h at 80 C in a vacuum oven, or 4 h at 60 C in an ordinary oven (a higher temperature may cause damage to filters in presence of oxygen). Store the dry filters in a desiccator over $CaSO_4$. They can be kept for several months but occasionally lose some hybridization capacity after two to three weeks. After storage, a 30-min bake at 80 C under vacuum, is advisable.

(f) *Probe DNA*

The filters are incubated with a mixture of denatured plasmid (Pl) DNA labelled with ^{14}C and chromosomal marker (Mu–1) DNA labelled with ^{3}H.

The amount of probe DNA should be in excess of the maximum expected amount of homologous DNA on the filter (Table I). Under the conditions described we have found that a linear response could be obtained with as little as a two-fold excess. A suitable amount, under the conditions described, is 0.2 μg of each species of probe DNA per filter. For the 48 filters of our hybridization we use a total of 10 μg each of Pl DNA and Mu–1 DNA.

TABLE I[a]

Prophage or plasmid	Copy number per chromosone origin	Molecular weight (megadaltons)	μg of DNA in 2 μg of bacterial DNA
Mu::*ilv*	1	24.8	0.037
λ::*attλ*	0.62	33.0	0.030
φ80::*att* φ80	0.54	30.4	0.024
R100–1	1	62.6	0.093
Pl	0.75	60.0	0.067
ColEl	10	4.4	0.065
pSC101	1.75	6.2	0.016

[a] Estimated amount of various prophages or plasmid DNA and chromosomal DNA loaded on filters. The cells are assumed to have been growing exponentially with a doubling time of 40 min. Under such conditions the amount of DNA per replicating chromosome will be 1.44 chromosome-equivalent and the number of replication origins per cell will be approximately 2.80 on the average (Sueoka and Yoshikawa, 1965; Cooper and Helmstetter, 1968; Chandler *et al.*, 1975; Bremer *et al.*, 1979). The values given for copy number are purely illustrative and do not necessarily come from a rigorous measurement.

An adequate specific activity for the ^{14}C-labelled DNA species would be 3500 c.p.m. μg^{-1} of DNA. Depending on the efficiency of the counting this could be achieved by labelling the culture used to produce the labelled phage DNA with ^{14}C-thymine at a final specific activity of 10–15 mCi mM^{-1}. For best discrimination in the scintillation counting of filters the ^{3}H-labelled DNA species should be two to three times more radioactive than the ^{14}C-labelled DNA. Radioactive probe DNA may also be prepared by nick translation (Rigby *et al.*, 1977).

(g) *Hybridization*

1. All the probe DNA needed for the hybridization experiment (0.2 μg × number of filters for each of the two species) is placed in 3 ml of 4 × SSC in a 15-ml screw cap tube. Add 3 ml of 1 N NaOH. Cap tightly. Immerse the tube, up to its cap, in boiling water for 10 min. The heat source must be sufficient to maintain boiling. This procedure will both denature the DNA and cut it to an average size of 1000 bases.

2. Add 3 ml of 1 N HCl and 1.5 ml of 20 × SSC. Complete to half the desired volume with 4 × SSC, adjust pH to approximately 7.0 and mix with an equal volume of formamide. The final volume should be 0.5 ml × (1 + number of filters) and be 2 × SSC, 50% formamide.
3. Place this mixture in a 300-ml beaker. Wet the filters with 2 × SSC, letting them sink into the liquid to avoid trapping air bubbles. Drain the filters briefly and place them into the hybridization mixture. When filters have sunk into mixture, top with a layer of mineral oil and cover the beaker tightly with Parafilm.
4. Incubate at 42 C for four or five days, preferably with gentle agitation, or with an occasional shaking by hand.
5. At the end of incubation, drain liquid and place the filters in a 500-ml beaker with 200 ml of a 2 × SSC, 50% formamide solution. Stir gently with a magnetic stirrer at room temperature for 30 min. Drain liquid and repeat for 15 min, then for 10 min with 2 × SSC and 10 min with 0.2 × SSC.
6. Drain filters. Dry at 40–50 C. Count.

(h) *Calculations*

1. Calculate the average number of ^{14}C and ^{3}H counts bound to the calf thymus filters. Subtract this background from all the other counts. This background correction is assumed in all the following discussion.
2. Plot the ^{14}C (plasmid) and ^{3}H (reference marker) average counts versus the amount of homologous DNA loaded on the calibration curve filters. They should fit a straight line. Extrapolation to zero gives the non-specific hybridization level of the probe to *E. coli* DNA.
3. Calculate the amount of ^{14}C and ^{3}H counts hybridized to the filters loaded with plasmid-containing strain (LC357). Compute the average of the nine points.
4. Evaluate the corresponding amount of plasmid (Pl) and reference marker (Mu–1) DNA from the calibration curve.
5. Divide each by the molecular weight of the corresponding DNA species (plasmid or phage molecular weight). The ratio of the two numbers gives the copy number of the plasmid relative to the chosen reference marker.

2. *Plasmid replication*

To study plasmid replication rates under a given set of experimental conditions, the plasmid-containing strain is pulse-labelled with ^{3}H-thymidine (or whatever is suitable) and its DNA is hybridized against filters loaded with plasmid DNA. Here again two normalization procedures are essential: the use of a reference chromosomal marker and the use of a reference culture allowing a comparison between the "experimental" and the "normal" replication rates. For example, the rate of replication of the plasmid ColEl in a *dna*A$_{ts}$* mutant of *E. coli* could be studied by a comparison of cultures under permissive and non-permissive conditions or by a comparison between the mutant and its wild-type parent under the same conditions.

* *dna*A$_{ts}$ mutants are defective in initiation of DNA replication at the non-permissive temperature of 42°C.

In the first case, the best strategy is that outlined in Frey *et al.* (1979): the plasmid-containing strain is first labelled during exponential growth with ^{14}C-thymine; unincorporated label is removed by centrifugation and the cells are allowed to grow for one doubling time in non-permissive conditions (e.g. high temperature) and aliquots are pulse labelled at various times with ^{3}H-thymidine. In the second case, two cultures are prepared; the reference culture is labelled with ^{14}C and the experimental culture with ^{3}H. The two cultures are mixed before extracting the DNA. As an example we shall describe an experiment in which the replication of the plasmid ColEl is followed in a $dnaA_{ts}$ *E. coli* strain.

(a) *Strains and labelling procedure*

The strain used is MUT49, a *thy* $dnaA_{ts}$ strain lysogenized with the prophage Mu–1 inserted in *ilv*, close to the origin of chromosome replication *oriC*, and containing the plasmid ColEl. The *thy dnaA* + parental strain LC0129, without plasmid or prophage, is also used.

1. Grow a culture of the strain MUT49 at 30 C in minimal medium supplemented with 10 μg ml^{-1} of Casamino acids and 2 μg ml^{-1} of ^{14}C-thymidine at a specific activity of 46 mCi mM^{-1} (some strains might need a higher thymine concentration for normal replication fork velocity; Section II.A).
2. At $A_{450} = 0.10$ the cells are harvested and washed with prewarmed medium by centrifugation and resuspended at the same concentration in the same medium with unlabelled thymine. They are incubated at 30 C to an absorption of $A_{450} = 0.2$.
3. The culture is shifted to 42 C. 2-ml samples are taken at various times (taking care to avoid thermal shocks) and pulse labelled with 1 μg of ^{3}H-thymidine with a specific activity of 20 Ci mM^{-1}.
4. After 4 min incubation, the pulse is stopped by adding 2 ml of iced stop solution. (To make stop solution mix just before the experiment: 200 ml of ethanol, 4 ml of phenol and 56 ml of an 80 mM Na acetate – 8 mM EDTA solution at pH 5.5.) The samples can be stored at −20 C until used for hybridization.
5. A culture of the *E. coli* LC0129 control strain is labelled with ^{14}C-thymine as described in (1), stopped and frozen as described in (4).

(b) *Loading filters*

1. Stocks of purified Mu–1, ColEl, *E. coli* (LC0129) and calf thymus DNA are prepared by standard procedures.
2. Filters are loaded with 1 μg of DNA, for each of the DNAs listed by the method described above. Each point is determined in duplicate or triplicate. The ColEl CCC DNA must be linearized either by sonication, use of a suitable restriction enzyme or digestion in hot NaOH.

(c) *Hybridization*

1. Thaw the frozen labelled cellular DNA samples. Wash twice, by centrifugation, in 2 ml of TSE2–NaCN buffer (0.05 M Tris, 0.05 EDTA, 0.5 M NaCl, 0.01 M NaCN, pH 8.0) and resuspend in 0.5 ml of the same buffer. Transfer to 15-ml screw cap tubes.
2. Add 0.5 ml of 1 N NaOH, close cap tightly, plunge up to cap into a boiling water bath for 10 min.
3. Cool on ice. Add 0.5 ml of 1 N HCl and 0.1 ml of Tris 1 M at pH 7.5. Adjust pH to 7.5.
4. Add 0.5 ml 16 × SSC and 2.1 ml of formamide.
5. Wet the prepared filters with 2 × SSC. Place one each of each type of filter (calf thymus, *E. coli*, Mu–1 and ColEl) in glass scintillation vials (or, better, similar vials but with a slightly larger diameter). Add 2 ml of hybridization mixture. Cap tightly.
6. Incubate at 40 C for five days with constant or occasional agitation.
7. Pool all the filters (if they were marked with identification numbers), rinse them and count them as described above.

(d) *Treatment of the data from hybridization experiments.* Table II gives an example of the treatment of the data. The ^{14}C and ^{3}H counts binding to each of the probe filters (column A and B, respectively) have been corrected for background binding to filters charged with calf thymus DNA (approximately 150 c.p.m. ^{14}C in columns A and 500 c.p.m. ^{3}H in column B). For the calculation of non-specific binding, ^{14}C-labelled DNA from strains LC0129 was hybridized to filters containing *E. coli*, Mu–1, and ColEl DNA under the same conditions as the other hybridizations. The percentage of LC0129 binding to each filter, relative to that binding to filters loaded with *E. coli* chromosomal DNA (Chr), was evaluated (column G). The same percentage of the amount of ^{14}C or ^{3}H binding to the *E. coli* chromosome filters in the experimental points (columns A and B) was subtracted from the amounts binding to each of the other filters to give the final values corrected for background and non-specific binding (columns H and I). The ratio of ^{3}H/^{14}C binding (I/H) is calculated.

These general techniques have been employed to measure the origin and direction of chromosome replication in wild-type (Bird *et al.*, 1972; Louarn *et al.*, 1974), integratively suppressed Hfr (Bird *et al.*, 1976; Chandler *et al.*, 1977) and normal, F Hfr strains of *E. coli* (Chandler *et al.*, 1976). They have also been used to investigate the replication properties of wild-type (Chandler *et al.*, 1975), $dnaA_{ts}$ (Frey *et al.*, 1979) and *rep* mutants (Lane and Denhardt, 1974) of *E. coli*, the copy number of Pl (Prentki *et al.*, 1977) and the dependence of plasmid replication on host replication functions (Frey *et al.*, 1979; Van Brunt *et al.*, 1977). They are potentially applicable to a wide variety of organisms.

TABLE II

Example of the treatment of the data from the hybridizations[a]

DNA on filter	Raw data		Non-specific binding (LCO129)		Corrected values		Ratio $^3H/^{14}C$
	A	B		G	H	I	I/H
	^{14}C c.p.m.	^3H c.p.m.	^{14}C c.p.m.	% of chromosome binding	A − (G×ChrA)	B − (G×ChrB)	
Chr[b]	9326	53598	36032	—	9326	53598	5.7
Mu–1	1561	5185	577	1.6	1411	4327	3.1
colEI	563	7772	180	0.5	516	7504	14.5

[a] The calculations for the data are explained in the text.
[b] Chr; E. Coli chromosome.

C. Centrifugation and other methods

1. Dye–caesium chloride gradients

This method relies on the fact that at saturating concentrations of intercalating dyes such as ethidium bromide, covalently closed circular DNA binds less dye than linear or open circular DNA and thus has a greater buoyant density (Bauer and Vinograd, 1968; Chapter 6). This allows a determination of the percentage of total DNA that is covalently closed (plasmid DNA). The protocol given below is essentially that described by Womble *et al.* (1977) with minor modifications and consists of centrifuging a total lysate containing all the cellular DNA after gently shearing. It is important that all the cellular DNA be loaded onto the gradient in order to avoid the inevitable losses of plasmid DNA that occur during selective removal of chromosomal DNA (Section II.C). Although this method is simple and straightforward, it suffers from several disadvantages when precise estimates of copy number are required. The major disadvantage is that only a minimum estimate can be obtained since any nicked plasmid DNA will band in the same position as linear bacterial DNA. This problem can be exacerbated by the presence of a variable fraction of the plasmid DNA in the form of relaxation complexes (Clewell and Helinski, 1969). On treatment of such protein–DNA complexes with some detergents, notably SDS, the supercoiled DNA is converted to a nicked circular form. Solutions of caesium chloride–ethidium bromide exert a similar effect (Clewell and Helinski, 1969). For ColEl, 20–80% of the plasmid DNA can be found in this form depending on the culture conditions (Clewell and Helinski, 1972).

Another problem, usually ignored, is that since the amount of total cellular DNA is used as a reference unit, care must be taken to ensure that cells are always grown under identical conditions. The DNA content of bacteria (per mass or optical density unit) is a function of growth rate (Schaechter *et al.*, 1958) as is the copy number of some plasmids (Engberg and Nordström, 1975; Pritchard *et al.*, 1977). This particular problem can be compounded by the use of low-thymine-requiring strains, discussed in Secion II.A, in which the DNA content can depend on the concentration of thymine present in the culture medium.

Method

1. A fresh overnight culture of the strain MX213 (*ilv*::Mu–1 *thy leu* λ*ind*) containing the plasmid is diluted 500- to 1000-fold into M9 medium (Adams, 1959) supplemented with 0.4% glucose and 0.2% Casamino acids (Difco) and containing 2 μg ml^{-1} of ^{3}H- or ^{14}C-thymine (1.0 μCi μg^{-1}). The culture is grown to $A_{450} = 0.3$–0.6 ($\sim 5 \times 10^7$ cells per millilitre).

2. The cells (10 ml) are harvested, washed in DNA buffer (10 mM Tris-HCl, pH 8.0, 50 mM EDTA) and resuspended in 1 ml of the same buffer; lysozyme (0.1 ml of a 5 mg ml^{-1} solution) is added and the suspension is incubated at 37°C for 10 min. 10 μl of 25% SDS are then added, followed by 0.1 ml of proteinase K (20 mg ml^{-1}), and the lysate is incubated first at 37°C for 2 h, then at 65°C for 30 min. Finally the lysate is sheared by gently drawing it into a 1-ml plastic disposable pipette 20 times.

3. For preparation of the density gradient 0.5 ml of ethidium bromide (2.5 mg ml^{-1}) is added to the lysate and the volume adjusted to 3.7 ml with DNA buffer Caesium chloride (3.45 g) is then added: the refractive index of the solution should be between 1.3890 and 1.3900. The mixture is poured into a polyallomer tube and the tube is filled with mineral oil and centrifuged at 40 000 r/min for 40 h at 15°C in a Beckman 50 Ti rotor.

4. The gradient is fractionated by piercing the bottom of the tube and collecting the drops (approximately 250) on Whatman 3MM paper strips (2 cm wide, ruled at 2-cm intervals). The strips are washed in a beaker three times with ice-cold 10% trichloracetic acid, and then with ethanol. After drying, the strips are cut up and the radioactivity corresponding to each drop is counted.

5. The lower peak of radioactivity, typically 1–5% of the total, corresponds to plasmid DNA and the fraction of the total radioactivity in this peak gives an estimate of the plasmid copy number. When comparing derivatives of the same plasmid with different molecular weights the results should be corrected for this difference since one is, in effect, measuring the weight of plasmid DNA.

A specific problem with some plasmids is that they segregate in the absence of selection. In these cases, selective media should be used and the fraction of plasmid-free cells in the culture should be determined by plating samples of the culture.

2. Preparation of replicative forms

Dye–caesium chloride gradients can also be used to isolate replicating molecules for analysis by electron microscopy (Chapter 7). This kind of analysis can be used to determine the origin and direction of plasmid replication. It is usually essential to enrich for replicative forms of the plasmid. In the most widely used technique (Lovett *et al.*, 1976) thymine-requiring cells are starved for thymine for one generation time then given a short pulse of thymine to allow rounds of replication to start. The pulse is rapidly terminated and the cells are gently lysed. Following the end of labelling, the lysates are then cleared by centrifugation (Clewell and Helinski, 1969) resulting in a supernatant enriched for plasmid DNA. This is centrifuged in a caesium chloride–ethidium bromide gradient. The region of the gradient between the linear and covalent closed circular DNA species contains replicating molecules. Although this technique works well for small plasmids, it has not been successful in our hands for obtaining replicative forms of large plasmids such as R100. The technique we have used for these plasmids is rather different: replicating molecules are allowed to incorporate bromouracil and, following complete lysis of the cells, rather than the production of a cleared lysate, they are separated on a gradient of caesium chloride making use of the fact that they are lighter than bulk DNA, probably because of an association with proteins or lipids (Silver *et al.*, 1977).

An alternative to synchronization by thymine starvation which is applicable to large plasmids in wild type cells is the use of hydroxyurea at subinhibitory concentrations. The effect of treatment of a culture with hydroxyurea is to reduce greatly the rate of movement of replication forks resulting in an accumulation of replicating molecules (Perlman and Rownd, 1975).

3. Analysis of plasmid replication by separation of CCC forms

Centrifugation techniques can also be used to analyse plasmid replication by measuring the incorporation of radioactivity into plasmid DNA species. A cleared lysate is produced and centrifuged. Any appropriate technique such as sedimentation in neutral or alkaline sucrose gradients or dye–caesium chloride equilibrium centrifugation can be used. For the analysis of covalently closed circular DNA, alkaline sucrose affords greater resolution since, up to a pH of 12.5, such species form a more compact structure than at neutral pH, whilst nicked circular and linear species are denatured under these conditions (Vinograd *et al.*, 1965).

4. Enzyme assay and antibiotic resistance

In principle, if the product of any plasmid-specified gene is synthesized in proportion to the number of gene copies (i.e. plasmids), copy numbers can be estimated by assaying the gene product. This can be a rapid and easy technique for the analysis of many samples, provided that the proportionality between enzyme level and plasmid copy number is rigorously established. Normally this requires the prior isolation of plasmid copy mutants. Examples include β-galactosidase assay for determining the copy number of an F' lac plasmid (Pritchard *et al.*, 1975) and β-lactamase (Tn3) assay for the multiple antibiotic resistance plasmid Rl (Uhlin and Nordström, 1977). The chloramphenicol acetyltransferase and streptomycin adenylase enzymes encoded by Rl also show copy number dependent synthesis (Uhlin and Nordström, 1977). These three Rl-encoded enzymes display similar behaviour in *S. typhimurium* and in *E. coli* (Stougaard *et al.*, 1979). Another example is the synthesis of a bacteriocin in *Serratia marcescens* (Timmis and Winkler, 1973).

The Rl-encoded β-lactamase enzyme is particularly useful since both the level of enzyme within the cell and the level of resistance conferred on the cell are proportional to the number of plasmid copies (Uhlin and Nordstrom, 1977). This is not true for chloramphenicol acetyltransferase or streptomycin adenylase (Uhlin and Nordström, 1977). This proportionality extends over at least a ten-fold range which means that copy numbers can be estimated simply by plating bacteria on different concentrations of ampicillin to find the lowest concentration that prevents colony formation. For Rl harboured by *E. coli* this is approximately 400 μg ml^{-1}. Copy mutants can be isolated by plating on high concentrations of the antibiotic, typically 1000–2000 μg ml^{-1}. The ampicillin gene is carried on a transposon, Tn3, which can be easily transposed onto other plasmids thus making the technique applicable to a wide variety of plasmids. A further application of the minimum inhibitory concentration of ampicillin is in the complementation analysis of copy mutants. If the mutant plasmids carry Tn3, whilst the wild-type plasmid is Ap^s, it is simple to see whether or not the presence of the wild-type plasmid reduces the copy number of the mutants (Molin *et al.*, 1981).

III. Curing and segregation of plasmids

A. Curing

It is often important or useful to obtain a microbial strain free of plasmid DNA. While certain plasmids, in certain bacterial hosts, undergo spontaneous segregation (and deletion), the majority of plasmids are stable, and plasmid-free cells are only rarely observed. In the case of stable plasmid species, agents must be employed which either increase the rate of spontaneous segregation (curing agents) or enrich for rare segregant clones. Unfortunately there is not yet a standard technique applicable to the large spectrum of plasmid–host systems currently under investigation.

Several of the currently available techniques are listed below. We have included only those procedures which are well characterized. It should be borne in mind, however, that failure to cure a certain trait does not necessarily mean that the trait is host-specified since many plasmids are refractory to curing. Nor is loss of a specific trait evidence that the plasmid under consideration has been cured since certain treatments may lead to selection for plasmid-deletion derivatives. In general, physical loss of the plasmid is best demonstrated by its absence as a CCC species using either density centrifugation of cleared lysates of the strain in caesium chloride–ethidium bromide gradients (Clewell and Helinski, 1969) or the more rapid procedures involving the analysis of partially purified plasmid DNA on agarose gels (e.g. Birnboim and Doly, 1979; Klein *et al.*, 1980; Chapters 6 and 9). In certain cases even this criterion may not be sufficient since many plasmids are able to undergo integration into the host chromosome and thus may not appear as

CCC molecules. In these cases, more sensitive techniques such as Southern blotting (Southern, 1975) of total DNA and hybridization with a plasmid-specific probe must be employed to demonstrate plasmid loss.

Agents that have been employed in isolating plasmid-free cells include intercalating dyes (Hirota, 1960; Bouanchaud *et al.*, 1969; Hahn and Ciak, 1971), coumermycin (Danislevskaya and Gregerov, 1980) and novobiocin (Novick, 1969), rifampicin (Riva *et al.*, 1973; Bazzicalupo and Tocchini-Valentini, 1972), mitomycin (Rheinwald *et al.*, 1973), sodium dodecylsulphate (SDS) (Tomoeda *et al.*, 1968; Salisbury *et al.*, 1972), temperature (May *et al.*, 1964; Stadler and Adelberg, 1972), limiting thymine (Clowes *et al.*, 1965; Pinney and Smith, 1971) and protoplast formation and regeneration (Hopwood, 1980; Novick *et al.*, 1980).

1. Intercalating dyes

Acriflavine, acridine orange, quinacrine and ethidium bromide have variously been used. Their mechanism of action seems to be a preferential inhibition of plasmid replication (Hohn and Korn, 1969).

Method. Grow overnight cultures, inoculated at a concentration of about 10^2–10^4 organisms per millilitre, in a series of tubes containing nutrient broth (pH 7.6) and various concentrations of the curing agent. In the case of acridine orange curing of *E. coli* K12 or C600, concentrations of between 10 and 100 μg ml^{-1} are used but the optimal concentration depends both on the bacterial strain and the particular agent. After overnight growth at 37°C, the culture tube that contains the highest concentration of curing agent that still allows visible growth should be plated on nutrient agar plates and isolated colonies tested for loss of the phenotype of interest. The success of this technique depends critically on the pH of the medium (Hirota, 1960) probably because of changes in permeability of the cells over the critical range (Silver *et al.*, 1968).

The method has been used successfully in curing members of the Enterobacteriaceae of the plasmid F and its derivatives (Hirota, 1960; Stouthamer *et al.*, 1963), of ColV-K94 (Kahn and Helinski, 1964) and of certain antibiotic resistance plasmids (Bouanchaud *et al.*, 1969). Other plasmids are refractory to curing by this technique. They include ColE1, ColE2 (Kahn and Helinski, 1964; Ozeki *et al.*, 1962), the antibiotic resistance plasmids of the FII (Watanabe and Fukasawa, 1962; Salisbury *et al.*, 1972) and I (Salisbury *et al.*, 1972) incompatibility groups and pSC101 (Wechsler and Kline, 1980). Intercalating dyes may also be useful in curing some staphyloccal plasmids (Bouanchaud *et al.*, 1969; Rubin and Rosenblum, 1971).

2. Coumermycin and novobiocin

These agents are known to inhibit DNA gyrase (Gellert *et al.*, 1976) and presumably exert their effect by preferentially inhibiting the DNA gyrase-dependent supercoiling of the plasmid molecule and thus plasmid replication (Gellert *et al.*, 1976).

Method. The procedure is identical to that for acridine curing. With coumermycin, curing of ColE1 derivative plasmids from *E. coli* C600 occurs at concentrations between 1 and $7\,\mu$g ml^{-1} (optimum $5\,\mu$g ml^{-1}). This concentration does not significantly reduce the viable count of the culture.

The technique has been successfully employed in curing high copy number ColE1-derived plasmids such as pMB9 and pBR322, and also pSC101 (Danilevskaya and Gragerov, 1980). It has also been used to cure certain *S. aureus* strains of penicillinase plasmids (Novick, 1969).

3. Rifampicin

Rifampicin, an inhibitor of RNA polymerase, has been used in curing plasmids both from *E. coli* and *S. aureus*. The effect of this antibiotic is presumably a preferential inhibition of an RNA polymerase-dependent step in the replication of certain plasmids.

Method. Again, the technique is similar to that for acridine curing. The range of rifampicin concentrations should be between 5 and 10 μg ml^{-1} for *E. coli* (Riva *et al.*, 1973). For *S. aureus*, much lower concentrations of the drug (0.01 μg ml^{-1}) have been employed (Johnston and Richmond, 1970). The size of the inoculum, temperature of incubation and the composition of the medium are all important factors (Riva *et al.*, 1973).

The technique has been used to cure plasmid F and its derivatives from *E. coli* (Riva *et al.*, 1973; Bazzicalpo and Tocchini-Valentini, 1970) and certain *S. aureus* plasmids (Johnston and Richmond, 1970).

4. Thymine limitation

This technique can only be used with a thymine-requiring auxotroph of the particular strain. It has only been employed, to our knowledge, with *E. coli*.

Method for curing. An overnight culture grown in 50 μg ml^{-1} of thymine in minimal medium is diluted to give approximately 10^7 organisms per millilitre into tubes containing minimal medium supplemented with various concentrations of thymine (usually between 0 and 25 μg ml^{-1}). The cultures are incubated overnight and plated at a suitable dilution onto thymine-supplemented nutrient agar. Individual colonies are then screened for plasmid loss.

Certain bacterial strains carry, in addition to the *thyA* mutation, a secondary mutation at the *dra* or *drm* locus, which enables them to grow on lower thymine concentrations (Section II.A). The thymine concentration required for growth of each strain should, therefore, be determined in advance.

This technique has been employed in curing the plasmid F, and plasmids which are refractory to curing by acridine orange, such as ColE1 and ColE2 (Clowes *et al.*, 1965).

5. Sodium dodecylsulphate (SDS)

The physical basis for this method of curing is the differential sensitivity to SDS of cells carrying conjugal plasmids and plasmid-free cells (Tomoeda *et al.*, 1968). Plasmid-carrying cells are presumed to be more sensitive to SDS because of the presence of plasmid-specified pili on the cell surface.

Method. An overnight culture is inoculated at a concentration of about 10^3–10^4 organisms per millilitre into rich medium containing 10% SDS and the culture is incubated for 48–72 h at 37°C. In the case of *S. aureus*, concentrations of 0.002% SDS have been employed (Sonstein and Baldwin, 1972). While most cells undergo lysis, the survivors are enriched for plasmid-free cells. Some pH dependence has been reported, with an optimum between pH 7.0 and 7.6 and, at least in the case of *E. coli*, growth in a synthetic medium may decrease the effectiveness of the technique (Tomoeda *et al.*, 1968). Care should be exercised when using the technique since it has been demonstrated that it may, in many cases, select cells carrying deletion derivatives of the plasmids, rather than cells from which the plasmid has been lost (Tomoeda *et al.*, 1968; Inuzuka *et al.*, 1969).

This technique has been employed to cure Enterobacteriaceae of the plasmid F (Tomoeda *et al.*, 1968), FII incompatibility group plasmids which are refractory to curing by intercalating dyes (Tomoeda *et al.*, 1968; Salisbury *et al.*, 1972) and I incompatibility group plasmids (Salisbury *et al.*, 1972). It has also been used with limited success in curing *S. aureus* plasmids (Sonstein and Baldwin, 1972).

6. Protoplast formation and regeneration

Recently it has been shown both in *S. aureus* (Novick *et al.*, 1980) and in the Streptomycetes (Hopwood, 1980) that protoplast formation and regeneration can lead to the loss of certain plasmids. Although the conditions involved are likely to vary from organism to organism, we think that attention should be drawn to it here as a general technique which is potentially applicable to a wide variety of organisms. We refer the reader to the references cited above and to Chapter 2 for further information.

7. Curing using incompatibility

This technique also has a potentially wide application. It demands, however, the availability of unstable or temperature-sensitive replication mutants of plasmids of similar type to the plasmid which is to undergo curing. It also requires that these derivatives carry a suitable selective marker which can be used to discriminate against the resident plasmid, that the resident plasmid confers a phenotype which can be used to screen for its loss and that suitable transformation, transduction or conjugation systems exist. The technique is based on plasmid incompatibility (Chapter 2), i.e. the inability of two similar plasmids to exist stably in the same cell. The derivative plasmid is introduced into the organism and selection for it is maintained for several generations of growth. Cells which have lost the resident plasmid are then grown for several generations under conditions which lead to the loss of the incoming plasmid (*e.g.* at the non-permissive temperature for a temperature-sensitive replication mutant).

This technique has been successfully employed in curing *S. cerevisiae* of its 2 μm plasmid (Toh-E and Wickner, 1981) and, in our laboratory, to cure strains of the pSC101 plasmid (P. Linder, unpublished data).

8. Additional enrichment procedures

In many cases, the curing methods described above can be used in conjunction with a procedure which enriches for plasmid-free cells. For example, in the case of antibiotic resistance, if the plasmid of interest specifies resistance to an antibiotic whose action is bacteriostatic (e.g. tetracycline), growth of the culture in the presence of this drug and a second bacteriocidal drug (e.g. penicillin, ampicillin or cycloserine) to which the cells are sensitive will result in enrichment for tetracycline-sensitive (non-growing) cells. Cycling the culture in rich medium with and without both drugs results in selection against tetracycline-resistant, plasmid-carrying cells in the population. The method is identical to that often employed in enrichment of auxotrophic mutations (Miller, 1972).

B. Segregation

Estimates of the stability of plasmids under certain conditions can be used to determine the extent of incompatibility between two plasmids (Cabello *et al.*, 1976), the manner in which host replication functions are involved in replication (Frey *et al.*, 1979) and, under special conditions, plasmid copy numbers (Hohn and Korn, 1969; Frey *et al.*, 1979). It has also been used to locate specific regions of plasmid genomes which are presumably involved with partitioning plasmid molecules to daughter cells during growth (Meacock and Cohen, 1980; Molin *et al.*, 1979; Miki *et al.*, 1980). Two methods are in current use and are described below.

1. Segregation curves

The first simply determines the relative proportion of segregant clones over many generations of cell growth. These are plotted on a semilogarithmic scale as a function of the number of generations of growth and the slope of the curve then gives the segregation rate (segregation per cell per generation). The disadvantage of this method is that it depends on the assumption that segregants and plasmid-carrying cells have identical growth rates. This is not always true.

In cases where plasmid replication can be arrested instantaneously, giving a segregation rate of 0.5 per cell per generation, extrapolation of the curve to zero time yields an estimate of the plasmid copy number. However, any disturbance in the growth of the culture during this treatment influences the interpretation of the results (e.g. Lane *et al.*, 1979).

2. The fluctuation test

The second method, the fluctuation test (Luria and Delbrück, 1943), was developed to measure mutation frequency and is not influenced by differences in growth rate of plasmid-carrying and plasmid-free cells in the population. A number of small tubes are inoculated with few cells so that a substantial number of the resulting cultures contain no segregants after overnight growth. The proportion of cultures in which no segregation has occurred is then ascertained and the average number of segregants calculated per culture according to the zero term in the Poisson distribution: $P(o) = e^{-s}$, where $P(o)$ is the proportion of cultures which carry no segregants and s is the average number of segregants per culture. Assuming that the number of cells in each overnight culture is considerably higher than the initial inoculum, the number of generations of growth which the cultures have undergone can be approximated by division of the total number of cells by $\log_e 2$. The rate of segregation per cell per generation can then be calculated using the average number of segregants per culture(s) and the mean number of generations.

It should be noted that with both these methods, the results will be sensitive to plasmid conjugal transfer during growth, if the plasmid under consideration is transmissible. Conditions in which this transfer does not occur, e.g. low cell densities, should be employed in these cases.

Acknowledgements

The experiments performed in our laboratory were supported by grant No. 3.591.79 from the Swiss National Science Foundation. We would like to acknowledge the important contributions of our collaborators: R. Bird, P. Beguin, M. Clerget, A. Epstein, J. Frey, M. Funderburgh, G. Kellenberger-Gujer, D. Lane, P. Linder, J.-M. Louarn, J. Louarn, M. Pougeon, P. Prentki, M. Ragenbass, D. Rifat, Y. Roth and L. Silver.

References

Adams, M. H. (1959). "Bacteriophages", p. 446. Wiley (Interscience), New York.
Bauer, W. and Vinograd, J. (1968). *J. Mol. Biol.* **33**, 141–171.
Bazzicalupo, P. and Tocchini-Valentino, G. P. (1972). *Proc. Natl. Acad. Sci. U.S.A.* **69**, 298–300.
Bird, R. E., Louarn, J., Martuscelli, J. and Caro, L. (1972). *J. Mol. Biol.* **70**, 549–566.
Bird, R. E., Chandler, M. and Caro, L. (1976). *J. Bacteriol.* **126**, 1215–1223.
Birnboim, H. C. and Doly, J. (1979). *Nucleic Acids Res.* **7**, 1513–1523.
Bonner, J., Kung, G. and Bekhor, I. (1967). *Biochemistry* **6**, 3650–3653.
Bouanchaud, D. H., Scauizzi, M. R. and Chabbert, Y. A. (1969). *J. Gen. Microbiol.* **54**, 417–425.
Brack, C. (1981). *Crit. Rev. Biochem.* **10**, 113–169.
Bremer, H., Churchward, G. and Young, R. (1979). *J. Theor. Biol.* **81**, 533–545.
Burton, K. (1956). *Biochemistry* **62**, 315–323.
Cabello, F., Timmis, K. and Cohen, S. (1976). *Nature (London)* **259**, 285–290.
Chandler, M., Bird, R. E. and Caro, L. (1975). *J. Mol. Biol.* **94**, 127–132.
Chandler, M., Silver, L., Roth, Y. and Caro, L. (1976). *J. Mol. Biol.* **104**, 517–523.
Chandler, M., Silver, L. and Caro, L. (1977). *J. Bacteriol.* **131**, 421–430.
Churchward, G., Estiva, E. and Bremer, H. (1981). *J. Bacteriol.* **145**, 1232–1238.
Clewell, D. B. and Helinski, D. R. (1969). *Proc. Natl. Acad. Sci. U.S.A.* **62**, 1159–1166.
Clewell, D. B. and Helinski, D. R. (1972). *J. Bacteriol.* **110**, 1135–1146.
Clowes, R. C., Moody, E. E. M. and Pritchard, R. H. (1965). *Genet. Res.* **6**, 147–152.
Cooper, S. and Helmstetter, C. E. (1968). *J. Mol. Biol.* **31**, 519–540.
Danilevskaya, O. N. and Gragerov, A. I. (1980). *Mol. Gen. Genet.* **178**, 233–235.
Denhardt, D. T. (1966). *Biochem. Biophys. Res. Commun.* **23**, 641–646.

Doty, P., Marmur, J. Eigner, J. and Schildkraut, C. L. (1960). *Proc. Natl. Acad. Sci. U.S.A.* **46**, 461–476.

Engberg, B. and Nordström, K. (1975). *J. Bacteriol.* **123**, 179–186.

Frey, J., Chandler, M. and Caro, L. (1979). *Mol. Gen. Genet.* **174**, 117–126.

Frey, J., Chandler, M. and Caro, L. (1981). *Mol. Gen. Genet.* **182**, 364–366.

Gellert, M., Mizuuchi, K., O'Dea, M. H., Itoh, T. and Tomizawa, J.-L. (1977). *Proc. Natl. Acad. Sci. U.S.A.* **74**, 4772–4776.

Gillespie, D. and Spiegelman S. (1965). *J. Mol. Biol.* **12**, 829–842.

Hahn, F. E. and Ciak, J. (1971). *Ann. N.Y. Acad. Sci.* **182**, 295–304.

Hirota, Y. (1960). *Proc. Natl. Acad. Sci. U.S.A.* **46**, 57–64.

Hohn, B. and Korn, D. (1969). *J. Mol. Biol.* **45**, 385–395.

Hopwood, D. A. (1980). *In* "International Symposium on Actinomycete Biology" (K. P. Schaal, Ed.). Fischer, Stuttgart.

Inuzuka, N., Nakanupa, S., Inuzuka, M. and Tomoeda, M. (1969). *J. Bacteriol.* **100**, 827–835.

Johnston, J. H. and Richmond, M. H. (1970). *J. Gen. Microbiol.* **60**, 137–139.

Kahn, P. L. and Helinski, D. R. (1964). *J. Bacteriol.* **88**, 1573–1579.

Kahn, P. L. and Helinski, D. R. (1965). *J. Bacteriol.* **90**, 1276–1282.

Klein, R. D., Selsing, E. and Wells, R. D. (1980). *Plasmid* **3**, 88–91.

Kourilsky, P., Marcaud, L., Sheldrick, P. and Luzzati, D. (1968). *Proc. Natl. Acad. Sci. U.S.A.* **61**, 1013–1020.

Kourilsky, P., Leidner, J. and Tremblay, G. Y. (1971). *Biochimie* **53**, 1111–1114.

Lane, D. and Denhardt, D. (1974). *J. Bacteriol.* **120**, 805–814.

Lane, D., Chandler, M., Silver, L., Bruschi, A. and Caro, L. (1979). *Mol. Gen. Genet.* **168**, 337–340.

Legault-Démare, J., Desseaux, B., Heyman, T., Séror, S. and Ress, G. P. (1967). *Biochem. Biophys. Res. Commun.* **28**, 550–557.

Louarn, J., Funderberg, M. and Bird, R. E. (1974). *J. Bacteriol.* **120**, 1–5.

Lovett, M. A., Katz, L. and Helinski, D. R. (1974). *Nature (London)* **251**, 337–340.

Luria, S. E. and Delbrück, M. (1943). *Genetics* **28**, 491.

Lycett, G., Orr, E. and Pritchard, R. H. (1980). *Mol. Gen. Genet.* **178**, 329–336.

McConaughy, B. L., Laird, C. D. and McCarthy, B. J. (1969). *Biochemistry* **8**, 3289–3295.

Maniatis, T., Jeffrey, A. and van de Sande, H. (1975). *Biochemistry* **14**, 3787–3794.

Marmur, J. and Lane, D. (1960). *Proc. Natl. Acad. Sci. U.S.A.* **46**, 453–460.

Marmur, J., Rownd, R. and Schildkraut, C. L. (1963). *Prog. Nucleic Acid Res.* **1**, 231–300.

May, J. W., Houghton, R. H. and Perret, C. J. (1964). *J. Gen. Microbiol.* **37**, 157–169.

Meacock, P. A. and Cohen, S. N. (1980). *Cell* **20**, 529–542.

Meijs, W. H. and Schilperoort, R. A. (1971). *FEBS Lett.* **12**, 166–168.

Miki, T., Easton, A. M. and Rownd, R. H. (1980). *J. Bacteriol.* **141**, 111–120.

Miller, J. H. (1972). "Experiments in Molecular Genetics". Cold Spring Harbor, New York.

Molin, S., Stougaard, P., Uhlin, B. E., Gustafson, P. and Nordström, K. (1979). *J. Bacteriol.* **138**, 70–79.

Molin, S., Stougaard, P., Light, J., Nordström, M. and Nordström, K. (1981). *Mol. Gen. Genet.* **181**, 123–130.

Novick, R. P. (1969). *Bacteriol. Rev.* **33**, 210–235.

Novick, R. P., Sanchez-Rivas, C., Gruss, A. and Edelman, J. (1980). *Plasmid* **3**, 348–358.

Nygaard, A. P. and Hall, B. D. (1964). *J. Mol. Biol.* **9**, 125–142.

O'Donovan, G. (1978). *In* "DNA Synthesis Present and Future" (I. Molineux and M. Kohiyama, Eds), pp. 219–252. Plenum, New York.

Ozeki, H., Stocker, B. A. D. and Smith, S. M. (1962). *J. Gen. Microbiol.* **28**, 671–687.

Perlman, D. and Rownd, R. H. (1975). *Mol. Gen. Genet.* **138**, 281–291.

Pinney, R. J. and Smith, J. T. (1971). *Genet. Res.* **18**, 173–177.

Prentki, P., Chandler, M. and Caro, L. (1977). *Mol. Gen. Genet.* **152**, 71–76.

Pritchard, R. H. (1974). *Philos. Trans. Soc. London Ser. B* **267**, 303–336.

Pritchard, R. H. and Zaritsky, A. (1970). *Nature (London)* **226**, 126–131.

Pritchard, R. H., Chandler, M. and Collins, J. (1975). *Mol. Gen. Genet.* **138**, 143–155.

Rheinwald, J. G., Chakrabarty, A. M. and Gunsalus, I. C. (1973). *Proc. Natl. Acad. Sci. U.S.A.* **70**, 885–889.

Rigby, P., Dieckman, M., Rhodes, C. and Berg, P. (1977). *J. Mol. Biol.* **113**, 237–251.

Riva, S., Fietta, A., Berti, M., Silvestri, L. G. and Romero, E. (1973). *Antimicrob. Agents Chemother.* **3**, 456–462.

Robberson, D., Aloni, Y., Attardi, C. and Davidson, N. (1971). *J. Mol. Biol.* **60**, 473–484.

Rubin, S. J. and Rosenblum, E. D. (1971). *J. Bacteriol.* **108**, 1200–1204.

Salisbury, V., Hedges, R. W. and Datta, N. (1972). *J. Gen. Microbiol.* **70**, 443–452.

Schaechter, M., Maaløe, O. and Kjelgaard, N. O. (1958). *J. Gen. Microbiol.* **19**, 592–606.

Silver, L., Chandler, M., Boy de la Tour, E. and Caro, L. (1977). *J. Bacteriol.* **131**, 929–942.

Silver, S., Levine, E. and Spielman, P. M. (1968). *J. Bacteriol.* **95**, 333–339.

Sonstein, S. and Baldwin, J. N. (1972). *J. Bacteriol.* **109**, 262–265.

Southern, E. M. (1975). *J. Mol. Biol.* **98**, 503–517.

Stadler, J. and Adelberg, E. A. (1972). *J. Bacteriol.* **109**, 447–449.

Stougaard, P., Molin, S. and Nordström, K. (1979). Plasmid Rl in *Salmonella typhimurium*: molecular instability and gene dosage effects.

Stouthamer, A. H., de Haan, P. G. and Bulten, E. J. (1963). *Genet. Res.* **4**, 305–317.

Sueoka, N. and Yoshikawa, H. (1965). *Genetics* **52**, 747–757.

Timmis, K. and Winkler, V. (1973). *Mol. Gen. Genet.* **124**, 207–217.

Toh-E, A. and Wickner, R. B. (1981). *J. Bacteriol.* **145**, 1421–1424.

Tomoeda, M., Inuzuka, M., Kubo, N. and Nakamura, S. (1968). *J. Bacteriol.* **95**, 1078–1089.

Uhlin, B. and Nordström, K. (1977). *Plasmid* **1**, 1–7.

Van Brunt, J., Waggoner, B. and Pato, M. L. (1977). *Mol. Gen. Genet.* **150**, 285–292.

Vinograd, J., Lebowitz, J., Radloff, R., Watson, R. and Laipis, P. (1965). *Proc. Natl. Acad. Sci. U.S.A.* **53**, 1104–1111.

Warnaar, S. O. and Cohen, J. A. (1966). *Biochem. Biophys. Res. Commun.* **24**, 554–558.

Watanabe, T. and Fukasawa, T. (1961). *J. Bacteriol.* **81**, 679–983.

Watanabe, T. and Ogata, G. (1966). *J. Bacteriol.* **91**, 43–50.

Weschsler, J. and Kline, B. C. (1980). *Plasmid* **4**, 276–280.

Wetmur, J. G. and Davidson, N. (1968). *J. Mol. Biol.* **31**, 349–370.

Womble, D. D., Taylor, D. P. and Rownd, R. H. (1977). *J. Bacteriol.* **130**, 148–153.

Yahara, I. (1971). *J. Mol. Biol.* **57**, 373–376.

6
Isolation and Purification of Plasmid DNA

J. GRINSTED AND P. M. BENNETT

Department of Microbiology, University of Bristol, Medical School, Bristol, UK

I. Introduction

The main problem to be overcome in the preparation of plasmid DNA is its separation from chromosomal DNA, since the plasmid usually comprises no more than about 5% of the total DNA. The physical characteristics that permit separation are the relatively small size of plasmids, their covalently closed structure, and the fact that they are not bound to other cellular components in a lysate. (It should be noted that chromosomal DNA is very large (in *Escherichia coli*, for example, about 4000 kilobases), so that lysis of the bacteria and manipulation of the lysate inevitably results in random shearing of the molecules. In general, the size of the resulting fragments of chromosomal DNA will depend on the vigour with which the lysate has been handled.) In this chapter, we start by describing the properties of covalently closed circular (CCC) DNA that permit its separation from other forms of DNA. Methods that are successfully used in this laboratory for the isolation of plasmid DNA are then described. Other chapters in this volume describe related techniques and these will be referred to as appropriate. There are a number of books on the market that contain advice on the sort of techniques that are described here; we especially recommend the manual entitled "Molecular Cloning" from Cold Spring Harbor (Maniatis *et al.*, 1982).

METHODS IN MICROBIOLOGY
VOLUME 17   ISBN 0–12–521517–7

II. Nature of CCC DNA

Plasmids are isolated as circular molecules that are covalently closed in each of the two single strands. Since the two single strands are wound round each other to give the double helix, a consequence of this covalent closure of both strands is that they are inextricably linked together; the strands cannot escape from each other even if the forces that normally keep them together in the double helix are broken. They are linked together by topological bonds. Such binding requires that both of the single strands be covalently closed, since a single break in just one strand will introduce a point of free rotation that will allow the now discontinuous strand to wind off the other and escape. This topological binding is the basis of methods of plasmid isolation which use high pH. At pH 12.5 the forces that hold the double helix together are disrupted (i.e. the DNA is denatured). When the solution is neutralized, the DNA can renature, provided that complementary strands can find each other again. With linear DNA, or circular DNA which is not covalently closed in both strands, the complementary strands would have completely separated from each other, but with CCC DNA this is not the case. Thus, CCC DNA will preferentially renature and can be separated from other forms of DNA, which will still be single-stranded.

The topological linking of the two single strands in CCC DNA is described by the linking number (α), which is the net number of times one of the strands crosses the other. The linking number of a CCC DNA molecule is a constant; it cannot be changed unless there is a break in one of the strands so that this strand can rotate with respect to the other. The linking number is related to the double helix in the following way.

$$\alpha = \alpha_0 + \Delta\alpha. \qquad (6\text{--}1)$$

where α_0 is approximately numerically equal to the number of turns of the double helix in a linear molecule of identical size, and $\Delta\alpha$ is the difference between α and α_0. With all naturally occurring CCC DNA, $\alpha < \alpha_0$. Thus, $\Delta\alpha$ is negative and the molecules are supercoiled in a right-handed sense with $\Delta\alpha$ approximately equal to the number of supercoils. Supercoiled molecules are strained with respect to the open form. Thus, supercoils can only be maintained if the two single strands of the double helix are constrained from rotating with respect to each other, as in CCC DNA. Wang (1980) and Bauer et al. (1980) give straightforward descriptions of the properties of CCC DNA.

α_0 is determined by the dimensions of the double helix (see above). If these are changed in CCC DNA, then $\Delta\alpha$ must also change in step because α is constant (see above). α_0 can be changed by the addition of ethidium bromide (EB); this drug intercalates the base pairs of the double helix, lengthening and unwinding it (Radloff *et al.*, 1967). Thus, in the presence of EB, α_0 of CCC DNA is decreased. With natural CCC DNA (where $\alpha < \alpha_0$ in the absence of EB, see above), the consequence of adding increasing concentrations of EB will be that $\Delta\alpha$, which starts at some negative value, will become zero and then, as the concentration of EB increases, will become positive. To put it another way, right-handed supercoils will be removed and will eventually be replaced by left-handed supercoils. Since supercoiled molecules are in a state of strain (see above), unwinding of the supercoils is energetically favoured and the establishment of supercoils is disfavoured. Thus, when $\alpha < \alpha_0$ (at low concentrations of EB) EB will preferentially bind to CCC DNA (compared to other forms of DNA); but when $\alpha > \alpha_0$ (at high concentrations of EB) the reverse is the case since binding of the drug to CCC DNA will now result in the generation of supercoils. Thus, at high concentrations of EB, CCC DNA binds less of the drug than do other forms of DNA. This is the basis of CsCl/EB gradients; binding of EB to DNA reduces its density and since, at high drug concentrations CCC DNA binds less of the drug than other forms of DNA, its density will be reduced less. This density difference is exploited with the CsCl density gradient.

III. Rapid methods for analysis of plasmid DNA

There are numerous methods by which plasmids can be separated from chromosomal DNA without the need for CsCl/EB gradients. It should be noted that such rapid preparations will invariably be contaminated to a greater or lesser extent with chromosomal DNA. For most purposes, however, this does not matter and such preparations will usually be adequate for analysis with restriction enzymes, for transformation and also in many cases for cloning. The great advantage of these methods of preparation is their speed and capacity: many preparations can be made at the same time. It should be noted that to take full advantage of these methods a microfuge is required (we use the Eppendorf 5414). Scaled-up versions of the methods for removing the bulk of chromosomal DNA are also used as the first stage in the preparation of purified plasmid DNA (Section IV).

A. Analysis of plasmid content of bacteria

In certain circumstances (e.g. in the preliminary screening of strains) a simple procedure that just displays the plasmids contained by a strain is required. Such methods involve lysis of the bacteria with SDS. This can be performed within a well of the agarose gel that is to be used for analysis (Eckhardt, 1978), or in an Eppendorf tube, followed by a clearing spin to remove the bulk of the chromosomal DNA. The plasmids are then displayed by electrophoresis through agarose gels. A suitable set of plasmids of known molecular weight run in the same gel will give an estimate of the sizes of the CCC plasmids. Such methods are extremely fast and the number that could be done in a day is limited only by the electrophoretic analysis (Chapter 9).

B. Rapid methods for preparation of plasmid DNA

To isolate plasmid DNA, first the cells have to be lysed, and second the bulk of the chromosomal DNA must be removed. These two requirements are related because the method of lysis and the vigour with which the lysate is treated will determine what methods for the removal of chromosomal DNA can be employed. For example, the method for *E. coli* described in detail below lyses the bacteria relatively gently (lysozyme followed by lysis with the detergent Triton X–100); the resulting lysate can be cleared of the bulk of its chromosomal DNA with a clearing spin (presumably the chromosomal DNA is attached in some way to membrane fragments). However, some bacteria are not lysed by this procedure, whereas others (including some strains of *E. coli*) are lysed but the chromosomal DNA does not pellet when the lysate is centrifuged.

Methods that should be applicable to a wide range of bacterial species are those that involve lysis with SDS followed by denaturation and selective renaturation; SDS should lyse most bacteria and dissociate DNA from proteins etc., and selective renaturation is dependent only on the properties of DNA, so that separation of the plasmid should not depend on the particular properties of the bacteria. Such a method is that of Birnboim and Doly (1979), which is described in detail in Chapter 9. We have used this technique to isolate plasmids from both wild type and laboratory strains of *E. coli* and also from strains of *Providencia stuartii*. We use 1–1.5 ml of an overnight broth culture and then follow the published procedure. This gives enough DNA for one restriction enzyme digest even from low copy number plasmids. The procedure works reliably with both small and large plasmids.

With respect to strains of *E. coli* that are used in the laboratory, we have found that Triton X–100 lysis followed by a clearing spin can give good results. Since such strains are used widely for experiments with plasmids, we shall describe in detail this method. The described procedure is for 10 ml of an overnight culture in nutrient broth in a Universal bottle. All manipulations are carried out at room temperature on the bench. Apart from the initial harvesting, 1.5-ml plastic Eppendorf tubes are used throughout and all centrifugation is carried out in a microfuge.

1. Harvest the culture in a bench-top centrifuge (spin for 10 min) and resuspend the bacterial pellet in 0.4 ml of sucrose (25%), Tris-HCl (50 mM, pH 7.5). Transfer the suspension to 1.5-ml plastic Eppendorf tube.
2. Add 50 μl of lysozyme solution (10mg ml^{-1} in water) and mix. Leave for 20 min (or a few minutes at 55°C).
3. Add 0.1 ml of Na$_2$EDTA (0.2 M, pH 8) and then 0.4 ml of Triton X–100 (2% v/v), Tris-HCl (50 mM, pH 7.5), EDTA (50 mM). Mix by inversion. Lysis usually occurs immediately, although in some cases the mixture may have to be left for a few minutes. In general, lysis is not complete, so a transparent solution should not be expected.
4. Spin for 5 min (this is the clearing spin). Remove supernatant with an automatic pipette. Alternatively, the pellet can usually be removed by sucking it into a pipette and pulling it out of the tube. Discard pellet.
5. Fill tube with buffered phenol (Section V describes its preparation). Vortex, then spin for 1 min (this is a phenol extraction to remove protein). Remove the aqueous (top) phase containing DNA, avoiding collecting the denatured protein at the interface (but don't worry if some of this is sucked up). Discard phenolic (bottom) phase.
6. Add about 1/10th volume of 4 M Na acetate (pH 6) and 6/10ths volume of isopropanol (typically, there will be about 0.8 ml to which will be added 70 μl of Na acetate and 0.5 ml of isopropanol). Mix by inversion and then spin for 5 min. Remove supernatant by decanting, or with a pipette, and discard.
7. Add 1 ml of ethanol and spin for 1 min. Decant and discard supernatant.
8. Dissolve pellet in 0.5 ml of Tris-HCl (10 mM, pH 7.5), EDTA (0.1 mM) containing boiled RNAase A (10 μg ml^{-1}). (It is not necessary to remove the last drop of ethanol before dissolving.) Leave for 10 min.
9. Add 50 μl of Na acetate (4 M) and 0.3 ml of isopropanol. Mix by inversion. Spin for 5 min. Discard supernatant.
10. Add 1 ml of ethanol and spin for 1 min. Discard supernatant.
11. Add 1 ml of ether and spin for 1 min. Discard supernatant.
12. Leave pellet to dry (for a few minutes) and then dissolve in 100 μl of Tris-HCl (pH 7.5), EDTA (0.1 mM).

The pellet should be readily visible after the first isopropanol precipitation; it will be dramatically diminished by the RNAase treatment; and it tends to come loose from the side of the tube when ethanol and, particularly, ether is added, so care must be taken at this stage. It should also be noted that the precipitated DNA is often distributed up the sides of the tube and will not become visible until it is dried.

10 μl of such a preparation should be sufficient for analysis with restriction enzymes (Chapter 8). In addition to being susceptible to restriction enzymes, such preparations can be used for transformation and in cloning experiments. As regards the speed of preparation, one person with two microfuges can make 48 preparations in 2–3 h.

IV. Preparation of pure plasmid DNA

Pure plasmid DNA is prepared by running lysates in CsCl gradients in the presence of high concentrations of EB (Section II). This treatment usually results in a density differential of 0.04–0.05 g ml^{-1} (depending on the EB concentration) between the chromosomal DNA and CCC DNA (the plasmid in this case). CsCl gradients are established by centrifugation and therefore, have to be run for several hours to establish the equilibrium gradient. Until relatively recently, angle rotors were usually used for CsCl gradients (e.g. Chapter 5); the time required to establish equilibrium gradients in these rotors is a minimum of 40 h. However, recently, vertical rotors have been introduced. In these the centrifuge tubes stand vertically in the rotor so that their length is parallel to the axis of rotation; CsCl gradients can be formed in these in as little as 5 h. During spinning, the gradient and any bands of DNA therein are obviously oriented with respect to the axis of rotation (i.e. the gradient is formed across the width of the tube). Surprisingly, perhaps, the gradient reorients smoothly as the rotor slows down so that at rest the bands are horizontal.

Prior to CsCl/EB gradient centrifugation, bacteria are treated with one of the methods discussed in Section III to remove the bulk of the chromosomal DNA, otherwise the gradients will be overloaded. In the method that is described below, a scale-up of the Triton X–100 lysis/clearing spin method is used for this purpose. But, of course, the procedure actually adopted will depend on the actual strain to be used; the method here works well with laboratory strains of *E. coli*. The following is for 1 litre of overnight culture grown in nutrient broth.

1. Harvest the culture and resuspend in 10 ml of sucrose (25% w/v), Tris-HCl (50 mM, pH 7.5).
2. Add 0.6 ml of lysozyme solution (30 mg ml^{-1} in water) and mix. Leave at room temperature for 20–30 min (or 15 min at 37°C).
3. Add 5 ml of Na$_2$EDTA (0.2 M, pH 8) and 10 ml of Triton X–100 (2% v/v), Tris-HCl (50 mM, pH 7.5), EDTA (0.05 M). Mix by inversion.
4. Spin at 15 000 r/min and 5°C for 15 min (this is the clearing spin). This should give a fluffy, relatively compact pellet. (Spin for longer if necessary.) If the pellet occupies a substantial proportion of the tube, it is possible that the initial volume used to resuspend the bacteria was too small. Decant supernatant (discard pellet).
5. Add an equal volume of buffered phenol (Section V). Mix thoroughly by inversion and then spin for 5–10 min at 15 000 r/min. Remove the upper aqueous phase and discard the phenolic phase.
6. To 20 ml add 1.7 ml of Na acetate solution (4 M, pH 6) and 12 ml of isopropanol. Mix and then spin for 25 min at 15 000 r/min and 5°C. Decant and discard supernatant.
7. Fill tube with ethanol and spin briefly. Decant and discard supernatant.

8. Dry pellet and resuspend in 3.5 ml of Tris-HCl (10 mM, pH 7.5), EDTA (0.1 mM). Add 0.2 ml of EB solution (10 mg ml^{-1} in water) and 3.7 g of CsCl. Agitate gently to dissolve the CsCl.
9. Check the refractive index of the solution. This should be about 1.386 (density 1.55 g ml^{-1}). We use a simple sugar refractometer and aim for a reading of 34–35%. If the preparation is not cleaned up with phenol, the refractive index at this stage would be about 38% on our instrument.
10. The solution is put into a 5-ml polyallomer centrifuge tube (Dupont-Sorvall Cat. No. 03127). About 4.6 ml of solution is required to fill the tube. If necessary, add a CsCl solution of the same density. Spin in the vertical Sorvall rotor (Catalogue TV865) at 55 000 r/min and 15 C for 5 h, or at 48 000 r/min and 15 C overnight, in a Sorvall OTD65 centrifuge.

The tube is removed from the rotor and illuminated with ultra-violet light; the tube is transparent to ultra-violet light and the DNA appears as bright orange fluorescent bands. There is usually also a purple pellicle on top of the solution and running down the inside of the tube (this is protein) and a bright fluorescent strip running down one side of the tube (RNA). The pellicle can be removed (it sticks very nicely to a disposable plastic spatula); the upper band of chromosomal DNA is then removed with a syringe and discarded; then the lower band of plasmid DNA is removed with a clean syringe. If a second CsCl/EB spin is needed, this plasmid solution can immediately be diluted with a CsCl solution of the correct density (1.55 g ml^{-1}, see above), a little EB is added and the mixture spun again as before.

To extract the plasmid from the CsCl/EB solution the following procedure is used.

1. Dilute the solution three-fold with Tris-HCl (10 mM, pH 7.5) and distribute this solution into 1.5-ml plastic Eppendorf tubes such that each tube contains 0.8 ml (typically, two or three tubes will be required).
2. To each tube add 70 μl of Na acetate (4 M, pH 6) and 0.5 ml of isopropanol. Mix by inversion. Spin for 5 min in a microfuge at room temperature. Decant supernatant and discard.
3. Add 1 ml of isopropanol solution (40% v/v containing 0.2 M Na acetate, pH 6) to remove last drops of CsCl solution. Spin for 1 min. Decant and discard supernatant.
4. Add 1 ml of ethanol, spin and decant and discard the supernatant.
5. Dissolve and combine the pellets in a total of 0.8 ml of Tris-HCl (10 mM, pH 7.5).
6. Add equal volume of buffered phenol (Section V). Mix thoroughly and spin for 1 min. Remove the upper aqueous phase and discard the lower phase.
7. Add 70 μl of Na acetate (4 M, pH 6) and 0.5 ml of isopropanol. Mix and spin for 5 min. Remove and discard the supernatant.
8. Add 1 ml of ethanol, spin for 1 min, and remove and discard the supernatant.
9. Add 1 ml of ether, spin for 1 min and remove and discard the supernatant.
10. Dry pellet (a few minutes on the bench) and dissolve in, say, 500 μl of Tris-HCl (10 mM, pH 7.5), EDTA (0.1 mM).

This procedure for the extraction of plasmids from CsCl/EB solutions is very fast (about 15 min from rotor to a clean solution ready for analysis). It should be noted that no special effort is expended to remove the EB; the precipitations and the phenol treatment are quite sufficient. One other point about this procedure is that very often a red non-fluorescent band (it can be seen in daylight) is seen very close to the plasmid band in the CsCl/EB gradient (if it is coincident it quenches the fluorescence of the plasmid in the ultra-voilet). It is presumably a carbohydrate–EB complex (it does not occur if poly ethylene glycol is used for precipitation of the cleared lysate instead of isopropanol). Its position relative to the plasmid is easily manipulated by adjusting the amount of EB in the gradient (i.e. by changing the density of the plasmid), and it is not normally a problem. Some workers have dealt with this by doing an initial CsCl gradient in very low concentrations of EB (so that all the DNA bands together), and then taking this band and running it in a high concentration of EB (Halford and Johnson, 1981). The yield from this method is variable. Typically, starting with 1 litre of a culture of a strain containing a high copy number plasmid and ending with a 500-μl preparation, 1–2 μl should be adequate for visualization on an agarose gel.

V. Miscellaneous observations

To complete this chapter we comment on various aspects of the methods discussed above.

A. Flexibility

As with any technique, much time can be saved if important variables are distinguished from unimportant variables. Many of the details in the procedures described should not be considered as prescriptions; they are simply descriptions of what was done rather than what had to be done. On the other hand, relatively small changes in the important variables can have dramatic effects. So, if a particular technique does not immediately work with a particular strain, small changes in a published protocol may result in success.

B. Precipitation of DNA

DNA is usually precipitated from solutions either with ethanol or with isopropanol; the former is probably the most popular. It is usually recommended that after addition of the alcohol, the solution is cooled to $-20\,^\circ$C or $-70\,^\circ$C prior to spinning (with isopropanol solutions this will mean that freezing will occur). It is our experience that isopropanol precipitation at room temperature, leaving only 1 or 2 min for the precipitation to occur, works very satisfactorily for most purposes. Besides saving time, this has the advantage that isopropanol precipitation needs a smaller volume of the alcohol than does ethanol precipitation (say 0.6 volumes as opposed to 2), which can be very useful, and that the lower concentration of alcohol and the higher temperature gives a degree of selective precipitation of the DNA (e.g. RNA may stay in solution under these conditions). This method of precipitation is especially useful when purifying the DNA from CsCl/EB solutions (see above).

C. Phenol

We do not saturate our phenol with buffer. The solution is made up by taking 500 g of commercial phenol and adding to it 7.5 ml of NaOH (2 M), 130 ml of water, 6 ml of Tris-HCl (1 M, pH 7.5) and leaving the mixture overnight to liquefy. This gives a solution of about pH 7.5 and 10 mM Tris. We do not redistil the phenol; in our experience, even darkly coloured phenol works satisfactorily. Following extractions with phenol, many procedures recommend that the solution is extracted with chloroform or ether to extract residual phenol prior to precipitation. This is a waste of time; precipitation of the DNA followed by the normal washes (see above) removes all phenol.

It should also be noted that the material that many centrifuge tubes are made of is sensitive to many organic solvents, including phenol. So check before adding; it would be disastrous, for example, if you tried to do a phenol extraction in a polycarbonate centrifuge tube.

D. Chloramphenicol amplification

The relative amount of small multicopy plasmids (compared to chromosomal DNA) can often be increased by chloramphenicol amplification (Maniatis *et al.*, 1982). This involves incubation of the culture, prior to lysis, in the presence of chloramphenicol, under which conditions the chromosome stops replicating while the plasmids continue to replicate. This can give very high yields of such small plasmids. The method is not applicable to large plasmids.

References

Bauer, W. R., Crick, F. H. C. and White, J. H. (1980). *Sci. Am.* **243**, 100–113.
Birnboim, H. C. and Doly, J. (1979). *Nucleic Acids Res.* **7**, 1513–1523.
Eckhardt, T. (1978). *Plasmid* **1**, 564–568.
Halford, S. E. and Johnson, N. P. (1981). *Biochem. J.* **199**, 767–777.
Maniatis, T., Fritsch, E. F. and Sambrook, J. (1982). "Molecular cloning. A Laboratory Manual". Cold Spring Harbor, New York.
Radloff, R., Bauer, W. and Vinograd, J. (1967). *Proc. Natl. Acad. Sci. U.S.A.* **57**, 1514–1521.
Wang, J. C. (1980) *Trends Biochem. Sci.* **5**, 219–221.

7

Electron Microscopy of Plasmid DNA

H. J. BURKARDT

*Department of Microbiology and Biochemistry, University of Erlangen,
Federal Republic of Germany*

A. PÜHLER

Department of Genetics, University of Bielefeld, Federal Republic of Germany

I. Introduction

Since the development of a suitable preparation technique for DNA molecules, which was achieved by the introduction of spreading techniques using basic protein monolayers (Kleinschmidt and Zahn, 1959), electron microscopes (EM) have been used routinely to study plasmid molecular biology. There are several reasons for their widespread use in plasmid research, namely that most EM techniques are relatively quick in comparison to other molecular biological methods, their accuracy is only surpassed by DNA sequencing and one can actually see what happens to the DNA

METHODS IN MICROBIOLOGY
VOLUME 17 ISBN 0-12-521517-7

molecules under investigation. So electron microscopy always gives information about single individual molecules, in contrast to DNA gel techniques,
for instance, which average a whole population of molecules. This in-
dividuality has two consequences: to obtain an unambiguous result from an
EM study of plasmids statistical evaluation may be required; some peculia-
rities within a population of DNA molecules may be detected only by an EM
technique. Electron microscopy can help solve the following questions in
plasmid research.

1. Molecular weight determination by contour length measurements.
2. Detection of inverted repeats in plasmids (IS sequences, transposons) by
   homoduplex experiments.
3. Plasmid–plasmid homology and therefore detection of insertions, deletions and
   inversions by heteroduplex analysis.
4. Gross nucleotide composition by AT-mapping and secondary structure mapping.
5. In combination with other molecular biological methods: promotor mapping by
   RNA polymerase binding studies and visualization of transcription complexes or
   transcription products by R-loop mapping.
6. Study of basic molecular biological events in which nucleic acids are involved,
   such as replication, recombination, transcription and translation.

This chapter will concentrate on molecular weight determination, homo- and
heteroduplexing and AT-mapping because all these methods are based on the
same preparation technique for DNA visualization, are relatively simple and
so can be performed in every EM laboratory without the need for complicated
and expensive apparatus and chemicals.

II. Technical requirements for electron microscopy of nucleic acids

A transmission electron microscope as shown in Fig. 1 is the main technical
requirement. It is not necessary to have a sophisticated one, because, for all the
techniques described in this chapter (and even for most other DNA
techniques) the required magnification is moderate, about 10 000-fold. There
are no resolution problems because in plasmid research only lengths of
complete DNA molecules or segments, and not DNA fine structure, are of
interest. A vacuum evaporator is useful for preparing specimen support films
and contrasting DNA preparations. A room with no through-pass or a special
preparation box is recommended because all DNA preparations are sensitive
to contamination from the environment and to draughts etc.

  For DNA preparation, grids with carbon or Parlodion films may be used.
The type of film preferred depends on which one is normally used in the EM
laboratory. For beginners we recommend Parlodion films because they are

easier to prepare, the quality is reproducible and the adsorbtion rate of DNA is high. A simple recipe for preparation of Parlodion films is as follows.

1. Arrange copper grids on a filter paper in a water-filled Büchner funnel.
2. Clean the water surface using a water jet pump. Place one drop of a water-free Parlodion solution in iso-amyl acetate (1.5–3%) onto the water surface, in the middle of the funnel. After evaporation of the solvent, which will take 5–7 min, the Parlodion will form a thin film on the surface of the water. To prepare the Parlodion solution, cut dry Parlodion into small pieces and bake them at 80°C overnight. This reduces the water content of the Parlodion. Put the pieces in a tightly sealed flask with the organic solvent and dissolve by gently shaking it over a period of a few days. Parlodion which is predissolved in ethanol or ether might be less useful because of possible water contamination which causes holes in the final film.
3. Remove this first film and discard it (it is used to clean the water surface).
4. Prepare a second film in the same manner.
5. The copper grids are covered with the film when the water is allowed to flow out of the funnel.
6. Before use, the grids, covered with a film of Parlodion, are dried while still on the filter paper. Removal of the wet grids from this paper damages the film.
7. Film thickness can be roughly estimated by its shininess. Very thin films are merely dull, thicker ones are slightly glossy. Films which are too thick for use exhibit a strong gloss or even interference colours.

III. Cytochrome C preparation methods: classical spreading and droplet technique

As mentioned in Section I, for EM preparation a DNA molecule has to be stabilized by a special support film. The first films which were introduced were basic protein monolayers of which cytochrome c (Cyt c) has been used most widely because of its easy availability and properties, described below.

1. The molecule is small and globular (giving a fine background grain).
2. At the water–air interface it denatures, forming a monolayer which is stable on the water surface.
3. In the neutral pH range it has a net positive charge that can interfere with the negative charges of nucleic acids and result in unfolding and binding of those molecules.

The following two Cyt c spreading methods are in use:

1. The spreading method, which is the original Kleinschmidt technique (Kleinschmidt, 1968).
2. The droplet technique, which is a simple modification of the former (Lang and Mitani, 1970).

(a)

Fig. 1. View and cross-section of a transmission electron microscope.

(b)

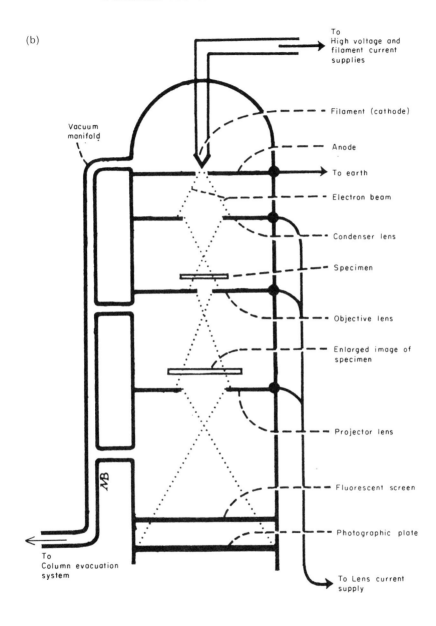

A. Spreading method

This method uses a hyperphase which is spread over a hypophase (Fig. 2). The hyperphase consists of buffer, Cyt c and DNA. The hypophase consists of a less concentrated buffer solution or pure water. The advantage of this two-phase system lies in the possibility of changing parameters in both phases independently, which may be required by the type of nucleic acid under investigation. For example, to spread single-stranded DNA the water has to be partially replaced by denaturing agents such as formamide or dimethylsulphoxide (DMSO) to avoid single-stranded snap-back structures or heavy coiling of a totally single-stranded molecule. The concentration of such agents is always higher in the hyper- than in the hypophase. For routine use the hyperphase can be prepared as a stock solution, containing 60% formamide, which can be used equally well for spreading double-stranded and single-stranded DNA.

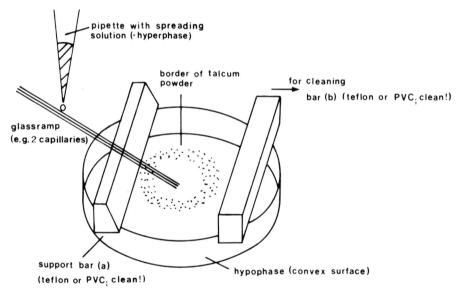

Fig. 2. Spreading apparatus.

The recipe for formamide spreading is laid out below. Note that the purity of formamide is critical for the hyperphase (not for the hypophase) and can be checked by optical density measurement. It should not exceed 0.2 A_{270} (reference: water). The quality of formamide can be improved by re-crystallization or distillation.

1. Preparation of hyperphase

1. Prepare a stock solution: 60% formamide (purified), 0.2 M Tris, 0.02 M EDTA adjusted with 1 N HCl to pH 8.5. The stock solution can be kept frozen at −20 C for months.
2. Mix 10 μl of stock solution and 10 μl of DNA solution. This ratio is valid for DNA concentrations of about 1–10 μg ml^{-1}; if the DNA is more concentrated, dilute it with 1 mM EDTA.
3. Add 0.4–0.5 μl of Cyt c (5 mg ml^{-1}) immediately before spreading.

2. Preparation of hypophase

1. Mix in a bottle 10 ml of formamide, 1 ml of 1 M Tris and 1 ml of 100 mM EDTA, fill up with double-distilled water and adjust pH with 1 N HCl to 8.5–8.7. (Alternatively: mix a 100 ml solution containing 10% formamide, 10 mM Tris and 1 mM EDTA and adjust pH with 1 N HCl to 8.5–8.7).
2. Use hypophase within a few hours.

3. Spreading

1. Spread 2–5 μl of the hyperphase over the hypophase as indicated in Fig. 2.
2. Before the first and between two spreadings the surface of the hypophase is cleaned by wiping it with the plastic bar.
3. Pick up parts of the Cyt c film with its adhering nucleic acid by touching the hyperphase with a copper grid with a support film. The area of the hyperphase can be made visible by sprinkling some talcum powder in front of the ramp. After spreading the powder marks the border of the spread hyperphase.

B. Droplet method

The droplet method (Fig. 3) is simpler because it is a one-phase system; unfortunately, however, results are mostly very poor when preparing single-stranded DNA. Therefore we recommend this method only for DNA double-strand preparations.

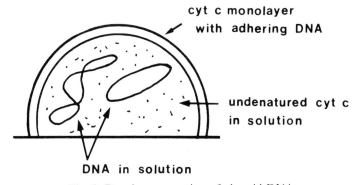

cyt c monolayer
with adhering DNA

undenatured cyt c
in solution

DNA in solution

Fig. 3. Droplet preparation of plasmid DNA.

1. Prepare in a test-tube 0.2 M ammonium acetate buffer, 1 mM EDTA, pH 7.
2. Add Cyt c from a 0.1% stock solution (in water) to a final concentration of 0.00025%.
3. Add to 0.25 ml of this mixture about 0.5–5 μl of DNA solution (depends on DNA concentration).
4. Pipette this volume in three to four droplets on a clean hydrophobic surface (e.g. a new plastic Petri dish).
5. Protect the droplets against dust and wait for 0.5–1 h until the Cyt c film has formed and DNA has adsorbed to it.
6. Pick up Cyt c film and adsorbed DNA by touching the droplet surface with a grid.

IV. DNA contrasting by shadowing and staining

Like most biological specimens DNA has no heavy atoms to give sufficient contrast in the bright field EM, so additional contrasting is required for visualization (unless special and complicated dark field EM methods are applied). Staining with solutions of heavy metal salts, shadowing with heavy metal or a combination of both techniques are possible. For normal preparation with Parlodion-coated grids we recommend the last technique which results in excellent contrast. The stain and shadowing also thicken the diameter of the nucleic acid and therefore improve the visibility of the fine filaments of nucleic acids.

Procedure

1. Dip grids with film and DNA immediately after preparation in staining solution, which is 10^{-5} M uranyl acetate and 10^{-4} N HCl in 90–95% ethanol. (This can be cheap alcohol, which is denatured by petroleum ether. Pure alcohol damages Parlodion film.) The staining solution is freshly prepared by diluting a 100-fold more concentrated aqueous stock solution. The stock solution is stable in the dark for several months. To reduce the amount of uranyl precipitates on the grid, filtering (pore diameter <0.2 μm) the stain solution is recommended.
2. Remove excessive stain by submerging the grid in 90–95% ethanol without stain.
3. Dry grid in the air; a possible fluid bath in petroleum ether accelerates drying.
4. Shadow DNA with Pt, Pt/Ir or similar alloy in the shadow casting machine. To obtain an even contrast, especially of circular molecules, rotary shadowing is required.
   We use the following shadow casting conditions:
   vacuum about 10^{-5} Torr
   distance (wire-specimen) about 4.5 cm
   angle about 5°
   amount about 3.5 cm wire (φ 0.1 mm)

V. Evaluation of electron micrographs:
configuration and contour length of plasmid DNA

A well-spread (droplet method) and contrasted plasmid molecule is shown in
Fig. 4(a); Fig. 4(b) is a typical example of one which is poorly spread. The
reason for the bad preparation may be contaminating agents in the DNA
solution (detergents), bad Cyt c (stock solution too old) or contamination of
buffer. Such a simple DNA visualization can give the following information.

1 Presence or absence of DNA in a plasmid isolation experiment.
2 Quality of isolated DNA (contamination, fragments because of contaminating
   nucleases).
3 Approximate concentration of DNA.
4 Form of DNA: linear, circular, supertwisted.
5 Molecular weight of DNA.

For the last point some more evaluation work is necessary. Molecular weight
determination by EM is, in principle, a contour length measurement of the
nucleic acid molecules (Lang, 1970). These lengths can be determined by
tracing the molecule contour on an enlarged drawing or directly on an
enlarged projected EM negative. Several types of instruments are available for
tracing. The most simple and cheapest is a distance measurer for maps, but
sophisticated measurers with computer evaluation are also available. As
individual molecules are measured, a length distribution will result. We
evaluate a minimum of about 20 molecules of one DNA species. Besides the
mean length, the respective standard deviation should always be quoted. It
indicates the quality of the length determination and should not exceed $\pm 2\%$.
To get a reliable absolute molecular length a calibration of the magnification
of microscope and evaluation system is essential. For double-stranded nucleic
acids, an external calibration is sufficient, because the molecules are relatively
resistant to preparation artefacts. For this purpose, all molecules should be
photographed at one microscope magnification, which is calibrated by a
carbon replica grating. For single-stranded nucleic acids an internal standardization is recommended because these molecules are very sensitive to
stretching and have a prominent tendency to shorten themselves by forming
snap-back structures. Internal calibration is achieved by adding a known
single-stranded DNA, e.g. $\varphi X174$ bacteriophage DNA, to the DNA sample
to be studied (Stüber and Bujard, 1977). The length can be determined in
$\varphi X174$ DNA units. An analogous internal standardization is also possible
with double-stranded DNA (e.g. ColE1 DNA may be used as a standard). At
an ionic strength of 0.1–0.5 (which is the case for both the droplet and
spreading methods) the following factor for double-stranded DNA can be
used to calculate the molecular weight: 1 μm of DNA $= 2.07 \times 10^6$ D (≈ 3 kb).

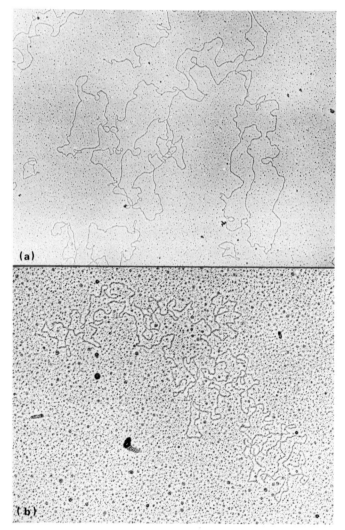

Fig. 4. Plasmid DNA molecule prepared according to the droplet technique: (a) well spread; (b) poorly spread.

VI. Homoduplex experiment: detection of inverted repeats

Inverted repeats (IR) are DNA sequences which appear in two or several copies in one DNA molecule, with examples in both possible orientations. They are parts of transposons and IS sequences and, therefore, common in plasmids. They can be detected readily by a homoduplex experiment. This involves denaturing, renaturing and then spreading the DNA. Denaturation means separating the strands of double-stranded DNA; renaturation is the reverse process. Nevertheless, after renaturation, the parental type of molecule is not always restored. In particular, when renaturation times are short, there is not sufficient time for complementary single strands to find each other. Complementary sequences, however, within one strand will find each other quickly, as they are situated on the same molecule. Provided that the IRs are small in comparison to the total DNA molecule (as is the case for IS sequences in plasmids) then the majority of the DNA molecule remains single stranded, allowing a second annealing with a complementary single-strand DNA molecule. In this case, however, a complete restoration of the parental molecule is impossible, because the IRs on one strand have undergone intramolecular annealing. Such a process leads to a special structure which has been called an "underwound loop" (Kleckner et al., 1975; Burkardt et al., 1978a). The reactions in a homoduplex experiment are summarized in the scheme of Fig. 5; Fig. 6 shows an example of a plasmid with an underwound loop. This structure is a good indicator of IRs because it has a very characteristic appearance under the microscope, whereas the annealing of IRs in a single-stranded molecule often cannot be discerned from a normal DNA crossover, particularly when the IRs are small. Length measurements of the underwound loops (= distance of IRs from each other), however, are best obtained from the structure which results from a short period of renaturation. Therefore we suggest that homoduplex experiments be performed using two renaturation times.

Procedure

1. Denaturation

    1. Mix 5 μl of purified formamide, 1 μl of 1 M phosphate buffer pH 7 and 3 μl of DNA (about 10 μg ml^{-1}).
    2. Boil in a water bath for 1.5 min.

2. Renaturation

    1. Add 1 μl of 2 M NaClO$_4$ and renature at 40 C for 5 min and 30 min. The short time mainly allows complementary sequences on the same DNA strand to anneal. The long time mainly results in molecules with underwound loops.

3. Spreading

    1. Dilute 2 μl of the renaturation mix in 10 μl of purified formamide and 8 μl of 1 mM EDTA.
    2. Add 0.4 μl of Cyt c (5 mg ml^{-1}) to complete the hyperphase and spread over 30% formamide, 10 mM Tris, 1 mM EDTA, pH 8.5–8.7.

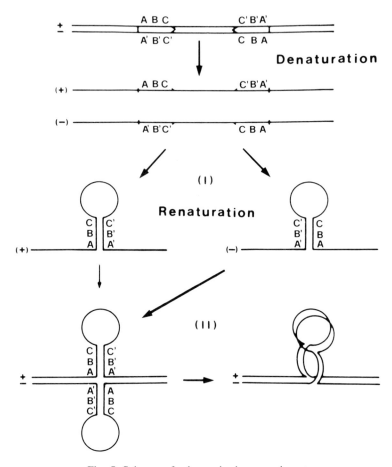

Fig. 5. Scheme of a homoduplex experiment.

The method is based on a well-balanced ratio between the different denaturing and renaturing agents: denaturation is favoured by heat and formamide, renaturation is favoured by high salt concentrations.

VII. Heteroduplex analysis: demonstration of homology

This is probably the most useful EM DNA technique and was, for a long time, the only widely used method to test physically the relationship between DNA molecules and to detect physically alterations in DNA, such as deletions, insertions, substitutions or inversions (Davis and Davidson, 1968; Davis *et al.*, 1971; Westmoreland *et al.*, 1969). Even today when other methods such as

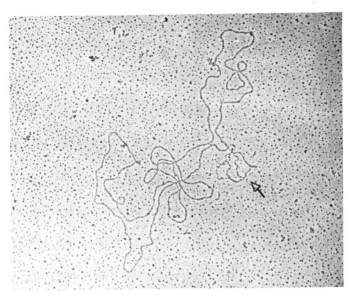

Fig. 6. Plasmid DNA molecule with an underwound loop (marked by arrow).

Southern blotting or DNA sequencing can be used to solve similar problems, heteroduplex mapping can compete with these methods because it has the advantages of being, in general, more exact than the former and far less time and money consuming than the latter. As in homoduplex analysis, heteroduplex analysis consists of a biochemical part and an EM preparation part. The biochemical part also requires a hybridization step. This time, however, duplex structures are formed between related, but different, DNA species. The following points should be kept in mind.

1. Structures are only visible under the EM if their size exceeds the resolution limit of the DNA preparation, i.e. 50–100 base pairs.
2. Two strands are regarded as homologous even when each third base is false (resolution limit of biochemical hybridization).

In Fig. 7(a–e) all types of heteroduplex molecules are shown. For a correct interpretation it is essential that one can clearly distinguish between double-stranded and single-stranded DNA. When heteroduplex molecules are well prepared the single-stranded DNA appears slightly thinner and more kinky than the double-stranded part (cf. Fig. 6). It is also important that the DNA has as few crossovers as possible in order to determine, unambiguously, as for example, an insertion point relative to another marker. When the re-naturation time is too long, especially in the presence of nicked DNA, hybridization can take place between single-stranded regions of different

(a)
   Insertion

(b)
   Deletion

(c)
   Inversion

(d)
   Substitution = deletion of a DNA segment and insertion of a
                  different DNA segment with different or equal length

(e)
   Homology of a short segment

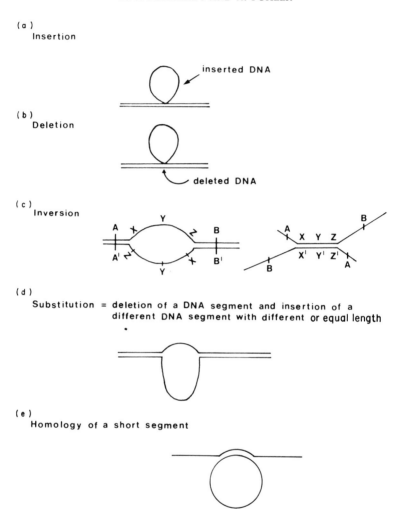

Fig. 7. Types of heteroduplices: (a) and (b) DNA molecule exhibiting an insertion or deletion single-stranded loop; (c) DNA fragment with an inversion bubble; (d) DNA molecule with a substitution bubble; (e) heteroduplex between a linear fragment and a plasmid DNA showing a region of homology.

heteroduplex molecules leading to uninterpretable structures and a DNA network. This occurs in particular with incomplete heteroduplices which consist of a total single-stranded molecule and a single-stranded fragment partner (from nicked DNA). So only DNA preparations with a low proportion of nicked DNA should be used for heteroduplex experiments. This can be estimated by the ratio of open circular and supertwisted DNA. The ideal ratio is 1:1 because in such a DNA preparation the likelihood of an open circular DNA molecule carrying more than one nick is low. These open circular molecules, however, are required for heteroduplex formation because the denatured single strands of supertwisted DNA molecules cannot be separated from each other. They remain interlocked and are, therefore, incapable of heteroduplex formation.

The number of heteroduplex molecules that can be evaluated is reduced by the above-mentioned limitations. In addition, most of the single-stranded DNA molecules will not give rise to heteroduplices but will restore the parental molecules because the plus and minus strands are in the same reaction mixture. So, having performed a heteroduplex experiment, the number of unambiguous heteroduplex structures may be low, especially in complicated DNA hybrid molecules with more than one possible single-stranded structure. This means that patience is required when surveying the specimens under the EM.

Procedure

1. Mix 5 μl of purified formamide, 1 μl of 1 M phosphate buffer pH 7, 1.5 μl of DNA$_1$ (about 10 μg ml^{-1}) and 1.5 μl of DNA$_2$ (about 10 μg ml^{-1}).
2. Denature, renature and spread as in a homoduplex experiment.

VIII. Partial denaturation: gross nucleotide composition of plasmid DNA regions

Partial denaturation is a technique by which a specific physical pattern can be assigned to a double-stranded nucleic acid. In addition to this physical characterization it also yields information about the gross nucleotide composition by marking AT- and GC-rich molecule regions. So, like heteroduplexing, it can be used to identify plasmids, to test relationships between plasmids and, in addition, to study evolutionary aspects of plasmids. AT-mapping can also be used as a preliminary indicator method to look for promotors or other DNA regions which are distinguished by a high AT content. It does not have the accuracy of DNA sequencing but surpasses this newer method by its speed and simplicity. The principle of the method is the following: a double-stranded DNA molecule can be separated into its single strands when heating it beyond its melting point (this is used in all hybridization experiments). When the temperature is raised to a point just below the melting point the strands will not be separated totally; rather denaturation (= strand separation) starts in weak DNA regions. Weak regions are defined by a high content of AT bases because these two organic bases form only two hydrogen bonds between each other (in comparison to three between G and C) and stacking forces between AT pairs are weaker than between GC pairs. Partial denaturation can also be achieved by chemical methods with denaturing agents such as alkali, DMSO or formamide (Inman, 1966; Inman and Schnös, 1970). In the microscope the unpaired (denatured) regions can be seen as bubbles on an otherwise duplex structure, if renaturation is prevented (e.g. by chemical fixation) and if a resolution limit of 50–100 bp is exceeded. An example of a partially denatured plasmid molecule is presented in Fig. 8.

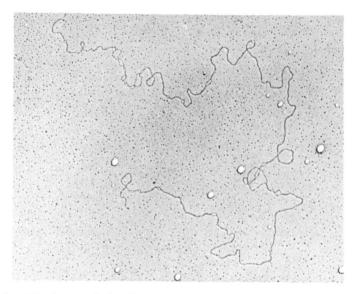

Fig. 8. Partially denatured plasmid molecule which has been linearized by restriction enzyme digestion.

The evaluation of such partially denatured molecules is the most laborious task of a partial denaturation experiment. It has to be a statistical assessment because strand separation is a statistical process and differs to some extent from one molecule to another. The first step consists of measuring separately, and in sequence, all native and denatured regions of a molecule. This, and the further evaluation, is very much facilitated when an additional physical marker to act as a start and as an end point for the measurements is present. For circular plasmid molecules linearization, before partial denaturing, with a restriction enzyme that has a single cleavage site is useful. The extent to which further evaluation can be taken depends on whether a computer together with a suitable program are available (or not). When access to a computer is not possible the measured molecular segments are drawn to scale on a paper strip (e.g. line for native, box for denatured region) and then the paper strips are aligned so as to obtain maximum congruence of denatured and native segments.

The final diagram (AT map) emerges when all molecules are counted which are denatured at the molecular segments $x_0 \ldots x_n$. The size of one segment x_i depends on the resolution of the EM and the evaluation system. A typical system is shown in Fig. 9. The abscissa equals the total molecule length and is subdivided into the $x_0 \ldots x_n$ segments. The ordinate indicates the percentage of molecules of the whole population which are denatured in a given x_i segment. In some instances, in particular when you have fairly large plasmid molecules which are only slightly denatured, it is advantageous in our experience not only to construct diagrams based on this resolution limit, but also to enlarge artificially the denatured sites, by anything up to 3% of the total molecule length, which results in clearer AT maps that are easier to interpret than the originals (Burkardt *et al.*, 1978b). The reason for this map improvement is the following. When the denaturation bubbles are rather small and sparingly distributed along the DNA, naturally identical denaturation sites of two molecules frequently may not occupy quite the same

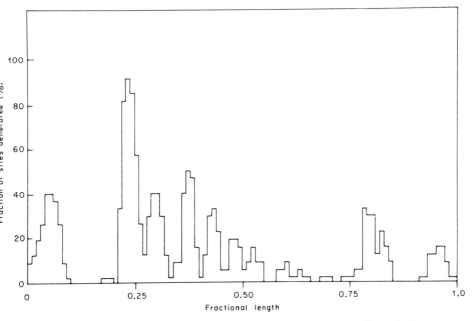

Fig. 9. Plasmid AT map. Abscissa equals total molecule length, ordinate indicates proportion of individual molecules which are denatured at a given fractional length.

position in the $x_0 \ldots x_n$ frame, because they are more or less displaced by preparation artefacts and false tracing and measuring. So in a system with high resolution they contribute, by error, to different denaturation peaks. However, if they are sufficiently enlarged until they overlap then they contribute to the same peak, which corresponds better to the natural conditions. The map presented in Fig. 9 was constructed using such a manipulation. When using a computer to analyse your data you can incorporate this provision into the program (including bubble enlargement). The computer will then generate the possible variations of the map of your denatured and measured molecules in a very short time.

Procedure

1. Partial denaturation

1. Prepare denaturation stock: 0.25 ml of DMSO, 0.21 ml of 0.2 M phosphate buffer, 0.001 M EDTA, pH 7 and 0.14 ml of formaldehyde (37%).
2. Mix 0.03 ml of denaturation stock and 0.02 ml of DNA ($\sim 10 \ \mu g \ ml^{-1}$).
3. Heat to 50–60°C for 10–20 min.

The exact denaturation conditions required depend on the $(G+C)$% ratio of the DNA to be studied and have to be found in a series of denaturation experiments. Formaldehyde reacts with the free amino groups of unpaired bases in DNA single strands so preventing normal reannealing of the DNA. Unbound formaldehyde disturbs, however, the Cyt c spreading and therefore has to be removed before spreading.

2. Formaldehyde removal

1. Prepare in a Pasteur capillary pipette (ϕ about 7 mm) a small Sephadex G50 column (5 cm long); equilibrate with 1 mM EDTA.
2. Apply 20 μl of denaturation mix on top of the column.
3. Elute with about 500 μl of 1 mM EDTA.
4. Collect three 20-μl fractions.
5. Mix 10-μl fraction with 10 μl of hyperphase mix (Section III).

The column has to be calibrated for use. This is achieved by testing the system with radioactively-labelled DNA or using the EM to screen the fractions for DNA molecules.

IX. Molecular structure of P type plasmids: an example of DNA analysis by electron microscopy

The use of the EM in analysing plasmids will be demonstrated in this last section of the chapter. Plasmid RP4 serves as an example, some other P type plasmids are RP1, RP8, R68, R68.45 and RK2. These molecules are typical resistance plasmids, isolated from *Pseudomonas aeruginosa* (except RK2, which was isolated from *Klebsiella*); all carry resistance genes to ampicillin, kanamycin and tetracycline. They belong to the same incompatibility group P. When we obtained these plasmids a few years ago their broad host range, which rendered them prominent among all other plasmids so far known, had just been discovered (Datta *et al.*, 1971). Since molecular data were sparse at that time we undertook an EM analysis of these plasmids. A Cyt *c* droplet preparation enabled a portrait of these molecules for the first time (Fig. 10) and confirmed and extended molecular weight determinations made by sucrose gradient centrifugation (Burkardt *et al.*, 1978b). A summary of the length measurement data revealed, within the range of error, identical lengths for RP1, RP4, R68 and RK2, whereas R68.45 was slightly longer (0.6-μm increase) and RP8 was 50% longer (12-μm increase) than the other plasmids (Table I). The different lengths of the latter two plasmids correspond well with their different biological properties.

1. R68.45 shows enhanced chromosomal mobilizing ability (sex factor activity) in comparison to RP1, RP4, R68 and RK2.
2. RP8 has a narrow host range in comparison to all other P type plasmids and is freely transferable only between Enterobacteriaceae and *P. aeruginosa*.

These findings, namely size and genetic characters (identical resistance genes but differences in host range and chromosome mobilizing ability), led us to

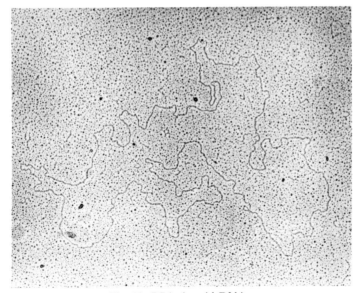

Fig. 10. RP4 plasmid DNA.

TABLE I
Lengths of P type plasmids

Plasmid	Contour length
RP1	18.9 μm
RP4	19.1 μm
RP8	31.3 μm
R68	19.1 μm
R68.45	19.7 μm
RK2	18.2 μm

question the identity and relationship of these P type plasmids. Therefore various heteroduplex experiments were performed. We started with RP1 and RP4 against RP8 because we knew from partial denaturation experiments (Burkardt *et al.*, 1978b) and biochemical hybridization studies from other groups (Holloway and Richmond, 1973) that RP8 should show extensive homology with both RP1 and RP4. Figure 11 shows a heteroduplex between RP4 and RP8 which clearly demonstrates that the hybrid molecule is composed of a double-stranded section and a single-stranded section (which was the only single-stranded structure). Length measurements of these parts proved the following interpretation to be correct: RP8 is constituted from an

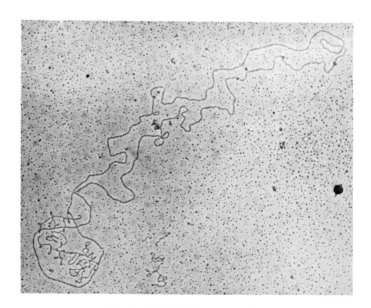

Fig. 11. RP4/RP8 heteroduplex.

entire RP4 molecule and a piece of additional DNA; it can therefore be regarded as an insertion mutant of RP4. A similar interpretation followed an examination of heteroduplices of R68.45 and RP4 (Fig. 12): R68.45 is composed of an RP4 type molecule with a 0.6-μm insertion (Riess *et al.*, 1980). Heteroduplices between RP1, RP4, R68 and RK2 exhibited no such heterologies. This series of heteroduplex experiments revealed the following relationship (at the EM resolution level): RP1 = RP4 = RK2 = R68 = R68.45—0.6-μm insertion = RP8—12-μm insertion (Burkardt *et al.*, 1979). RP1/RP8 heteroduplices displayed a characteristic single-stranded structure, which was later also found in all heteroduplex experiments with P type plasmids (Fig. 6), in addition to the single-stranded insertion loop. This structure resembled neither an insertion loop nor a substitution or inversion bubble and could not be interpreted by us at that time. The solution to the problem emerged when more was known about the genetics of P type plasmids and when we performed long-time homoduplex experiments. Genetic investigations detected the first transposon, Tn1, as a part of RP4 (Hedges and Jacob, 1974). This could be visualized by us as an underwound loop in a typical homoduplex experiment, as described in Section VI. As a heteroduplex experiment utilizes the same preparation techniques as a long-time homoduplex experiment, the occasional appearance of underwound loops was explained.

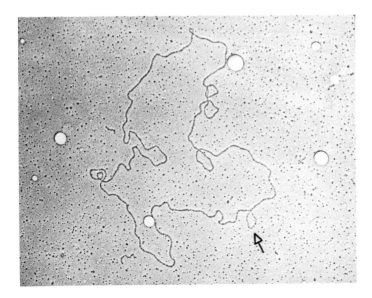

Fig. 12. RP4/R68.45 heteroduplex. R68.45 insertion is marked by an arrow.

Partial denaturation experiments, originally performed to assign specific patterns to each P plasmid, were compared to detect relationships (Burkardt *et al.*, 1978b). The relationship question was solved more decisively by heteroduplex experiments which are more suitable for this (Burkardt *et al.*, 1979). The AT-mapping, however, yielded information about the gross nucleotide composition of P type plasmids. By comparing these maps with genetic maps we were able to determine the relative AT content of the RP4 genes (Burkardt *et al.*, 1980). An example for RP4 is shown in Fig. 13. The correct alignment of the partial denaturation and genetic maps was facilitated by using two single restriction enzyme sites on RP4, specifically those for *Eco*RI, and *Hind*III. Without going into detail one can deduce from this figure an unusually high relative AT content for the two resistance gene regions of ampicillin (located on Tn*1*) and kanamycin. This finding may reflect evolutionary aspects of the RP4 plasmid, namely that these gene regions were not part of a primitive RP4 precursor but were acquired from different DNA sources during plasmid evolution.

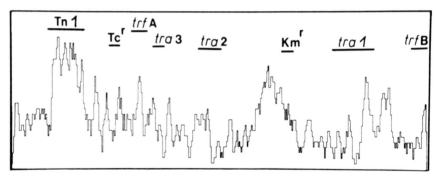

Fig. 13. Partial denaturation map of RP4 showing the relative AT content of some RP4 genes.

The EM story of IncP plasmids does not end here. Applying other EM methods, not described in this chapter, we have been able to map *E. coli* RNA polymerase binding sites on RP4 DNA and have obtained evidence of active, but as yet unknown, RP4 genes (Burkardt and Wohlleben, 1981). We intend to continue the investigation by analysing, under EM, microscopic transcription complexes so as to identify active promotors and to determine the direction of transcription from each of them.

References

Burkardt, H. J. and Wohlleben, W. (1981). *J. Gen. Microbiol.* **125**, 301–309.
Burkardt, H. J., Mattes, R., Schmid, K. and Schmitt, R. (1978a). *Mol. Gen. Genet.* **166**, 75–84.
Burkardt, H. J., Mattes, R. E., Pühler, A. and Heumann, W. (1978b). *J. Gen. Microbiol.* **105**, 51–62.
Burkardt, H. J., Riess, G. and Pühler, A. (1979). *J. Gen. Microbiol.* **114**, 341–348.
Burkardt, H. J., Pühler, A. and Wohlleben, W. (1980). *J. Gen. Microbiol.* **117**, 135–140.
Datta, N., Hedges, R. W., Shaw, E. J., Sykes, R. B. and Richmond, M. H. (1971). *J. Bacterial.* **108**, 1244–1249.
Davis, R. W. and Davidson, N. (1968). *Proc. Natl. Acad. Sci. U.S.A.* **60**, 243–250.
Davis, R. W., Simon, M. and Davidson, N. (1971). *Methods Enzymol.* **21**, 413–428.
Hedges, R. W. and Jacob, A. E. (1974). *Mol. Gen. Genet.* **132**, 32–40.
Holloway, B. W. and Richmond, M. H. (1973). *Genet. Res., Camb.* **21**, 103–105.
Inman, R. B. (1966). *J. Mol. Biol.* **18**, 464–476.
Inman, R. B. and Schnös, M. (1970). *J. Mol. Biol.* **49**, 93–98.
Kleckner, N., Chan, R. K., Tye, B. K. and Botstein, D. (1975). *J. Mol. Biol.* **97**, 561–575.
Kleinschmidt, A. K. (1968). *Methods Enzymol.* **12**, 361–377.
Kleinschmidt, A. K. and Zahn, R. K. (1959). *Z. Naturforsch.* **14b**, 770–779.
Lang, D. (1970). *J. Mol. Biol.* **54**, 557–565.
Lang, D. and Mitani, M. (1970). *Biopolymers* **9**, 373–379.
Riess, G., Holloway, B. W. and Pühler, A. (1980). *Genet. Res., Camb.* **36**, 99–109.
Stüber, D. and Bujard, H. (1977). *Mol. Gen. Genet.* **154**, 299–303.
Westmoreland, B. C., Szybalski, W. and Ris, H. (1969). *Science* **163**, 1343–1348.

8

Use of Restriction Endonucleases

W. P. DIVER* AND J. GRINSTED

Department of Microbiology, University of Bristol, Medical School, Bristol, UK

I. Introduction

Restriction endonucleases are enzymes that recognize specific sequences of DNA (usually 4, 5 or 6 base pairs) and subsequently cut the phosphodiester backbone of the molecule. We are concerned exclusively with Class II restriction enzymes in this chapter; these require only magnesium ions for activity and cleave both strands of the DNA at specific points either within the recognition site or just outside it. The term restriction derives from the discovery of such enzymes; strains that contain them restrict bacteriophage growth by initiating degradation of the bacteriophage DNA, thus rendering it biologically inactive. A necessary corollary for a cell that contains a restriction enzyme is some system that will ensure that the cell's own DNA is not degraded. This protection is usually provided by modification of the DNA such that the sites recognized by the restriction enzyme are methylated; these methylated sites are not susceptible to the enzyme. A formal restriction role for most restriction enzymes has not been demonstrated, and only in a few cases has a corresponding modification system been shown.

The specificity of restriction enzymes is the cornerstone of molecular genetics. In particular, genetic engineering and DNA sequencing would be impossible without restriction enzymes. Other chapters in this volume deal with the specific uses of these enzymes. For instance, examples of the strategy used to map DNA sequences with restriction enzymes are given in Chapters 9 and 10. Our aim in this chapter is to discuss their use in general terms and to

---

* Present address: Molecular Biology Unit, Research School of Biological Sciences, Australian National University, Canberra A.C.T., Australia.

METHODS IN MICROBIOLOGY
VOLUME 17 ISBN 0-12-521517-7

describe how easy they are to use in the laboratory. We should like to draw attention to the admirable Cold Spring Harbor manual entitled "Molecular Cloning" (Maniatis et al., 1982); this covers all aspects of cloning, including the use of restriction enzymes, in technical detail.

II. Choice and sources of restriction enzymes

The selection of the actual restriction enzymes to be used depends on the DNA that is to be analysed, and on the purpose of the digestion. The procedure taken with a new DNA sequence, such as a newly isolated plasmid, would be to construct a map of the sites recognized by various enzymes (Chapter 9). One might start with available enzymes that recognize 6 base pair (bp) sequences (and thus cut, on average, once every 4096 bp—4^6) to find a few points of reference to work from; then other enzymes that might cut more frequently could be used. If simply trying to show whether two plasmids were the same or not, it might be sufficient to digest both with an enzyme that gives many fragments and compare the patterns obtained. Complete lists of all known restriction enzymes and their recognition sites are published regularly in, for instance, *Nucleic Acids Research* (Roberts, 1983).

A large number of restriction enzymes are available commercially from numerous firms. In our experience commercially available enzymes are usually dependable and our main criterion in selecting the source is cost. One of the consequences of the rapidly increasing use of these enzymes and the competition between the various firms supplying them is that the cost is decreasing, in some cases quite dramatically. However, they are still expensive.

If cash is short, an alternative to the commercially available enzymes is laboratory-made preparations. These can be simply prepared, and 1 or 2 litres of culture can give 5 ml of preparation, 1 μl of which is sufficient for most analytical uses. A method that can be used depends on two columns (in fact, in some cases, the product of the first column is of sufficient purity for most purposes) and is written up in detail in Greene et al. (1978). Although custom-built columns, peristaltic pumps, gradient makers and fraction collectors certainly make life a little easier with such preparations, none are essential. So, for instance, disposable syringes can be used as columns, columns can be fed by gravity and gradient makers are simple to rig up (or the column can simply be eluted step-wise with increasing concentrations). Finally, it is our experience that such enzyme preparations can be carried out at room temperature, so not even a cold room is required.

III. Use of restriction enzymes

Restriction enzymes are not particularly fastidious in their requirements: the only necessary cofactor is magnesium ions. The other parameters that have to be considered are pH, ionic strength and temperature. The conditions for each enzyme recommended by the suppliers are often widely different and one is strictly enjoined to follow the recommendations to the letter. However, the concentrations of the components of the buffers are often very flexible and it is our experience that most restriction enzymes work adequately in 50 mM Tris-HCl, 5 mM $MgCl_2$, pH 7.5 at 37 C. (It should be noted that Tris buffers have a high temperature coefficient: for instance, a 50 mM solution of Tris-HCl which is pH 8.0 at 25 C is pH 8.6 at 5 C and pH 7.7 at 37 C.) We make up our Tris buffers by mixing Tris base and Tris-HCl (from Sigma) in the proportions given in the tables supplied by Sigma. We do not pretend that these conditions necessarily correspond to the ideal conditions for every enzyme, and there are certainly some enzymes which we would use in different buffers (see below), but the use of a single buffer is very convenient, particularly when the DNA is to be digested with more than one enzyme. Recently, BRL have introduced core buffer (50 mM Tris pH 8, 10 mM $MgCl_2$, 50 mM NaCl) which they now recommend for many of their enzymes.

With a few enzymes different conditions are to be recommended or are required. For instance EcoRI often gives extra bands in low ionic strength and it is sensible to add 100 mM NaCl to the digestion buffer; high ionic strength is also recommended for SalI. The normal temperature of incubation is 37 C, but a few enzymes (e.g. TaqI) are used at much higher temperatures. Most of the enzymes are relatively catholic with respect to pH. However, a few either require high pH (9–10) for significant activity (e.g. SmaI) or work better under such conditions (e.g. BglI and BglII). One other point to bear in mind is that glycerol will be added to the reaction mixture with the enzyme (see below) and it has been reported that some enzymes cut DNA in unexpected places when the glycerol concentration is higher than 5% (Maniatis et al., 1982).

Enzymes are usually stored in 50% glycerol solutions so that they can be kept at −20 C without freezing. Before removing a sample of enzyme from the stock solution it is sensible to give the vial a quick (1 s) spin in a microfuge to ensure that all the preparation is at the bottom (there might be only a few microlitres of the solution). (This procedure is useful whenever there is a problem with droplets on the sides of tubes.) For most analytical purposes we aim to add 1 μl of the enzyme preparation. If necessary, the stock solution should be diluted to achieve a suitable concentration of the enzyme (commercial preparations are often very concentrated). Since dilution often results in loss of enzyme activity, care must be taken if dilution is necessary; only small aliquots of the stock should be diluted at any one time with the storage buffer containing 50% glycerol. The activity of enzyme preparations is usually assayed with λ DNA, and different manufacturers measure the activity in slightly different ways. So the quoted activities from different commercial sources are not necessarily the same. Furthermore, it must be remembered that, just because a certain amount of preparation completely digests 1 μg of λ DNA in 1 h, it does not therefore follow that the same amount of the preparation will necessarily completely digest some other DNA with exactly the same kinetics. (For example, if the experimental DNA has many more sites than does λ DNA, differences would be expected.) Furthermore, the purity of the DNA can have an affect; preparations that are not very clean (rapid preparations for instance, see below) are often affected more slowly than pure preparations.

The rapid methods of preparing plasmid DNA (Chapters 6 and 9) normally give DNA that is satisfactory for analysis with restriction enzymes. For certain specific purposes (e.g. molecular cloning or DNA sequencing or analysis with the electron microscope) the DNA would probably have been purified further (Chapter 6) because steps after the digestion with the restriction enzyme might require it. It should also be remembered that there are some restriction enzymes whose recognition sites can contain the site recognized by either the *Escherichia coli dam* or *dcm* methylases. (These sites are GATC and CCA/TGG, respectively.) Thus, these sites can be methylated in *E. coli* and some restriction enzymes do not act at recognition sites methylated in this way. If these enzymes are used to digest DNA isolated from *E. coli*, then the DNA has to be prepared from a *dam* or *dcm* mutant (Maniatis *et al.*, 1982).

Digestions are usually carried out in small (0.4- or 1.5-ml) plastic tubes. For analytical purposes we might mix the following in a 0.4-ml tube:

1. 10 μl of DNA solution (usually in 10 mM Tris, pH 7.5, 0.1 mM EDTA);
2. 5 μl of Tris-HCl (150 mM, pH 7.5 at 37 C), MgCl₂ (15 mM);
3. 1 μl of enzyme preparation.

The amount of DNA would be in the range 0.1 to 1 μg: the actual amount of any DNA preparation to add to give suitably bright bands on the gel (see below) is determined empirically. The tube is then vortexed and incubated at 37 C for 1 h. 5 μl of EDTA (0.2 M, pH 8), sucrose (40% w/v), bromophenol blue (1.5 mg⁻¹ ml⁻¹) are then added and the mixture vortexed. The sample is now ready for loading on a gel (see below). This "stop mix" would not be added to restriction enzyme digests that are to be subjected to further enzyme treatments (e.g. ligation or labelling with radioactivity), but here it may be necessary to inactivate the restriction enzyme. This can normally be done by heating the mixture at 65 C for 10 min; there are, however, some enzymes that are resistant to this treatment (e.g. *BamHI, TaqI, HindIII*). Such enzymes can be inactivated with phenol: the mixture can simply be phenol-extracted, followed by precipitation of the DNA (Chapter 6), or a drop of buffered phenol can be added to the solution and, after vortexing, can be removed by extraction with water-saturated ether.

IV. Analysis of restriction enzyme digests

Restriction enzyme digests can be analysed on either agarose or polyacrylamide gels. In general, the latter would be used for low molecular weight fragments (less than 1 kb), and the former for larger fragments. However, agarose can be used for small fragments too. Details of acrylamide gels are given in Chapter 13 and of agarose in Chapter 9. We should like to make a few points about agarose gels. The concentrations used vary between 0.3% (to resolve fragments of maybe 100 kb) and 2.5% to resolve fragments as short as 100 bp. We weigh out the agarose, add an appropriate volume of electrophoresis buffer (we use Tris-borate; Chapter 9) and melt and dissolve the agarose by heating directly over a bunsen. The liquid is continually stirred or there is a danger of charring (especially with agarose at 1.5% and over); care must also be taken that the solution does not boil over. The agarose solution can then be poured into an appropriate gel former (Chapter 9); concentrated solutions set very rapidly and it is wise to pour the solution at 100 C into prewarmed apparatus. It should be borne in mind when pouring the gels that the use of very hot solutions with cold glass plates might crack the plates, and that pouring the gel when it is at a temperature close to its setting point often results in air bubbles in the gel that are almost impossible to remove. Once poured the gel should form in 15–20 min (this can be accelerated if the whole apparatus is put in a cold room or a refrigerator). Details of running gels are described in Chapter 9.

After running, the fragments in the gel are visualized by examination in ultra-violet light (310 nm is best): on illumination with ultra-violet light, ethidium bromide (which is included in the electrophoresis buffer) fluoresces strongly when bound to DNA. It should be noted that ethidium cannot be incorporated into polyacrylamide gels (presumably it is oxidized by the perchlorate) and these have to be stained prior to exposure to ultra-violet light (after electrophoresis, they are simply immersed in electrophoresis buffer containing 1 μg ml^{-1} of ethidium bromide for 15–30 min). It should also be noted that SDS electrophoreses with the marker dye and complexes all the ethidium it encounters. Consequently, gels with samples containing SDS have to be stained even if ethidium had been included in the running buffer.

Finally, a few words about the appearance of the bands. In general, horizontal gels give sharper bands: with vertical gels the bands often "smile", particularly those of higher molecular weight. (It is alleged that using Ficoll in the stop buffer instead of sucrose prevents this effect, but we have not found that it makes any difference.) On the other hand, large samples can be loaded with vertical apparatus (100 μl in a 1-cm $\times$ 0.3-cm well) and give sharp bands. Finally, open circular DNA forms of plasmids often give bands with downturned sides (the opposite of smiles). This is so marked that it can be used as a diagnostic feature for open-circular DNA.

References

Greene, P. J., Heyneker, H. L., Bolivar, F., Rodriguez, R. L., Betlach, M. C., Covarrubias, A. A., Backman, K., Russel, D. J., Tait, R. and Boyer, H. W. (1978). *Nucleic Acids Res.* **7**, 2373–2380.
Maniatis, T., Fritsch, E. F. and Sambrook, J. (1982). "Molecular Cloning. A Laboratory Manual". Cold Spring Harbor, New York.
Roberts, R. J. (1983). *Nucleic Acids Res.* **11**, r135–r163.

9

Analysis of Clones

C. M. THOMAS

Department of Genetics, University of Birmingham, Birmingham, UK

I. Introduction

Analysis of clones, for the purpose of this chapter, covers the analysis of plasmid DNA and its expression in any bacterial clone. The aim of such an analysis, in general, is to locate and study a gene or genes of interest. The plasmids could be naturally occurring or could be recombinants constructed *in vitro* from restriction endonuclease-cleaved fragments ligated into a suitable

METHODS IN MICROBIOLOGY
VOLUME 17 ISBN 0-12-521517-7

cloning vector. In the case of naturally occurring plasmids, the aim of the analysis may be to determine their size and restriction maps, to examine whether they carry particular sequences and to localize on the plasmid genomes the regions of interest. For putative hybrid plasmids, starting with a population of bacterial clones, analysis may involve determining which clones carry hybrid plasmids, analysis of which hybrids carry DNA sequences of interest or produce gene products of interest and finally analysis of plasmid DNA to locate and characterize the gene(s) of interest. The emphasis of this chapter will be on the analysis of hybrid plasmids, but methods useful for the analysis of large and/or low copy number plasmids, which are more likely to occur among naturally occurring plasmids, will also be dealt with.

Many methods have been developed to analyse plasmids and it is beyond the scope of this chapter to cover, in detail, all the methods that could be useful. Some of these methods are dealt with in other chapters in this volume and also in other recent volumes (e.g. "Methods in Enzymology', Vols 65 and 68). The aim of this chapter is, therefore, to outline the various steps in clone analysis, reviewing recent developments and describing some of the standard methods that are in current use.

A major consideration in creating and analysing hybrid plasmids is to adopt a strategy that will minimize the amount of work involved in achieving a particular goal. To this end a number of methods have been devised to make the isolation of hybrid plasmids more efficient and these are described in Section II. Selection of the desired hybrid plasmid depends on one of a number of strategies and these are discussed in Section II. In general, it is worthwhile carrying out this stage of the analysis as exhaustively as possible so that only those clones which are of genuine interest will be selected. The second half of the chapter deals with methods for isolation and analysis of the plasmid DNA in clones of interest. For obvious reasons the majority of methods have been developed during work with *Escherichia coli*. Many of them are more generally applicable, but in some cases specific methods have been developed in other species.

II. Isolation of clones carrying hybrid plasmids

A. Introduction

The construction of a library of genomic DNA fragments, inserted into plasmid vehicles involves no selection for genetic information on the inserted DNA fragments. Hence a simple method, other than gene expression, is necessary to identify hybrid plasmids, otherwise considerable effort may be expended in analysing transformants to determine whether hybrid plasmids have been obtained. Screening transformants for inactivation of plasmid antibiotic resistance markers due to the insertion of foreign DNA fragments in the resistance gene (insertional inactivation) is still widely used to detect hybrid plasmids. An alternative approach uses a plasmid that carries that part of the *E. coli lacZ* gene which produces the α peptide, which can complement β-galactosidase activity in certain *lacZ* deletion strains (e.g. M15, Langley *et al.*, 1975). Insertions into the plasmid's single *Eco*RI site (in the *lacZ* segment) prevent α peptide formation (Rüther, 1980; Fig. 1) and so eliminate the ability to complement. Production of β-galactosidase can be easily detected on agar plates because it hydrolyses 3-chloro-4-bromo-indolyl β-galactoside (X-gal) (present at 80 μg ml^{-1}) to give a strong blue colour. Plasmid transformants can be directly screened for insertion of foreign fragments at the *Eco*RI site because the relevant colonies remain white.

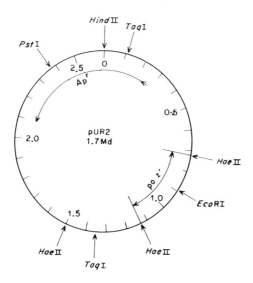

Fig. 1. A circular restriction map of pUR2. The scale is in kilobases. Insertions of fragments larger than 100 base pairs at the *Eco*RI site inactivate the *lacZ* gene α fragment (from Rüther, 1980).

A number of methods designed to yield 90–100% hybrid plasmids from the initial transformation are also available. One method involves treatment of the cleaved plasmid cloning vehicle with bacterial alkaline phosphatase (100 units per 10 pmol of 5′ phosphate, i.e. 13.5 μg of singly-cut pBR322, 10 mM Tris-HCl pH 8.0, 64 C for 60 min) prior to ligation to the fragments to be inserted (Fig. 2) (Ullrich *et al.*, 1977). This treatment removes the 5′ phosphate groups which are necessary for covalent joining of DNA fragments by DNA ligase. Hence recircularization of the vehicle DNA so treated is, in principle, impossible. Very few transformants, if any, should be obtained because the linear molecules function very inefficiently in transformation of *Escherichia coli* (probably due to DNA degradation on entry). However, initial cleavage of the plasmid DNA and/or 5′ phosphate removal may not be 100% efficient. It is advisable therefore to make a stock of treated plasmid DNA which can be tested by ligation and transformation and then retreated, if necessary, to lower the background number of transformants to a very low level. Addition of the fragments to be inserted, which carry 5′ phosphate groups at both ends, allows joining of plasmid vehicle and fragment in one strand at each junction (Fig. 2).

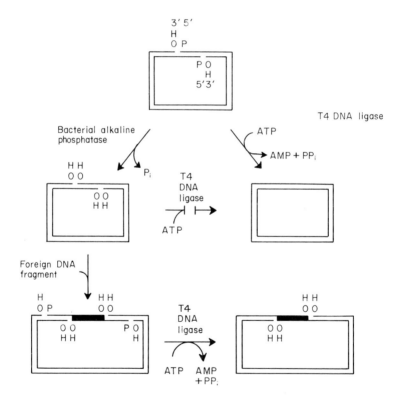

Fig. 2. Use of bacterial alkaline phosphatase to remove 5′ phosphate groups from linearized plasmid cloning vehicle to prevent recircularization by T4 DNA ligase. Addition of foreign DNA fragments with 5′ phosphates allows ligase to form circular hybrids with single-strand nicks which are repaired *in vivo* after transformation.

These circular molecules with single-strand gaps can be repaired by the host after transformation so that the majority of transformants obtained should be hybrids. Another method employed to select hybrids is to use a cosmid cloning vehicle. In this case hybrid plasmid molecules are introduced into the host by transduction, following *in vitro* packaging of the hybrid DNA molecule into bacteriophage particles (Collins, 1979; Hohn and Hinnen, 1980). This method selects hybrids on the basis of size—the cosmid alone cannot be packaged but the cosmid plus inserted foreign DNA fragments in a particular size range can be packaged.

A number of more specific methods for selecting hybrid DNA molecules have been developed and are described in the following sections.

B. Selection for inactivation of a tetracycline resistance gene

Expression of tetracycline resistance determinants makes cells more sensitive to a number of chemicals, for example fusaric acid, a lipophilic chelating agent, possibly because one component of the mechanism of resistance to tetracycline may be a reduction in the level of membrane divalent cations that are required for entry of the antibiotic into the cell (Bochner *et al.*, 1980). This differential sensitivity has been used to select against tetracycline-resistant bacteria. In the original report a rich growth medium, similar to L-Broth, was used, but subsequently it was discovered that this was suitable only for certain slow-growing strains. Thus, by omitting glucose from the medium and reducing the tryptone concentration to 0.5%, general bacterial growth on the medium was reduced. As a consequence the differential sensitivity of tetracycline-resistant and sensitive bacteria to fusaric acid increased sufficiently to reduce the background growth for most strains to acceptable levels (Maloy and Nunn, 1981). The selective agar is prepared as follows: to the basic medium of 15 g of agar, 5 g of tryptone, 5 g of yeast extract and 10 g of NaCl per litre, sterilized by autoclaving, are added as separate sterile solutions, 10 g of $NaH_2PO_4.1\ H_2O$, 4 ml of chlortetracycline hydrochloride solution (12.5 mg ml^{-1} in broth and autoclaved), 6 ml of fusaric acid solution (2 mg ml^{-1}) and 5 ml of $ZnCl_2$ solution (20 mM). This medium will inhibit the growth of cells that express tetracycline resistance genes like those of pBR322. Cells in which the tetracycline resistance determinant is inactive will grow Obviously an antibiotic which will select for the presence of the plasmid vehicle (e.g. penicillin at 300 μg ml^{-1} for pBR322) has to be included in the medium.

C. Selection for activation of a tetracycline resistance gene

Roberts *et al.* (1980) have constructed a derivative of plasmid pBR322, namely, pTR262, in which the rightward promotor (p_R) of bacteriophage λ has replaced the normal promotor for expression of tetracycline resistance (Fig. 3). The cI gene of λ that produces the λ transcription repressor is included to inhibit transcription from p_R under normal circumstances. Insertion of DNA fragments into restriction sites in the cI gene inactivates the repressor and the tetracycline resistance gene is expressed. Selection for tetracycline resistance allows, therefore, selection of hybrid plasmids with fragments inserted in the cI gene. The two sites used for cloning are *Hind*III A↓AGCTT) and *Bcl*I (T↓GATCA). The use of *Hind*III linkers can increase the usefulness of this strategy for fragment cloning.

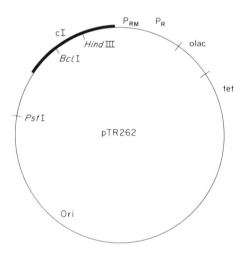

Fig. 3. A circular restriction map of pTR262 (5.4 kb approximately). Insertions into the *Hind*III or *Bcl*I sites inactivate the cI gene and allow transcription of Tc^r from p_R (from Roberts *et al.*, 1981).

D. Inactivation of a kanamycin resistance gene

Direct selection for hybrid plasmids carrying fragments that are inserted into and thus inactivate a kanamycin resistance gene can also be achieved. This technique uses strains derived from C600 that have mutations that alter the ribosomes so that growth is dependent on paromomycin (200 μg ml^{-1}), an antibiotic that interferes with translation in a manner analogous to streptomycin (Bjare and Gorini, 1971). Genes conferring resistance to kanamycin and neomycin specify enzymes which also inactivate paromomycin. Therefore carriage of such a gene by a paromomycin-dependent strain would inhibit its growth (Slutsky *et al.*, 1980). Thus, when such a strain is transformed with a ligated mixture of DNA fragments and cloning vehicle, where the cloning vehicle has been cleaved in its kanamycin resistance gene, any transformants recovered would be expected to carry hybrid plasmids. Religated vehicle would not be recovered. A plasmid suitable for such constructions would be pACYC177 (Chang and Cohen, 1978).

E. Inactivation of the Colicin E1 gene

Plasmid ColE1 derivatives that have an additional selective marker and have lost colicin E1 immunity, for example by insertion of the ampicillin resistance (β-lactamase) transposon Tn*3* into the colicin immunity gene, can be used for direct selection of clones carrying *Eco*RI DNA fragments (Ozaki *et al.*, 1980). ColE1 carries the colicin E1 gene that is inactivated by insertions at the *Eco*RI or *Xma*I sites of the plasmid. Induction of this gene by growth on nutrient agar in the presence of subinhibitory concentrations of mitomycin C ($0.1 \ \mu g \ ml^{-1}$), or by growth at 43 C severely inhibits the host, although under normal conditions the immunity gene protects against this. Thus only those cells in which the colicin E1 gene is inactive will grow well. This strategy provides a selection against bacteria carrying the parental non-hybrid plasmid.

F. Inactivation of the Mu *kil* gene

The *kil* gene of bacteriophage Mu, which is present on the *Eco*RI.C fragment, has been cloned into a number of plasmids. These hybrid plasmids kill Mu-sensitive hosts (Schumann and Lögl, 1980). Insertion of DNA fragments into restriction sites within the Mu DNA can interfere with *kil* expression. Use of the plasmids as cloning vehicles together with Mu-sensitive strains should provide a direct selection for hybrid plasmid formation. Sites known to be suitable for such insertional inactivation are *Hpa*I, *Hind*III and *Pst*I.

Examples of plasmids suitable for direct selection of hybrids are listed in Table I. For a more extensive list of plasmids that could be useful, see Bernard and Helinski (1980).

III. Screening of clones for the presence of particular genes or DNA sequences

A. Complementation

The presence of complete genes in hybrid plasmids can be detected by complementation analysis. Usually this test will be applied to a gene bank.

TABLE I

Examples of plasmid cloning vehicles for direct selection of hybrid plasmids by insertional inactivation

Plasmid cloning vehicle	Plasmid size	Selective marker	Gene inactivated	Suitable restriction sites	Selection procedure
pBR322 (Bolivar *et al.*, 1977)	4.36 kb	Ap^r	Tc^r	*Hind*III, *Bam*HI, *Sal* I	Fusaric acid resistance of Tc^s bacteria (Bochner *et al.*, 1980; Maloy and Nunn, 1981)
pTR262	5.4 kb (approx.)	λ immunity or Tc^r	λcI	*Hind*III, *Bcl*I	Reactivation of tetracycline resistance (Roberts *et al.*, 1980)
pACYC177 (Chang and Cohen, 1978)	3.67 kb	Ap^r	Km^r	*Hind*III, *Sma*I, *Xho*I	Growth of paromomycin-dependent bacteria (Slutsky *et al.*, 1980)
pKY2287	10.2 kb	Ap^r	Colicin E1	*Eco*RI, *Xma*I	Inactivation of induced Colicin E1 gene (Ozaki *et al.*, 1980)
pKN80	16.0 kb	Ap^r	Mu *kil*	*Hind*III, *Hpa*I	Inactivation of Mu gene lethal for Mu-sensitive hosts (Schumann and Lögl, 1980)
pKN001	10.3 kb	Tc^r	Mu *kil*	*Hind*III, *Hpa*I	

Generally, screening will be by complementation of defects in the equivalent host chromosomal genes, but it can equally well be applied to defects in genes on extrachromosomal elements. In practical terms, the use of complementation to screen a population of hybrid plasmids for the gene of interest mainly extends to genes where growth under specific conditions requires the presence of a functional gene product. However, the procedure can be applied when the gene product can be easily detected in some other way, for example, by enzyme assay linked to a colour change or the ability to show chemotactic response. In self-cloning experiments (where the DNA cloned comes from the same organism as that being used as the host), it is important to use a recombination deficient strain to prevent the formation of a functional gene by recombination between chromosomal sequences and a fragment of the gene of interest. Clone analysis will often involve hybrid plasmids carrying chromosomal DNA fragments from a species different from the host; in these cases complementation may be limited by the level of gene expression in the specific host used. Nonetheless interspecies complementation has been found. Thus, particular genes may be expressed in different Gram-negative species although the control of expression of the gene may be altered. Most extensively studied in this context are the *trp* genes (Nagahari and Sakaguchi, 1978; Nagahari *et al.*, 1979) and the β-galactosidase gene (Beringer, 1974; Baumberg *et al.*, unpublished data) of *E. coli*. Although there is some evidence for expression of genes from Gram-negative bacteria in a Gram-positive bacterium, the *E. coli* thymidylate synthetase gene in *B. subtilis* for example (Rubin *et al.*, 1980), this seems to be rare; it seems more common for genes from Gram-positive bacteria to function in Gram-negatives, in that expression of *B. subtilis* genes in *E. coli* has been demonstrated for a number of genes including *thy* (Ehrlich *et al.*, 1976), *leu* and *pyr* (Mahler and Halvorson, 1977; Chi *et al.*, 1978). Some genes of lower eucaryotes (*Saccharomyces cerevisiae* and *Neurospora crassa*) also complement *E. coli* defects (Struhl and Davis, 1977; Clarke and Carbon, 1978; Ratzkin and Carbon, 1977; Vapnek *et al.*, 1977). Since RNA processing may be one of the barriers to expression of eucaryotic genes in *E. coli*, the possibility of using a lower eucaryote in which to perform complementation tests has been explored for auxotrophic markers. Using yeast as a host, a bank of *Drosophila melanogaster* genomic DNA clones was screened for complementation of a number of growth defects; success was achieved with the yeast adenine biosynthesis locus *ade*-8 (Henikoff *et al.*, 1981). Characterization of the transcription product of the cloned fragment revealed that the *Drosophila* gene may not contain intervening sequences. It is unclear, therefore, whether this technique will be of general use to test for the presence of higher eucaryotic genes with intervening sequences.

The recent advances in transformation of eucaryotic cells with naked chromosomal DNA (Hinnen *et al.*, 1978; Wigler *et al.*, 1979a, b) have facilitated the task of screening bacterial clones containing hybrid plasmids by using the ability of these elements to rectify defects in specific cell lines. DNA of a hybrid plasmid can integrate into the eucaryotic chromosome by homologous recombination under conditions which select for transformation by a specific genetic marker. The hybrid can then be recovered by digesting total DNA isolated from these transformants with a restriction endonuclease, one that does not cut either within the gene of interest or the cloning vehicle. After circularizing this DNA, it can be reintroduced into a suitable bacterium by transformation and antibiotic selection (Perucho *et al.*, 1980).

B. Nucleic acid hybridization

To screen bacterial colonies for the presence of particular DNA sequences, cells are transferred to and lysed by alkali on a membrane to which denatured DNA will bind; the bound DNA is then allowed to react with a radioactive nucleic acid probe that will hybridize only with the particular sequence of interest. Hybridization can be visualized by autoradiography of the membrane after washing away non-hybridized radioactivity. A set of bacterial clones, which is a replica of that transferred to the membrane, is maintained on an appropriate medium. Once identified, clones of interest can be located and retested, if necessary, before further analysis. The basic method was reported by Grunstein and Hogness (1975) but certain adaptations have been introduced subsequently (Humphries *et al.*, 1978; Hanahan and Meselson, 1980). The procedure is summarized in Fig. 4. It is possible now, using the most sensitive techniques, to screen about 100 000 colonies simultaneously in a standard sized Petri dish. Once an area of growth, containing one or more colonies with the desired sequence has been identified, then those colonies can be respread to allow identification of specific clones.

Single-stranded DNA will attach to a number of different types of filter. Although ordinary filter paper (Whatman No. 540 or 541) can be used (Gergan *et al.*, 1979; H. E. D. Lane, personal communication), nitrocellulose or mixed nitrate/acetate ester filters are recommended [e.g. Millipore, Triton free (HAFT) or Gelman (GN–6)] since they give a more consistent binding and are less prone to smearing. Gridded filters, which are made by a number of manufacturers, may be useful for keeping track of the location of clones on a filter.

The moist, but not visibly wet, nitrocellulose filter is placed on the surface of a nutrient agar plate of standard size (avoid trapping air bubbles underneath) and inoculated with bacteria either by spotting clones onto it with a tooth pick, or by spreading a bacterial suspension over its surface or by contact with a replicating velvet. The bacteria are allowed to grow on the filter surface by

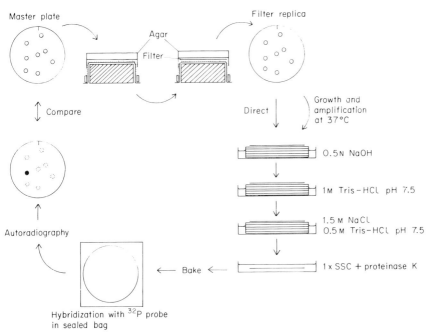

Fig. 4. Colony hybridization to screen for hybrid plasmids carrying particular DNA sequences. Colonies are transferred to filters, either Whatman 540, which are treated directly, or nitrocellulose which are incubated on medium and amplified with chloramphenicol before proceeding to lysis, etc. by placing on wads of filter paper soaked in a series of solutions (see text). After proteinase K treatment and baking at 80 C *in vacuo* the filter is hybridized with radiolabelled probe and autoradiographed. The autoradiograph is then compared with the master plate to locate the colonies of interest.

incubating it at 37 C or another appropriate temperature. When a colony size of about 1-mm diameter is attained, a replica is made by standard methods, if no duplicate set of the clones already exists. The sensitivity of the test can be increased by amplification of suitable plasmids (i.e. those where the vector has a ColE1 type replication system) by transfer of the filter to a nutrient agar plate containing chloramphenicol (200 μg ml⁻¹) followed by incubation at 37 C overnight. If Whatman filter paper is used, bacteria are transferred from a replicating velvet and lysed without further incubation. Cell lysis and subsequent neutralization are performed at room temperature by transferring the filter, bacteria upwards, to a series of wads of 3-mm Whatman filter paper (four or five sheets thick), soaked in the appropriate solution. The filter is dried on clean filter paper between each step. First the filter is transferred to 0.5 N NaOH for 10 min. This treatment lyses the bacteria and denatures the

DNA, which then sticks to the filter. To neutralize the alkali, the filter is transferred to 1.0 M Tris-HCl, pH 7.5 (10 min). This treatment is repeated twice before the filter is transferred to 1.5 M NaCl, 0.5 M Tris-HCl, pH 7.5 (10 min). Cell debris is removed from the filter by incubating it for 1 h at room temperature in a Petri dish containing 5 ml of 1 × SSC (0.01 M Na citrate, 0.1 M NaCl, pH 7.0) and 1 mg of proteinase K per millilitre. Alternatively, 2 × SSC, 0.1% (w/v) SDS can be used. The filter is rinsed with 2 × SSC, to remove residual traces of unlysed bacteria, since this contamination can increase the non-specific background. The filters are dried at 65°C and then baked for 2 h at 80°C in a vacuum oven. The baked filters are pretreated at 65°C for 2 h with 3 × SSC and 10 × Denhardt's solution [1 × Denhardt's solution is 0.02% polyvinyl pyrollidone, 0.02% Ficoll and 0.02% bovine serum albumin (Denhardt, 1966)] and then hybridized with a radioactive probe. If the radioisotopically labelled probe is RNA, the filter is wetted with 1.0 ml of hybridization buffer (5 × SSC, 50% formamide, 1 × Denhardt's solution and 0.1% SDS) containing the probe and then incubated at 37°C for 16 h under mineral oil, between sheets of cling film, or in sealed polythene bags, to prevent evaporation. The filter is washed twice for 30 min with 50 ml of 2 × SSC, then for 30 min with 50 ml of 2 × SSC containing 20 μg ml of pancreatic RNAase. Finally it is blotted dry.

For hybridization with labelled DNA, the DNA probe, in 0.9 ml of 0.01 M Tris-HCl pH 7.5 and 0.01 M EDTA, is heated in a boiling water bath for 5 min to denature the DNA. Then the solution is adjusted to the same conditions as for RNA probe hybridization (see above). Incubation is at 55°C for 16 h in a sealed unit (as above), after which the filter is washed, three times, in 100 ml 2 × SSC at 55°C for 60 min and then blotted dry.

Filters are autoradiographed using appropriate preflashed (Laskey and Mills, 1977) film (e.g. Kodak X OMAT RP) with intensifying screens (e.g. Ilford fast tungstate). Radiolabelled RNA probe can be produced by *in vivo* labelling with $^{32}PO_4$, or by *in vitro* transcription of DNA using ^{32}P-labelled UTP. DNA probe can be obtained by nick translation (Rigby *et al.*, 1977) of plasmid DNA containing the desired DNA sequences or of an appropriate purified DNA fragment, which avoids possible hybridization between cloning vehicles.

C. Probing with specific antibodies

If a protein has been purified and used to raise antiserum then these specific antibodies can be used to screen a population of bacterial clones for those carrying hybrid plasmids which direct the production of antigenically active polypeptides. The most direct method for using the antibodies is to allow them to interact with lysed colonies on an agar plate and to look for immune precipitates (Anderson *et al.*, 1979). Lysis of bacterial colonies, grown (after replica plating from master plates) on thin layers of N-Z bottom agar (1% N-Z amine A, 0.5% NaCl, 0.4% Casamino acids, 10 μg ml^{-1} of thiamine, 1.5% bacto agar) at 30°C for 24–48 h can be achieved by heat induction at 42°C for 4 h if a λ lysogen with a temperature-sensitive phage repressor is used as host. Alternatively, bacteria can be lysed after colony growth by exposure to air saturated with chloroform vapour for 10 min, followed by overlaying with 4.5 ml of 0.6% agarose in 0.1 M Tris-HCl, 0.01 M EDTA, pH 8.0 containing 0.5 ml of salt-free lysozyme solution (5 mg ml^{-1} in 0.1 M Tris-HCl, 0.01 M EDTA) for a standard sized Petri dish. The plates must be sufficiently dry before use otherwise the bacteria will not remain attached to the agar surface during the overlay step. After 1 h at 37°C, 0.5 ml of a 2% sarkosyl solution is added and 1 h later the sarkosyl is rinsed off with two washings of distilled water. The agar surface is dried (open) at 37°C for 1 h. The plates carrying the phage or biochemically-lysed bacteria are then overlayed with 2.5 ml of 0.6% molten agarose in water containing the antiserum at the correct concentration (determined previously by testing serial dilutions against known amounts of antigen placed in holes on an N-Z agar plate). Incubation at 37°C overnight is generally sufficient to allow formation of precipitin rings around colonies producing antigen.

An alternative way to use antibodies to screen bacterial clones is to transfer proteins from bacterial lysates on to a solid surface and then to identify those areas where antigen is bound using radioactively labelled antibody, followed by autoradiography to detect the antigen–antibody complex. The solid surface may bind all proteins from bacterial lysates (Hitzeman *et al.*, 1979) or may be coated with specific antibody so that only the antigen of interest from the bacterial lysates will be bound (Erlich *et al.*, 1979; Broome and Gilbert, 1978; Clarke *et al.*, 1979). The surface to which proteins in the bacterial lysate, or specific antibodies, are bound can be diazobenzyloxy-methyl-cellulose paper (Alwine *et al.*, 1977; Erlich *et al.*, 1979), polyvinyl plastic (Broome and Gilbert, 1978) or cyanogen bromide (CNBr)-activated paper (Clarke *et al.*, 1979; Hitzeman *et al.*, 1979). The bound antigen is then detected with ^{125}I-labelled antibody or with unlabelled antibody together with ^{125}I-labelled staphylococcal protein A. The three different types of complex formed are illustrated in Fig 5. The method of Hitzeman *et al.* (1979) has the potential advantage of not requiring the antigen to interact with two layers of antibodies and so it is useful for monovalent antigens or monoclonal antibodies where each antibody may interact with a single site on the antigen. The full details of these methods are beyond the scope of this chapter and the reader is referred to the original references.

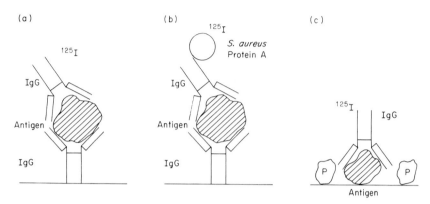

Fig. 5. Schematic diagram of the three types of complex that can be used to screen lysed colonies for specific antigens: (a) surface covered with specific antibody which attaches only specific antigen which is then detected with ^{125}I-labelled antibody (Broome and Gilbert, 1979; Clarke *et al.*, 1979); (b) as (a) except that the second layer of antibody is not labelled but is detected with ^{125}I-labelled staphylococcal protein A which specifically binds to IgG molecules (Erlich *et al.*, 1979); (c) lysate proteins (P) are attached to the surface directly and then specific antigen is detected as in (a) (Hitzeman *et al.*, 1979).

IV. Rapid isolation of plasmid DNA

A. Introduction

To decide which out of a large number of clones to study further it may be necessary to screen quickly the plasmid DNA from many colonies or cultures. A number of methods have been developed for this purpose, mostly for use with *E. coli*, but which can also be used with other bacterial species. The methods are simplest if native plasmid DNA is to be analysed. If the DNA is used in a transformation experiment or subjected to restriction endonuclease digestion, steps to remove inhibitory substances used to lyse the cells, such as phenol or SDS, must be introduced. Three main strategies have been employed for rapid screening of plasmid DNA. In the following sections these are discussed and the standard methods are described.

B. Electrophoresis of total cell lysates

When a whole cell lysate is electrophoresed in an agarose gel, plasmid DNA species will generally migrate as discrete bands whereas the fate of chromosomal DNA will depend on how it has been handled. Unfragmented chromosomal DNA will not enter the gel, whereas DNA fragments tend to migrate as a rather broad band, of about 10 kb, distinguishable from plasmid DNA. Unless the plasmid DNA species comigrates with these chromosomal fragments it can easily be seen providing it is isolated in sufficient quantity. Methods for separating plasmid DNA from chromosomal DNA by gel electrophoresis were developed for small high copy number plasmids (Telford *et al.*, 1977; Barnes, 1977), but these have few advantages over current methods that remove the majority of chromosomal DNA prior to electrophoresis. Lysis of cells in the gel well, followed by immediate electrophoresis has the advantage, however, that high molecular weight plasmids that might otherwise be lost due to shearing forces generated during manipulations can be visualized (Eckhardt, 1978). A vertical 0.7% agarose gel is prepared but the wells are not filled with buffer. One large freshly grown colony is transferred from the agar surface, using a toothpick or a stainless steel spatula, into 0.5 ml of lysis buffer (electrophoresis buffer +25% v/v glycerol, 1 μg ml^{-1} of preboiled RNAase, 20 μg ml^{-1} of fresh lysozyme). Alternatively, pelleted cells from 1 ml of overnight culture grown in nutrient broth can be used. The cells are resuspended by vortex mixing and then 0.1 ml is placed in a well. This is overlayed with 0.1 ml of SDS buffer (electrophoresis buffer, 10% glycerol, 0.2% SDS, bromophenol blue) and then with 0.1 ml of overlay buffer (electrophoresis buffer, 5% glycerol, 0.2% SDS). Finally each well is sealed with molten agarose. Electrophoresis buffer is added to both reservoirs and the gel is run at the lowest possible current (method of G. Ditta, personal communication). The SDS migrates into the bacterial suspension and the cells lyse. Plasmid DNA is released and migrates into the agarose leaving chromosomal DNA trapped in the well. The voltage is increased to 130–150 volts after 30 min. Because of its simplicity this procedure should work for most Gram-negative bacterial species, including *Rhizobium* sp. If problems of reproducibility are encountered then one modification is to resuspend the cells in 0.1% sarkosyl in TE buffer (50 mM Tris-HCl, 20 mM EDTA, pH 8.0) and then wash them with TE before resuspending them in the lysozyme mixture as described above. Increasing the RNAase concentration 100- to 1000-fold may also be beneficial. The SDS concentration may have to be increased to 2% instead of 0.2% to lyse some species such as *Pseudomonas solanacearum* (J. Denarié, personal communication). This method has resolved plasmids larger than 450 kb (Casse *et al.*, 1979).

C. Cleared lysate methods

Bacteria can be lysed gently in such a way that cell debris and chromosomal DNA can be pelleted by centrifugation, leaving a supernatant containing plasmid DNA. Such lysis can be achieved by producing protoplasts. The cells are digested with cell wall degrading enzymes (e.g. lysozyme for *E. coli* and *B.*

subtilis, lysostaphin for *S. aureus*) and then treated with lytic solutions containing one of a variety of detergents (Clewell and Helinski, 1969; Novick and Bouanchaud, 1971; Blair *et al.*, 1972; Hughes and Meynell, 1977). Phenol can be used instead of a detergent (Klein *et al.*, 1980), or, alternatively, cell suspensions can be treated directly with SDS, without prior lysozyme treatment (Kahn *et al.*, 1979). Recently, a method which combines lysozyme and detergent treatment with incubation in boiling water has been reported (Holmes and Quigley, 1981) and has the advantage of being very quick. Speed is the main advantage of the cleared lysate methods and they generally give good yields with relatively small, high copy number plasmids. They have the disadvantage that the lysis conditions which give the best yield of plasmid DNA and the least contamination by chromosomal DNA vary from strain to strain, and can even be affected by the plasmid involved. Thus, no one protocol is applicable in all situations. In addition the recovery of large low copy number plasmids can be very poor, probably due to complexes of plasmid with chromosomes and/or membranes. This poor recovery is not simply a matter of size since high molecular weight derivatives of small high copy number plasmids can, in general, be recovered in reasonable yield from both *E. coli* (C. Thomas, unpublished data) and *S. aureus* (R. Novick, personal communication). Cleared lysates generally contain some fragments of chromosomal DNA. While this does not normally interfere with the screening process, with or without restriction endonuclease digestion, the fragments can be removed, if necessary, by hydroxyl apatite chromatography (Colman *et al.*, 1978) or acridine yellow affinity chromatography (Vincent and Goldstein, 1981).

For analysis of plasmid DNA in single colonies of *E. coli*, cell lysis with SDS is effective (D. Sherratt, personal communication). A large colony, or the cell pellet from 0.5 ml of an overnight culture, is suspended gently in 200 μl of lysis buffer (1% SDS, 2% Ficoll, bromophenol blue in electrophoresis buffer) by stirring. The suspension is incubated at room temperature for 15 min and then spun in a microfuge at 4°C for 15 min. At this temperature SDS is precipitated and this helps to clear more than 90% of chromosomal DNA and cell debris from the supernatant. 50 μl of the supernatant can then be run on a suitable gel.

For rapid analysis of plasmid DNA in *S. aureus*, a cleared lysate method (R. Novick, personal communication) based on that of Novick and Bouanchaud (1971) is used. Overnight cultures are diluted in CY broth and then grown to OD_{675}1cm = 1.0 at 37°C. After harvesting, the cells are washed in SMM buffer (0.5 M sucrose, 0.02 M maleate pH 6.5, 0.02 M MgCl$_2$) and resuspended in SMM buffer at 20 times the cell density of the original culture. Fresh lysostaphin solution is added to 30 μg ml^{-1} and, after 30 min incubation at 37°C, an equal volume of 2% Brij58 (w/v), 100 mM EDTA is added and the solutions mixed by inverting the tube once. The chromosomal DNA is removed by spinning at 20 000 r/min ($\sim 30\,000 \times g$) for 45 min. The supernatant contains the plasmid DNA and can be cleaned up for transformation or restriction digestion by phenol extraction (with an equal volume of fresh water-saturated phenol, pH 7.0), to remove protein and denatured DNA, followed by either diethyl ether or chloroform extraction of the aqueous (upper) phase to remove dissolved phenol. Finally, the nucleic acids are precipitated by adding an equal volume of isopropanol (propan-2-ol) and storing the mixture at -20°C for 30 min. The DNA is recovered by centrifugation at approximately $10\,000 \times g$ for 10 min and resuspended in low salt buffer (e.g. 0.5 mM EDTA, 5 mM NaCl, 10 mM Tris-HCl, pH 7.5). The DNA can be analysed directly or after restriction endonuclease digestion. Alternatively, hydroxyl apatite chromatography can be used to remove proteins, RNA and chromosomal DNA fragments according to the method of Colman et al. (1978). However, since this method is less suitable than phenol extraction for multiple samples it is not described here.

The classical method of Triton X-100 cleared lysate preparation of plasmid DNA from E. coli is not described here because it is not as generally applicable as the method described in the next section, but details of this method can be found in Chapter 6.

D. Precipitation of chromosomal DNA after complete lysis

The most general methods for plasmid isolation involve complete cell lysis followed by selective precipitation of chromosomal DNA. This latter step has been achieved by coprecipitation of SDS and chromosomal DNA at high ionic strength in the cold (4°C) (Guerry et al., 1973) or by denaturing DNA at high pH followed by rapid renaturation using conditions where covalently closed circular plasmid DNA molecules return to a native form while chromosomal DNA anneals randomly to form an insoluble mass (Currier and Nester, 1976). This latter method has been adapted to small-scale microfuge plasmid preparations (Birnboim and Doly, 1979). A similar method on a rather larger scale has been reported by Casse et al. (1979). The advantages of these methods are that, because complete lysis is achieved using harsh conditions, the method is virtually independent of the particular bacterial strain or species, so long as there is a suitable enzyme to degrade the cell wall. The lysis conditions should also destroy any plasmid–chromosome or plasmid–membrane associations which might decrease the yield of low copy plasmids. In the author's experience, of the various methods tried, the method of Birnboim and Doly (1979) gives the best yield for small, high copy number plasmids and is also the best method for larger plasmids such as RK2 (56 kb). In Fig. 6 the results of isolation of plasmids pBR322 (4.36 kb) and RK2 by the

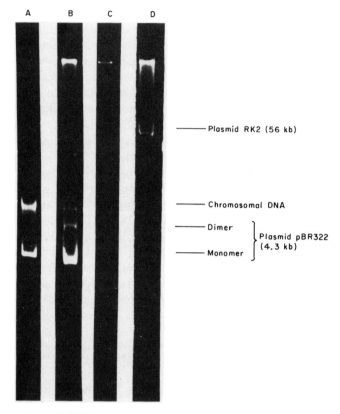

Fig. 6. Comparison of yield from the Triton X-100-cleared lysate (A and C) and the alkaline extraction (B and D) methods used for rapid isolation of plasmid DNA from *E. coli*, pBR322 (A and B) and RK2 (C and D). The difference in pBR322 mobility is due to ionic strength differences in the samples. Note the greater plasmid yield in track B compared with track A, with lower chromosomal DNA contamination.

Triton X-100-cleared lysate and alkaline extraction methods are compared. The latter procedure seems to be generally applicable to most Gram-negative species as well as to Gram-positive bacteria such as *B. subtilis* (S. D. Ehrlich, personal communication), thermophilic bacilli (Imanaka *et al.*, 1981) and *Streptococcus pneumoniae* (J. Denarié, personal communication) and even to yeast (Birnboim and Doly, 1979).

    The method is carried out as follows. Place one large colony, or the cell pellet from 0.5–1.0 ml of a fresh overnight culture, in a microfuge tube and resuspend, by vortexing, in 100 μl of lysis buffer (2 mg ml^{-1} lysozyme, 50 mM glucose, 10 mM EDTA, 25 mM Tris-HCl, pH 8.0); incubate for 30 min at 0°C (at 37°C for *B. subtilis*). Add 200 μl of alkaline SDS solution (1% w/v SDS, 0.2 N NaOH), vortex and incubate for 5 min at 0°C. The pH should be close to 12.4 but not more than 12.6 (above pH 12.6 plasmid DNA can be denatured irreversibly so it is important to keep the ratio of cells to solution volumes as described). 150 μl of 3 M sodium acetate pH 4.8 are then added lowering the pH and so allowing renaturation of plasmid DNA to its native form (chromosomal DNA becomes an insoluble mass because of interduplex annealing) and increasing the ionic strength sufficiently to precipitate protein–SDS complexes and RNA. After 10 min at 0°C the precipitate is pelleted by spinning for 5 min in a microfuge (~ 10 000 × g). The supernatant is removed, avoiding any lumps of precipitate which have floated free. An equal volume of isopropanol is added to the supernatant to precipitate plasmid DNA and RNA. After storage at −20°C for 30 min, pellet the precipitated plasmid DNA using a microfuge and resuspend it in low salt buffer (0.5 mM EDTA, 5 mM NaCl, 10 mM Tris-HCl, pH 7.5). From 1 ml of overnight culture, resuspend the pellet in 50 μl of buffer. Samples can be examined for supercoiled plasmid DNA directly: 2–5 μl should be ample to observe high copy number plasmids and 10–20 μl sufficient for low copy number plasmids. If the plasmid DNA is to be digested with restriction enzymes it must be further purified. Sodium acetate is added to a final concentration of 0.1 M (pH 8.0), followed by 2 volumes of cold ethanol or 1 volume of isopropanol. The mixture is stored at −20°C for 20 min. The DNA precipitate is collected as before by centrifugation and the resuspension and precipitation steps are repeated. Finally, dissolve the DNA in 50 μl of water. A few microlitres of this DNA solution should be sufficient for transformation, and restriction endonuclease digestions can be carried out by adding a sufficient volume of an appropriate concentrated restriction buffer to the desired volume of DNA solution to give the required final concentration. With *Pseudomonas* species and other species that produce a complex polysaccharide slime, it is common at this stage to obtain a precipitate that will not completely dissolve and may interfere with restriction endonuclease digestion and gel electrophoresis. Centrifugation of the suspension can remove this, leaving a clear supernatant which contains the nucleic acids.

The method of Casse *et al.* (1979) is similar to the method above but uses larger volumes and lyses bacteria directly with alkaline SDS instead of first producing protoplasts. A method which combines some of the same principles has been reported (Kado and Liu, 1981) but we have found in this laboratory that it is more difficult to obtain reproducible results with this method as compared to the method of Birnboim and Doly (1979) and poorer yields of both small and large plasmids were obtained.

V. Electrophoresis of plasmid DNA isolated from clones

A. Agarose gel electrophoresis

Apparatus for gel electrophoresis can be purchased from a number of commercial sources or made according to standard models (Studier, 1973). Electrophoresis can be carried out in Tris-acetate (50 mM Tris-acetate, pH 7.5–8.0, 1 mM EDTA) or Tris-borate (TBE) (89 mM Tris, 89 mM boric acid, 2.5 mM EDTA, pH 8.2) buffer. Half strength TBE is sufficient for most purposes. Ethidium bromide may be included at 0.1–0.5 μg ml^{-1} in the gel and tank buffers to allow visualization of the DNA under ultra-violet light illumination immediately after electrophoresis (Chapter 6). Horizontal agarose gels can be used at most agarose concentrations (0.4%–3% w/v), whereas vertical gels tend to collapse below 0.7% (w/v). Vertical gels have the advantage of larger well sizes; set against this, bands are more likely to have trailing edges than those in horizontal gels. To examine undigested plasmid DNA in the range 3–60 kb, 0.8% agarose is sufficient. For larger plasmids 0.7–0.75% agarose is suitable. Analysis of linear fragments throughout the range 0.3–10 kb can be done conveniently in 1% agarose gels. For larger fragments (i.e. > 10 kb) the percentage agarose should be decreased; conversely it should be increased for smaller fragments (Chapter 6). Gels are prepared by melting the agarose in an autoclave (5 min) or a boiling water bath. The molten agarose (at approximately 65°C) is poured into a mould formed by electrophoresis plates, spacers and a comb. The apparatus is first sealed at its seams with a small volume of very hot agarose which is allowed to set. Then the mould is filled with molten agar. The agarose is allowed to solidify and then the comb is removed. The gel is placed in the electrophoresis apparatus which is connected to a power pack so that the DNA migrates towards the anode, through the gel. The gel is run at 10 volts cm^{-1} until the bromophenol blue tracker dye reaches the bottom. Samples from cleared lysate or alkaline extraction methods, either with or without restriction endonuclease digestion, should be prepared by adding preboiled RNAase (20 μg ml^{-1} final concentration) to digest RNA, a tracking dye (generally bromophenol blue) and either glycerol (20% w/v final concentration) or ficoll (1–2% w/v final concentration) to increase the density of the DNA solution and so stop the sample rapidly mixing with the electrophoresis buffer. Ficoll tends to produce straighter bands, i.e. less curved than is found when glycerol is used. After electrophoresis, gels are placed on an ultra-violet transilluminator (Ultraviolet Products, C-6, 302-nm wavelength) and photographed with Polaroid film (Type 667) using a Kodak Wratten filter No. 16.

Sizes of the plasmids can be estimated by comparison with standard plasmids whose size has been determined independently; for example, by electron microscopy (Chapter 7). The plasmid standards can be isolated separately or from a strain carrying a range of plasmids (Macrina *et al.*, 1978).

B. Extraction of plasmid DNA from agarose or acrylamide

It may be desirable to extract plasmid DNA from agarose or acrylamide gels for a number of reasons. For example, when constructing a restriction map (see below), fragments produced by one enzyme can be analysed with a second enzyme, or fragments produced by partial digestion can be completely digested and these products analysed. If more than one plasmid species is present in the extract, as is often the case when analysing newly isolated bacterial strains, it may be necessary to separate supercoiled plasmid species in agarose gels, extract the plasmid DNA from the gel and then analyse the restriction patterns for each plasmid species separately. A number of methods exist for this purpose and most have been reviewed elsewhere (Smith, 1980; Southern, 1979). One group of methods depends on dissolving the agarose, for example, with sodium perchlorate (Wilke and Cortini, 1976) or potassium iodide (Blin *et al.*, 1975) and then separating the DNA from the agarose by hydroxyapatite binding or potassium iodide density gradient centrifugation. (It should be noted that the potassium iodide method cannot be used with gels made up in Tris-borate because of precipitation.) The use of low melting point agarose can make dissolution of the agarose easier (by simply increasing the temperature to 60°C); *n*-butanol extraction of the quaternary ammonium salt of the nucleic acid can be used to separate it from the agarose (Langridge *et al.*, 1980). Low melting point agarose can, in principle, be used in the initial run, so that a second digestion of DNA, without removal of the agarose, can be performed—after the first run the bands of interest are cut from the gel; the agarose is melted at 60°C, cooled to 37°C and the buffer conditions adjusted to those appropriate for the next restriction endonuclease digestion of the DNA. After digestion, the sample is applied to a second gel for analysis. While it is simple, this method can be very inefficient, since the presence of agarose may inhibit the activity of the restriction endonuclease.

DNA can be removed from gels without disrupting the gel completely, either by allowing it to diffuse into a buffer containing SDS (Maxam and Gilbert, 1977), or by squeezing liquid out of frozen samples (Thuring *et al.*, 1975). The level of recovery of DNA with both of these methods is variable. The former method is really only suitable for relatively small fragments (< 1 kb), whereas the latter is most suitable for large fragments in low percentage agarose. An alternative method is to electrophorese the DNA from the gel. The simplest method is to separate fragments on a gel, and then allow the fragments of interest to migrate into a catching devise incorporated into the gel—either a trap of dialysis bag (Yang *et al.*, 1979), a well filled with hydroxyapatite (Tabak and Flavell, 1978) or a strip of paper that will bind the DNA, e.g. DEAE–cellulose paper (Girvitz *et al.*, 1980; Dretzen *et al.*, 1981). The last method is the neatest since a slit, rather than a well, is cut in the gel. This may be of practical importance if bands are closely spaced. However, this method appears to be inefficient for recovery of covalently closed circular (CCC) DNA species. A more general method that can cope with closely spaced bands and isolation of CCC DNA is described below.

Cut the desired band out of the agarose slab (or acrylamide slab, Chapter 6) and place it in a glasswool-plugged 5-ml glass pipette that has been cut to widen the tip and shorten the length so that it is compatible with a vertical gel electrophoresis apparatus (Fig. 7). Dialysis tubing, just wide enough to fit the pipette tightly, is knotted at one end and placed over the lower end of the pipette (a rubber band is used to form a tight seal, if necessary). Dilute buffer (e.g. 40 mM sodium acetate, 0.1 mM EDTA, pH 8.2) is added to fill the pipette and the upper and lower tanks of the electrophoresis apparatus. The pipette with the dialysis sack is clamped in the lower tank; the buffer inside the pipette is connected to the upper tank by a U-shaped capillary tube. A potential difference of 500 volts is applied to the apparatus, which is run overnight. Before switching off, the current is reversed for 5 min to detach DNA from the dialysis sack. Then the contents are removed and the DNA is precipitated.

An even simpler technique exists. The gel slice is placed in a dialysis sack, which is filled with 5 mM tris, 4 mM sodium acetate, pH 8.0, and immersed in

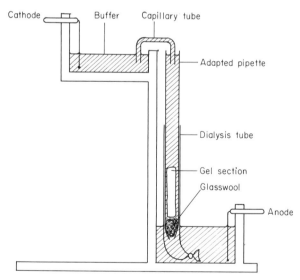

Fig. 7. Apparatus for electroelution of DNA from agarose or acrylamide gel slices.

the same buffer between two electrodes. A potential gradient of 10–15 volts cm^{-1} is applied (McDonnell et al., 1977). Thirty minutes should be sufficient for the DNA to migrate out of the gel and collect in the surrounding buffer.

VI. Analysis of cloned DNA fragments

A. Introduction

Once a bacterial clone carrying a hybrid plasmid of interest has been identified and the plasmid DNA isolated, the major objectives of further analysis will be to identify the smallest DNA segment carrying each gene of interest and to characterize transcription and translation of these genes. The reason for deleting all non-essential DNA is primarily to aid further fine structure analysis, such as DNA sequencing, introduction of specific mutations and identification of binding sites for proteins such as RNA polymerase. The first step in the location of the specific gene(s) within the cloned DNA segment is the construction of a restriction endonuclease cleavage site map.

B. Construction of a restriction endonuclease cleavage site map

DNA of hybrid plasmids can be characterized initially by digesting it with a restriction endonuclease that will cut at the junction between the plasmid cloning vehicle and the inserted fragment and analysing the resulting fragments by gel electrophoresis. The enzyme used will generally be the enzyme that was used to produce the original fragments for cloning. However, where enzymes such as Sau3A and MboI, which cut at many sites, have been used to produce random or overlapping fragments by partial digestion and these have been inserted into either a BamHI or BglII site (which produce the same cohesive ends as Sau3A and MboI) these latter sites will probably no longer exist. Furthermore, Sau3A and MboI cleavage patterns may be too complicated for simple analysis. In these circumstances sites close to the cloning site can be used for the initial digestion, e.g. EcoRI and SalI on either side of BamHI site in pBR322. The length of the inserted DNA can be estimated by summation of constituent fragments, the sizes of which can be calculated by comparison with standard DNA molecules such as bacteriophage λ DNA digested with HindIII (size range 25–2 kb; Allet and Bukhari, 1975), or smaller DNA molecules such as plasmid pBR322 (4362 bp), whose entire sequence is known (Sutcliffe, 1978), digested with various enzymes. The mobilities of the standard fragments are plotted against the logarithm of their molecular weights. For any particular gel this should generate what is essentially a linear relationship over the range of fragment sizes where estimates can be made most accurately. This calibration line is used to estimate the size of fragments of interest from their mobilities.

This initial characterization will allow a decision as to which clones to examine in more detail. For further analysis it may be necessary to make larger quantities of pure plasmid DNA (suitable methods are described in Chapter 6). (Before doing this the DNA already analysed should be used to transform a plasmid-free bacterial host using a low DNA to bacteria ratio to ensure that a strain is obtained that carries only the plasmid of interest; sometimes the initial hybrid construction introduces more than one plasmid into a cell line.)

A restriction map can be constructed by determining the number and size of fragments produced by any particular enzyme. Usually, enzymes with a 6 bp recognition sequence are tried first since, in general, they will cut least frequently. Then enzymes which are likely to cut more frequently, e.g. *Hinc*II or *Hae*II can be tried. Finally, if necessary, enzymes that recognize 4 bp sequences are employed. If the DNA segment contains more than one complete fragment for a particular enzyme (i.e. there are three or more sites for that enzyme within the sequence) then the order of these fragments can be determined only by further analysis. The simplest method is to digest the DNA with two enzymes before gel electrophoresis analysis. Ideally the sites for one of the enzymes should have been mapped accurately already. By determining which of the unmapped enzyme fragments is cut by the second enzyme, and from the sizes of the resulting fragments, the relative positions of the cleavage sites of the two enzymes may be deduced. This applies only to relatively simple cases. Where the test enzyme produces many fragments more laborious techniques are necessary.

The classical method for working out the order of fragments is to analyse partial digestion products (Danna *et al.*, 1973). The DNA is digested so that not all sites are cut by the enzyme. This is achieved by using optimal temperature and buffer conditions and varying the enzyme to DNA ratios and the time of incubation. In practice a series of incubation times should be used to obtain a range of partially digested intermediates. The sites which are cut are assumed to be chosen at random (an assumption not always found to be true in practice) to produce a series of fragments with overlapping segments. These contain different subsets of the restriction enzyme fragments of interest. Separation of these partial digestion products by gel electrophoresis, extraction of individual bands (as described earlier) and the analysis in turn of their products after complete digestion allows the determination of the order of fragments, so long as each site is present at the end of at least one partial digestion product. This method involves much work because it depends on the separation and the isolation of many different partial digestion products.

Two methods that depend on partial digestion, but avoid isolation of many intermediates, have been developed. The method of Smith and Birnstiel (1976) involves radioactive labelling of one end of the DNA segment of interest. This can be achieved by digesting the hybrid plasmid DNA with an enzyme that cuts outside the segment to be mapped. The 5′ phosphate groups are removed with bacterial alkaline phosphatase and then radioactive phosphate groups are attached using α ^{32}P-ATP and T4 polynucleotide kinase. (In principle, any end-labelling method should be suitable as an alternative.) The DNA fragment is then cut with a second enzyme, again outside the segment of interest, so as to separate the two 5′-labelled ends. The fragment of interest is then separated from the other by gel electrophoresis, extracted from the gel as described above and subjected to partial digestion for various lengths of time with the enzyme whose cleavage sites are to be mapped. After gel electrophoretic separation of the partially digested DNA alongside molecular weight markers, the pattern of radioactivity is determined by autoradiography. Radioactive fragments will have one end in common, the other end being at one of the restriction endonuclease cleavage sites of interest (Fig. 8). The estimated size of the fragments allows construction of a map since the differences between the lengths of adjacent fragments represents the distances between successive restriction sites. Obviously the accuracy of this method decreases as the distance from the labelled end increases. This means that the method is poor for determining the order of adjacent fragments that are very similar in size, except when these map very near to the labelled site.

An alternative method has been reported by Saint and Egan (1979). DNA is subjected to digestion for various lengths of time up to complete digestion. After electrophoretic separation the DNA is transferred to nitrocellulose filters by the method of Southern (1975). The filter is then hybridized with a radioactive probe made by nick translation (Rigby et al., 1977) of a single cloned fragment from the region of interest. In a complete digest this fragment will hybridize only to itself, but in partial digest it will hybridize to segments where it is joined to adjacent fragments. Estimation of the sizes of these partial digestion products allows the size of the adjacent fragments to be estimated.

If a hybridization probe exists for the gene of interest (e.g. radioactively labelled RNA or cloned DNA made from mRNA, i.e. cDNA) then this can be used in Southern blots (Southern, 1975) to determine which of the DNA fragments from the cloned DNA segment contain complementary sequences. This may be useful in determining on which DNA segment to concentrate further analysis.

C. Subcloning fragments from the original hybrid

One way of determining whether a specific DNA segment carries the function of interest is to subclone it from the original hybrid. A rather obvious point is

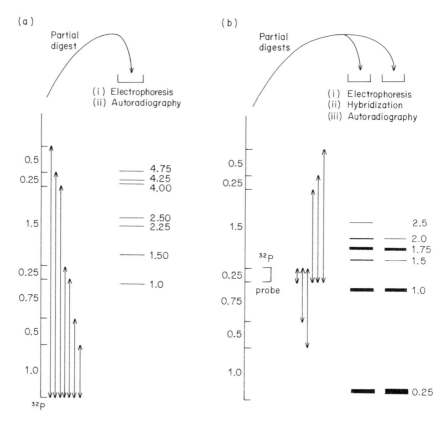

Fig. 8. Relationship between restriction map and data on radioactive bands produced with partial digestion for mapping methods of (a) Smith and Birnstiel (1976) and (b) Saint and Egan (1979).

that, in subcloning, it is often very convenient to choose a cloning vehicle with selective markers different from those of the first hybrid plasmid to avoid confusion or cross-contamination. If no convenient vehicle exists with the desired single sites, generally because the enzyme cuts too frequently, then alternative strategies may have to be employed. For a review of cloning vehicles see Bernard and Helinski (1980).

One method that is suitable for fragments produced by digestion with Sau3A and MboI (which produce a single-strand extension of 5′ GATC 3′) or TaqI and HpaII (3′ GC 5′) is to ligate these into plasmid cloning vehicles digested with BglII and BamHI (5′ GATC 3′) or ClaI (3′ GC 5′). A number of vehicles with single sites for these enzymes exist. Although the BglII, BamHI or ClaI sites may not be regenerated, appropriate analysis can establish the presence of the cloned fragments.

Of more general use is the addition of linker molecules to the ends of the fragment of interest (Rothstein *et al.*, 1979). Linkers are commercially available and consist of synthetic oligonucleotides which contain the recognition sequence for a specific restriction endonuclease. The DNA fragment of interest is rendered blunt-ended either by S_1 nuclease digestion or by filling in any single-strand segment using DNA polymerase and deoxyribonucleoside triphosphates. The fragment and 5' phosphorylated linkers are then mixed and ligated using a high concentration of T4 DNA ligase, which is suitable for blunt-ended ligation. The ligated DNA is digested with the restriction enzyme appropriate for the site on the linker to reduce the addition to a single linker at each end and to generate single-strand extensions. This DNA is then ligated to cleaved cloning vehicle DNA and hybrid molecules are isolated as described above.

If conclusions are to be drawn about the activity of genes on cloned fragments (e.g. the level of gene expression), then it is important to establish the relationship between the fragment and the cloning vehicle. The orientation of the DNA fragment can be determined by digesting the hybrid plasmid DNA with restriction enzyme(s) that cut asymmetrically within the cloned fragment and the cloning vehicle and analysing the fragment pattern. If possible, both orientations of insertion should be obtained to allow transcriptional and/or translational effects produced in one orientation (e.g. relative to a cloning vehicle promotor) to become apparent. It is not uncommon to find that a particular fragment can be inserted into the cloning vehicle in only one orientation. This is most likely due either to interference with cloning vehicle replication or to overproduction of a gene product which is lethal for the host when the fragment is inserted in the opposite orientation to the one observed. The exact reason can only be determined, if at all, by further analysis. The organization of transcription in plasmids pBR322 and pACYC184 has been reported (Stuber and Bujard, 1981) and this information may be helpful when analysing orientation effects observed with these plasmids.

D. Construction of deletion derivatives

Construction of a set of deletions which extend various distances into a cloned fragment, starting from a defined point within the cloning vehicle, may be useful for two main reasons. Firstly, by testing the set for expression of gene function, the smallest deletion to affect that function can be determined. Such results help to locate the relevant gene. Second, they can be used to facilitate nucleotide sequencing of a long DNA segment. While large-scale sequencing projects will often utilize fragments inserted into a single-stranded DNA phage vector so as to allow sequencing by the dideoxy method (Chapter 13), plasmids can be useful for combined sequence and functional analysis.

Recently, a method of creating a series of deletions in a DNA fragment, cloned at the *Pst*I site of pBR322, by inserting *Eco*RI linker molecules at random DNAase I-generated cuts, followed by deletion of the DNA between the new *Eco*RI site and the single *Eco*RI site of pBR322, has been reported (Frischauf *et al.*, 1980). Sequencing from the newly generated *Eco*RI site in the different derivatives then allows overlapping nucleotide sequences to be determined. An alternative strategy is to clone fragments into the *Hind*III site of pBR322 (Bolivar *et al.*, 1977) and to produce a series of deletions with one end point defined by the *Cla*I site of pBR322 which is next to the *Hind*III site while the other is generated by partial digestion with *Taq*I or *Hpa*II. Sequencing can start from the *Eco*RI site and is convenient because the cloned segment starts after approximately 20 bp of pBR322 DNA, so the 25% sequencing gel, which is normally used to determine the first few base pairs, can be omitted.

A general method of constructing a series of deletion derivatives using partial digestion with restriction endonucleases has been described (Kahn *et al.*, 1980). Most simply, the restriction map of the hybrid plasmid is examined to find unique sites that would be convenient as the focus of a series of deletions; 10 μg of the plasmid DNA is cut to completion with this enzyme. The enzyme is inactivated by heat. The restriction enzyme buffer is changed, if necessary, and then 1.5 μg of the DNA is withdrawn and five units of a restriction enzyme that is known to cut the DNA at many sites is added to the remainder of the DNA solution. After mixing, the solution is incubated at 37°C. Further aliquots of 1.5 μg of DNA are withdrawn after 1, 2, 5, 10 and 20 min. The restriction enzyme digestion is halted by mixing with 0.25 M EDTA (pH 8.0), to give a final concentration of 20 mM, and incubating at 65°C for 10 min. Each DNA sample is precipitated by adding an equal volume of isopropanol and then storing the preparation at −20°C for 30 min. The precipitates are pelleted in a microfuge, vacuum dried and then resuspended in ligation buffer. DNA ligase is added and the mixture is incubated at room temperature for a minimum of 2 h. Ligation should occur with molecules that have either not been cut by the second enzyme or that have been cut twice. The DNA is precipitated, resuspended in restriction buffer and digested with the enzyme used first, i.e. the one that cuts at the single site. This procedure should linearize those molecules that have religated without deletion. The DNA is then used to transform a suitable host. Only those molecules that retain the selective marker together with replication functions will become established. Ideally the number of transformants recovered should be small for the sample that was not digested partially with the second enzyme, since all the DNA should be in the form of linear molecules. With progressive partial digestion the number of transformants should increase to a maximum as more and more molecules lose the unique site, and then decline to zero as the DNA is more completely digested. Early time points are analysed preferentially. This method is based mainly on the much lower efficiency of linear as compared to circular plasmid DNA molecules to transform *E. coli*.

E. Analysis of transcription and translation

Transcription of cloned DNA fragments can be analysed *in vitro* using purified RNA polymerase holoenzyme and the appropriate DNA in binding studies (Seeburg and Schaller, 1975; von Gabain and Bujard, 1977). Alternatively, the products of transcription may be analysed (Carmichael and McMaster, 1980; Stüber *et al.*, 1978). *In vivo* studies of transcription can be carried out most simply by joining cloned fragments to transcription probes which consist of a gene lacking its own promotor. The *lacZ* gene of *E. coli*, without its normal promotor, is used extensively for this purpose, largely because quantitative changes in the level of β-galactosidase can easily be measured (Miller, 1972). Hence, the promotors on a cloned fragment may be identified by determining which orientation of the fragment activates the promotorless *lacZ* gene. Since enzyme activity is proportional to transcription activity, factors which affect the level of this transcription can also be investigated, simply by assaying the level of β-galactosidase during, or after, the change in conditions. A number of cloning vehicles suitable for cloning fragments adjacent to the *lacZ* gene, or next to the α fragment of the *lacZ* gene, have been constructed (Casadaban and Cohen, 1980). Experience acquired in this laboratory suggests that at least some of the plasmids carrying the α fragment (pMC632 and pMC692) may not be widely used for accurate measurements of transcription activity because, in some cases, uncontrolled transcription through the cloned fragment appears to be deleterious to the host. Under these circumstances there are strong pressures for loss of such transcription activity, presumably by mutation or DNA rearrangements. Alternative plasmids for investigating translation initiation signals have been constructed (Casadaban *et al.*, 1980).

To investigate the translation products of intact genes either mini cells (Chapter 12) or maxi cells (Sancar *et al.*, 1979) can be used. If the gene product is not produced in significant quantities, even when the gene is cloned in a high copy number plasmid, then that gene can be cloned downstream from a strong regulated promotor. A number of plasmids have been constructed for this purpose (Bernard and Helinski, 1980). Finally, and if necessary, *in vitro* translation of the cloned genes can be investigated (Zubay *et al.*, 1970; Gold and Schweiger, 1971).

VII. Concluding remarks

The isolation of bacterial clones carrying plasmids of interest and the characterization of their size and restriction enzyme cleavage map may, in fact, be only the beginning of a more detailed analysis. Many of the techniques for further analysis are dealt with in other chapters in this volume. In addition, techniques for *in vitro* mutagenesis and genetic analysis have been reviewed recently (Timmis, 1981). The exact course of clone analysis will depend on the particular aspect of the plasmids which is of interest. It is hoped that this chapter will have provided basic information (in the form of protocols and references to other papers on methodology) and suggestions about strategy that will form the starting point for most projects involving analysis of clones.

Acknowledgements

Work in this laboratory is supported by a Medical Research Council project grant. In preparation of this chapter I am indebted to many people who sent me details of current practice in their laboratories. Where specific information of this sort has been included it has been acknowledged in the text. Thanks are due to Chris Smith for valuable discussions and to Mrs M. Johnson, Ms S. Pipe and Mr B. Price for technical help.

References

Allet, B. and Bukhari, A. I. (1975). *J. Mol. Biol.* **92**, 529–540.
Alwine, J. C., Kemp, D. J. and Stark, G. R. (1977). *Proc. Natl. Acad. Sci. U.S.A.* **74**, 5350–5354.
Anderson, D., Shapiro, L. and Skalka, A. M. (1979). *In* "Methods in Enzymology" (R. Wu, Ed.), Vol. 68, Recombinant DNA, pp. 428–436. Academic Press, New York and London.
Barnes, W. M. (1977). *Science* **195**, 393–394.
Beringer, J. (1974). *J. Gen. Microbiol.* **84**, 188–198.
Bernard, H. U. and Helinski, D. R. (1980). *In* "Genetic Engineering" (J. K. Setlow and A. Hollaender, Eds), Vol. 2, pp. 133–167. Plenum, New York.
Birnboim, H. C., and Doly, J. (1979). *Nucleic Acids Res.* **7**, 1513–1523.
Bjare, U. and Gorini, L. (1971). *J. Mol. Biol.* **57**, 423–435.
Blair, D. G., Sherratt, D. J., Clewell, D. B. and Helinski, D. R. (1972). *Proc. Natl. Acad. Sci. U.S.A.* **68**, 210–214.
Blin, N., Gabin, A. V. and Bujard, H. (1975). *FEBS Lett.* **33**, 84–86.
Bochner, B. R., Huang, H. C., Schieven, G. L. and Ames, B. N. (1980). *J. Bacteriol.* **143**, 926–933.
Bolivar, F., Rodriguez, R. L., Greene, P. J., Betlach, M. C., Heyneker, H. L., Boyer, H. W., Crosa, J. H. and Falkow, S. (1977). *Gene* **2**, 95–113.
Broome, S. and Gilbert, W. (1978). *Proc. Natl. Acad. Sci. U.S.A.* **75**, 2746–2749.

Carmichael G. G. and McMaster, G. K. (1980). *In* "Methods in Enzymology" (L. Grossman and K. Moldave, Eds), Vol. 65, Part I, pp. 380–391. Academic Press, New York and London.

Casadaban, M. J., Chou, J. and Cohen, S. N. (1980). *J. Bacteriol.* **143**, 971–980.

Casadaban, M. J. and Cohen, S. N. (1980). *J. Mol. Biol.* **138**, 179–207.

Casse, F., Boucher, C., Julliot, J. S., Michel, M. and Dénarié, J. (1979). *J. Gen. Microbiol.* **113**, 229–242.

Chang A. C. Y. and Cohen, S. N. (1978). *J. Bacteriol.* **134**, 1141–1156.

Chi, N. T., Ehrlich, S. D. and Lederberg, J. (1978). *J. Bacteriol.* **133**, 816–821.

Clarke, L. and Carbon, J. (1978). *J. Mol. Biol.* **120**, 517–532.

Clarke, L., Hitzeman, R. and Carbon, J. (1979). *In* "Methods in Enzymology" (R. Wu, Ed.), Vol. 68, pp. 436–442. Academic Press, New York and London.

Clewell, D. B. and Helinski, D. R. (1969). *Proc. Natl. Acad. Sci. U.S.A.* **62**, 1159–1166.

Collins, J. (1979). *In* "Methods in Enzymology" (R. Wu, Ed.), Vol. 68, Recombinant DNA, pp. 309–327. Academic Press, New York and London.

Colman, A., Byers, M. J., Primrose, S. B. and Lyons, A. (1978). *Eur. J. Biochem.* **91**, 303–310.

Currier, T. C. and Nester, E. (1976). *Anal. Biochem.* **76**, 431–441.

Danna, K. J., Sack, G. H. and Nathans, D. (1973). *J. Mol. Biol.* **78**, 363–376.

Denhardt, D. T. (1966). *Biochem. Biophys. Res. Commun.* **23**, 641–646.

Dretzen, G., Bellard, M., Sassone-Corsi, P. and Chambon, P. (1981). *Anal. Biochem.* **112**, 295–298.

Eckhardt, T. (1978). *Plasmid* **1**, 584–588.

Ehrlich, S. D., Bursztyn-Pettigrew, H., Stroynowski, I. and Lederberg, J. (1976). *Proc. Natl. Acad. Sci. U.S.A.* **73**, 4145–4149.

Erlich, H. A., Cohen, S. N. and McDevitt, H. O. (1979). *In* "Methods in Enzymology" (R. Wu, Ed.) Vol. 68, Recombinant DNA, pp. 443–453. Academic Press, New York and London.

Frischauf, A. M., Garoff, H. and Lehrach, H. (1980). *Nucleic Acids Res.* **8**, 5541–5549.

Gergen, J. P., Stern, R. H. and Wensink, P. C. (1979). *Nucleic Acids Res.* **7**, 2115–2136.

Girvitz, S. C., Bacchetti, S., Rainbow, A. J. and Graham, F. L. (1980). *Anal. Biochem.* **106**, 492–496.

Gold, L. M. and Schweiger, M. (1971). *In* "Methods in Enzymology" (K. Moldave and L. Grossman, Eds), Vol. 20, pp. 537–542. Academic Press, New York and London.

Grunstein, M. and Hogness, D. S. (1975). *Proc. Natl. Acad. Sci. U.S.A.* **72**, 3961–3965.

Guerry, P., LeBlanc, D. J. and Falkow, S. (1973). *J. Bacteriol.* **116**, 1064–1066.

Hanahan, D. and Meselson, M. (1980). *Gene* **10**, 63–67.

Henikoff, S., Tutchell, K., Hall, B. D. and Nasmyth, K. A. (1981). *Nature (London)* **289**, 33–37.

Hinnen, A., Hicks, J. B. and Fink, G. R. (1978). *Proc. Natl. Acad. Sci. U.S.A.* **75**, 1929–1933.

Hitzeman, R. A., Chinault, A. C., Kingsman, A. J. and Carbon, J. (1979). *In* "Eukaryotic Gene Regulation" (R. Axel and T. Maniatis, Eds), Vol. 14, pp. 57–68. Academic Press, New York and London.

Hohn, B. and Hinnen, A. (1980). *In* "Genetic Engineering" (J. K. Setlow and A. Hollaender, Eds), Vol. 2, pp. 169–183. Plenum, New York.

Holmes, D. and Quigley, M. (1981). *Anal. Biochem.* **114**, 193–197.

Hughes, C. and Meynell, G. G. (1977). *Mol. Gen. Genet.* **151**, 175–179.

Humphries, P., Old, R., Coggins, L. W., McShane, T., Watson, C. and Paul, J. (1978) *Nucleic Acids Res.* **5**, 905–924.

Imanaka, T., Fujii, M. and Aiba, S. (1981). *J. Bacteriol.* **146**, 1091–1097.

Kado, C. I. and Liu, S. T. (1981). *J. Bacteriol.* **145**, 1365–1373.
Kahn, M., Kolter, R., Thomas, C., Figurski, D., Meyer, R., Remaut, E. and Helinski, D. R. (1979). *In* "Methods in Enzymology" (R. Wu, Ed.), Vol. 68, Recombinant DNA, pp. 268–280. Academic Press, New York and London.
Kahn, M., Ow, D., Sauer, B., Rabinowitz, A. and Calendar, R. (1980). *Mol. Gen. Genet.* **177**, 399–412.
Klein, R. D., Selsing, E. and Wells, R. D. (1980). *Plasmid* **3**, 88–91.
Langley, K. E., Villarejo, M. R., Fowler, A. V., Zamenhof, P. J. and Zabin, I. (1975). *Proc. Natl. Acad. Sci. U.S.A.* **72**, 1254–1257.
Langridge, J., Langridge, P. and Bergquist, P. L. (1980). *Anal. Biochem.* **103**, 264–271.
Laskey, R. A. and Mills, A. D. (1977). *FEBS Lett.* **82**, 314–316.
McDonnell, M. W., Simon, M. N. and Studier, F. W. (1977). *J. Mol. Biol.* **110**, 119–146.
Macrina, F. L., Kopecko, D. J., Jones, K. R., Ayers, D. J. and McCowen, S. M. (1978). *Plasmid* **1**, 417–420.
Mahler, J. and Halvorson, H. O. (1977). *J. Bacteriol.* **131**, 374–377.
Maloy, S. R. and Nunn, D. W. (1981). *J. Bacteriol.* **145**, 1110–1112.
Maxam, A. M. and Gilbert, W. (1977). *Proc. Natl. Acad. Sci. U.S.A.* **74**, 569–574.
Miller, J. (1972). "Experiments in Molecular Genetics". Cold Spring Harbor, New York.
Nagahari, K. and Sakaguchi, K. (1978). *Mol. Gen. Genet.* **158**, 263–270.
Nagahari, K., Koshikawa, T. and Sakaguchi, K. (1979). *Mol. Gen. Genet.* **171**, 115–119.
Novick, R. P. and Bouanchaud, D. (1971). *Ann. N.Y. Acad. Sci.* **182**, 279–294.
Ozaki, L. S., Maeda, S., Shimada, K. and Takagi, Y. (1980). *Gene* **8**, 301–314.
Perucho, M., Hanahan, D., Lipsich, L. and Wigler, M. (1980). *Nature (London)* **285**, 207–211.
Ratzkin, B. and Carbon, J. (1977). *Proc. Natl. Acad. Sci. U.S.A.* **74**, 5041–5045.
Rigby, P. W. J., Dieckman, M., Rhodes, C. and Berg, P. (1977). *J. Mol. Biol.* **113**, 237–251.
Roberts, T. M., Swanberg, S. L., Poteete, A., Riedel, G. and Backman, K. (1980). *Gene* **12**, 123–127.
Rothstein, R. J., Lau, L. F., Bahl, C. P., Narang, S. A. and Wu, R. (1979). *In* "Methods in Enzymology" (R. Wu, Ed.), Vol. 68, Recombinant DNA, pp. 98–109. Academic Press, New York and London.
Rubin, E. M., Wilson, G. A. and Young, F. E. (1980). *Gene* **10**, 227–235.
Rüther, V. (1980). *Mol. Gen. Genet.* **178**, 475–477.
Saint, R. B. and Egan, J. B. (1979). *Mol. Gen. Genet.* **171**, 103–106.
Sancar, A., Hack, A. M. and Rupp, W. D. (1979). *J. Bacteriol.* **137**, 692–698.
Schumann, W. and Lögl, Ch. (1980). *Mol. Gen. Genet.* **179**, 369–372.
Seeburg, P. H. and Schaller, H. (1975). *J. Mol. Biol.* **92**, 261–277.
Slutsky, A. M., Rabinovich, P. M., Yakubov, L. Z., Sineokaya, I. V., Stepanov, A. I. and Gordeyev, V. K. (1980). *Mol. Gen. Genet.* **180**, 487–488.
Smith, H. O. (1980). *In* "Methods in Enzymology" (L. Grossman and K. Moldave, Eds), Vol. 65, pp. 371–380. Academic Press, New York and London.
Smith, H. O. and Birnstiel, M. L. (1976). *Nucleic Acids Res.* **3**, 2387–2398.
Southern, E. M. (1975). *J. Mol. Biol.* **98**, 503–517.
Southern, E. (1979). *In* "Methods in Enzymology" (R. Wu, Ed.), Vol. 68, Recombinant DNA, pp. 152–176. Academic Press, New York and London.
Struhl, K. and Davis, R. W. (1977). *Proc. Natl. Acad. Sci. U.S.A.* **74**, 5255–5259.
Stuber, D. and Bujard, H. (1981). *Proc. Natl. Acad. Sci. U.S.A.* **78**, 167–171.
Stuber, D., Delius, H. and Bujard, H. (1978). *Mol. Gen. Genet.* **166**, 141–149.

Studier, F. W. (1973). *J. Mol. Biol.* **79**, 237–248.
Sutcliffe, J. G. (1978). *Nucleic Acids Res.* **5**, 2721–2728.
Tabak, H. F. and Flavell, R. A. (1978). *Nucleic Acids Res.* **5**, 2321–2332.
Telford, J., Boseley, P., Schaffner, W. and Birnstiel, M. (1977) *Science* **195**, 391–393.
Thuring, R. W. J., Sanders, J. P. M. and Borst, P. (1975). *Anal. Biochem.* **66**, 213–220.
Timmis, K. N. (1981). *In* "Genetics as a Tool in Microbiology" (S. W. Glover and D. A. Hopwood, Eds), Society for General Microbiology Symposium No. 31, pp. 49–109. Cambridge University Press, Cambridge.
Ullrich, A., Shine, J., Chirgwin, J., Pictet, R., Tischer, E., Rutter, W. J. and Goodman, H. M. (1977). *Science* **196**, 1313–1319.
Vapnek, D., Hautala, J. A., Jacobson, J. W., Giles, N. H. and Kushner, S. R. (1977). *Proc. Natl. Acad. Sci. U.S.A.* **74**, 3508–3512.
Vincent, W. S. and Goldstein, E. S. (1981). *Anal. Biochem.* **110**, 123–127.
Von Gabain, A. and Bujard, H. (1977). *Mol. Gen. Genet.* **157**, 301–311.
Wigler, M., Pellicer, A., Silverstein, S., Axel, R., Urlaub, G. and Chasin, L. (1979a). *Proc. Natl. Acad. Sci. U.S.A.* **76**, 1373–1376.
Wigler, M., Sweet, R., Sim, G. K., Wold, B., Pellicer, A., Lacy, E., Maniatis, T., Silverstein, S. and Axel, R. (1979b). *Cell* **16**, 777–785.
Wilkie, N. M. and Cortini, R. (1976). *J. Virol.* **20**, 211–221.
Yang, R. C. A., Lis, J. and Wu, R. (1979). *In* "Methods in Enzymology" (R. Wu, Ed.), Vol. 68, Recombinant DNA, pp. 176–182. Academic Press, New York and London.
Zubay, G., Chambers, D. A. and Cheong, L. C. (1970). *In* "The Lactose Operon" (J. R. Beckwith and D. Zipser, Eds), pp. 375–391. Cold Spring Harbor, New York.

10

Analysis of Plasmids with Transposons

T. J. FOSTER

Microbiology Department, Trinity College, Dublin, Ireland

I. Introduction

Transposons are discrete sequences of DNA that can move from one replicon to another by a process of recombination called transposition or translocation. Many types of transposons are found in nature. The size of the

METHODS IN MICROBIOLOGY
VOLUME 17 ISBN 0-12-521517-7

TABLE I

Properties of some useful transposons

Transposon	Antibiotic resistance markers	Size (kb)	Length of inverted repeats	Transposition frequency	Insertion specificity	Polarity	References to restriction map	Other references
Tn1,2,3 (=TnA)	Ap^r	4.9	Short 38 bp	High	Regional	One orientation	Heffron et al. (1979)	Hedges and Jacob (1974) Heffron et al. (1975)
Tn5	Km^r	5.4	Long 1450 bp	High	Low	Both orientations	Jorgensen et al. (1979)	Berg et al. (1975)
Tn7	Tp^{r}Sm^r	14	Short	Moderate	Low	Both orientations	Barth and Grinter (1977)	Barth et al. (1976)
Tn10	Tc^r	9.3	Long 1400 bp	Low	Hot spots	Both orientations	Jorgensen and Reznikoff (1979) Kleckner et al. (1978)	Kleckner et al. (1975) Foster et al. (1975)

elements can vary markedly from one to another and many different properties can be transposable. The transposable markers may be antibiotic resistance determinants, toxins and other virulence factors, or metabolic properties. Transposons have been discovered in many species of both Gram-negative and Gram-positive bacteria. This chapter is primarily concerned with the better characterized transposons of Gram-negative bacteria (Table I). The properties of transposable elements have been reviewed extensively elsewhere (Cohen, 1976; Kleckner, 1977; Nevers and Saedler, 1977; Kleckner, 1977, 1981; Calos and Miller, 1980; Starlinger, 1980).

Transposons retain their structural integrity during transposition. Transposition does not require DNA base sequence homology between the donor and recipient replicons and occurs independently of *recA*-controlled homologous recombination. Transposable elements are divided into two general groups: (a) the insertion sequences (IS), which are short (700–1500 bp) stretches of DNA that do not confer any known phenotype on the cell, and (b) more complex elements, transposons (Tn), which do confer a phenotype, most commonly resistance to an antibiotic, on the cell. Structurally, transposons consist of a unique DNA sequence, flanked by either direct, or, more usually, inverted nucleotide sequence repeats. Transposons can be divided into two types on the basis of their structure (Fig. 1). One type (e.g. TnA) has very short flanking inverted repeats (38 bp). Some elements of this type have been shown to encode functions involved in transposition with the genes located in the non-repeated central DNA sequence. The second type has larger inverted repeats which, in some cases, have been shown to be IS elements which act in

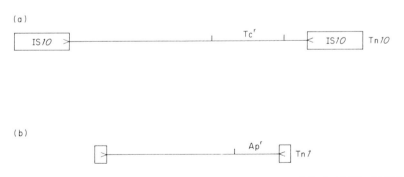

Fig. 1. Structure of the drug resistance transposons Tn*10* and Tn*1*. (a) The 9300 bp transposon Tn*10* which encodes tetracycline resistance. The *tet* genes occupy 2000 bp in the central non-repeated region. The terminal inverted repeat sequences (IS*10*) are 1400 bp long. (b) Tn*1* is one of a family of ampicillin resistance transposons. It has 38 bp inverted repeats (not drawn to scale). The *β*-lactamase gene occupies 850 bp to one side of the transposon. The rest of the non-repeated region determines functions required for transposition.

concert to transpose the intervening DNA sequences which may encode, for example, antibiotic resistance. The transposition functions of these transposons are encoded by the flanking IS elements.

The process of transposition is illustrated in Fig. 2. Replicon A, which carries the transposon, interacts with replicon B, the transposon sequences are replicated and a copy of the transposon is inserted into replicon B. The final products of the reaction are a derivative of replicon B which carries a copy of the transposon and the donor replicon A. In the case of complex transposons such as TnA, an intermediate structure has been detected. This comprises a cointegrate formed from replicons A and B with a copy of the transposon at both plasmid junctions. The two copies of the transposon are carried as direct repeats. A site-specific recombination between the two copies of the transposon releases the transposition product, replicon B::TnA, and the transposon donor. Transposition via cointegrates has been proposed as the mechanism for several TnA-like transposons (Tn1, Tn3, Tn21, Tn501, Tn1721), but cointegrates do not seem to be obligatory intermediates in the transposition of insertion sequences or compound transposons, which transpose by virtue of the insertion sequences that flank the element. In these cases transposition appears to occur directly, as indicated in route (A) (Fig. 2). Several models have been proposed to explain transposition (Grindley and Sherratt, 1978; Arthur and Sherratt, 1979; Shapiro, 1979; Galas and Chandler, 1981; Harshey and Bukhari, 1981).

A short stretch of DNA (often 5 or 9 bp) is duplicated in the recipient genome during transposition and these short direct repeats flank the transposon at its new location. This suggests that cleavage of recipient DNA during transposition is staggered by 5 or 9 bp and that the duplication is generated by a repair process following insertion of the transposon (Shapiro, 1979; Arthur and Sherratt, 1979).

There are several important consequences of the insertion of a transposon into a "recipient" DNA sequence.

1. A discrete sequence of DNA of characteristic size and structure is integrated. Thus the insertion can be readily mapped physically by heteroduplex analysis (Chapter 7) or restriction enzyme analysis (Chapters 8 and 9).
2. The transposon may integrate into a gene and cause a mutation. Insertion mutations have characteristic properties which are discussed in a later section.
3. The recipient genome has a selectable marker associated with the site of insertion.

The application of drug resistance transposons to microbial genetic analysis has been reviewed extensively (Kleckner et al., 1977) and practical details have

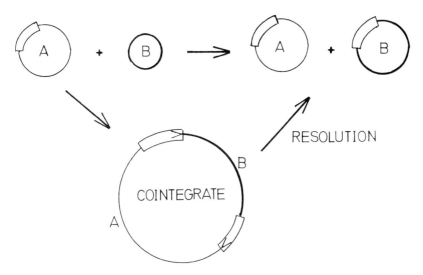

Fig. 2.   The transposition pathway. Replicon A carries a transposable element, which is represented by the open box. After transposition replicon B has acquired one copy of the transposon and the donor replicon (A-Tn) has been regenerated. The cointegrate structure is thought to be an intermediate in transposition but it is not certain if it is obligatory in all cases. One copy of the donor and recipient replicons are fused together flanked by directly repeated copies of the transposon. The resolution step generates the final products of transposition.

also been published (Davis *et al.*, 1980). It is not intended to duplicate this material in this chapter. However, it should be pointed out that it is now possible to perform genetic manipulations in organisms where no genetic system was previously available. These include the isolation of auxotrophic mutations, provision of portable regions of homology for chromosome transfer and the generation of deletions. Some simple protocols for transposon manipulation are given in Chapter 11.

II. Techniques for selecting transposition

The methods that have been devised to select for the insertion of a transposon into a new replicon are of two general types: (a) the selection of cells in which the transposon has survived the elimination of the donor replicon and (b) the selection of replicons which have acquired the transposon from another replicon in the cell. Here transposition occurs before DNA transfer to the new host.

A. Transposition into bacteriophages

Lysogenic bacteriophages which do not normally transfer bacterial DNA by generalized transduction are convenient vectors for detecting and characterizing transposons, particularly those encoding an antibiotic resistance. The phage is propagated on a strain harbouring the transposon, either by induction of a lysogen or by lytic infection. The phage lysate is then used to transduce antibiotic resistance to a sensitive recipient strain. The transductants are, in general, lysogens of those phages which have picked up the transposon. These lysogens may be induced to form high frequency transducing (HFT) lysates. HFT preparations may consist of defective particles only, of a mixture of defective particles plus a helper or entirely of non-defective elements.

1. Lambda in Escherichia coli

Lambda packages its DNA during the lytic cycle by recognition and cleavage of the *cos* site to produce single-stranded complementary ends. The amount of foreign DNA that can be incorporated into λ is restricted by the size limitations imposed by this packaging mechanism. The upper size limit for foreign inserts into wild type λ is 11% of the length of the wild type phage genome (i.e. a maximum of 5 kb). However, several deletion derivatives of λ are suitable for picking up transposons (Kleckner *et al.*, 1977, 1978; Shapiro and Sporn, 1977). Deletion *b221* is 22% (10 kb) shorter than the wild type phage and the *b515* and *b519* deletions together remove 9.6% (4.5 kb). The combination of *b515 b519* together with the *nin5* deletion removes 15% (7 kb), whereas with the *imm434* substitution 12% (6 kb) is removed.

The transposon is picked up following lytic growth of the phage and transduction of antibiotic resistance. If the phage is cI^+ int^+, transduction experiments should be performed at high multiplicity to favour lysogeny. Alternatively, an *hfl* recipient can be used to increase lysogenization and improve the chances of recovery (Berg *et al.*, 1975). Phages that are *att int* or *cI* (*b221* deletions are *att int*) cannot form lysogens but transductants can be selected by infecting a cell that already carries a λ prophage. The transducing phage will integrate into the lysogen by homologous recombination to form a double lysogen. Alternatively, use can be made of the fact that N^- mutants form autonomous plasmids. A λN^- amber mutant is grown lytically on an Su^+ host carrying the transposon. Infection of an Su^- recipient will allow the transposon-carrying λ plasmids to be selected (Kleckner *et al.*, 1978).

The lysogens should generate HFT lysates after induction. If the transposon has inserted into an essential phage gene then HFT lysates will not be formed unless a helper phage is present. The plaque toothpick pick-and-stab procedure described by Kleckner *et al.* (1978) for detecting λ :: Tn*10* phages should be suitable for other transposons.

2. *P22 in* Salmonella typhimurium

P22 packaging operates by a headful mechanism. P22 carrying a transposon (e.g. P22-Tn*10*) is too large to be packaged completely. However, P22-Tn phages can be readily selected by lytic propagation of the phage on the transposon-containing host, followed by transduction of an appropriate recipient and selection of drug-resistant lysogens. Lysogens will be formed by co-infection with a wild type phage. Induction of these transductants will yield HFT lysates in which the Tn-carrying phages are defective (Kleckner *et al.*, 1977).

3. *Pl in* Escherichia coli

Phage Pl also packages its DNA by a headful mechanism,. It can accommodate small transposons such as Tn*9* (Gottesman and Rosner, 1975; Rosner and Gottesman, 1977) and Tn*5* (Kuner and Kaiser, 1981) and still package its DNA normally. However, attempts to incorporate larger transposable elements (e.g. the r-det of R100) into plaque-forming phages resulted in the selection of deletions within the transposon (Iida and Arber, 1977).

4. *fd in* Escherichia coli

Derivatives of the single-stranded filamentous DNA phage fd incorporating transposons Tn*5* and Tn*903* have been reported (Herman *et al.*, 1978; Nomura *et al.*, 1978). The phage particles increase in length (from 0.95 μm to 1.7 μm in the case of fd-Tn*5*). Recombinant phages grow more slowly than wild type, so care must be taken to ensure that the transposon-carrying phage is not overgrown. Advantages of the use of a filamentous phage vector are that the size of the transposon should not prevent its detection by a phage pick-up method and single-stranded DNA is readily available for electron microscope and DNA sequence analysis (Chapters 7 and 13 respectively).

B. Bacteriophage vectors as donors of transposons

The principle of methods which use phage vectors to donate transposons is to infect a recipient cell with a specialized transducing phage which carries the transposon under conditions where the phage cannot lysogenize or replicate lytically. Ideally, each drug-resistant transductant colony is derived from an independent transposition event into the chromosome (or a plasmid) of the recipient cell. The proportion of plasmid-linked insertions relative to those in the chromosome will depend on the size and copy number of the plasmid and the ease of transposition into the two replicons. Controls should be performed to ensure that the drug-resistant transductants are due to true transpositions, particularly when characterizing a new system. No phage DNA should be present in the transductants. This can be demonstrated by lack of immunity to superinfection and by the failure of marker rescue experiments with mutant phages. Furthermore, the appearance of auxotrophs at a frequency of about 1% is a convenient indication of transposition.

1. *Lambda in* Escherichia coli

Derivatives of λ-carrying transposons Tn5, Tn9 or Tn10, which are suitable for mutagenesis experiments, have been described (N. Kleckner, personal communication; Rosner and Gottesman, 1977; Kleckner *et al.*, 1978). The best derivatives for donating Tn5 and Tn10 have mutations which remove the attachment site (*att*) and integration function (*int*) (e.g. the *b221* deletion). They also have a temperature-sensitive repressor mutation cI_{857} which prevents repressed phage genomes being maintained after infection. In addition, amber mutations in replication gene *O* (*Oam29*) and/or *P* (*P80*) prevent the phage from replicating lytically. The phage can be propagated in a suitable Su^+ host. To select transpositions from the phage, an Su^- strain is infected at a multiplicity of 0.5–1.0 plaque-forming units (p.f.u.) per cell, incubated at room temperature for 60 min, and then plated on antibiotic agar. Each drug-resistant colony obtained by this method is derived from an independent transposition event because outgrowth of cells after infection does not occur. The selection of tetracycline-resistant colonies due to transposition of Tn10 is improved by incorporating 2.5 mM sodium pyrophosphate into the growth medium. This reduces the background growth of Tc^s cells and prevents reinfection of cells on the plate by stray phage.

This method of selecting transpositions can be extended to plasmid genomes carried in the recipient cell. This is particularly appropriate for generating Tn5 insertions in small multicopy plasmids (Section II.E.1). The advantages of this approach are that Tn5 transposition is derepressed when the phage vector enters a new host (Section III.C.) and a high proportion of the transposition events (1:20–1:50) are in the plasmid.

2. *Phage P22 in* Salmonella typhimurium

Derivatives of P22 which carry Tn10 have been used to generate mutations in the chromosome of *S. typhimurium* (Kleckner *et al.*, 1975; Kleckner *et al.*,

1977). Following induction of a P22-Tn*10* lysogen, only defective particles are formed. Double infections, which occur at high multiplicities of infection, result in wild type phage genomes being reconstructed by recombination and drug-resistant transductants being formed by lysogenization. Two suitable methods for selecting transpositions are (a) infection of recombination deficient (*recA*) and attachment site deficient (*ata*$_{P22}$) recipients with a P22-Tn*10* variant defective in phage recombination functions (*erf*) (Kleckner *et al.*, 1975); and (b) the P22 variant now preferred for mutagenesis is P22-Tn*10 int c2-ts* 12⁻ 13⁻ (Kleckner *et al.*, 1977). Amber mutations in genes *12* and *13* prevent replication in an Su⁻ host, whereas the *int* and *c2* mutations prevent lysogenization. The rationale and methods for transposon mutagenesis with P22 are analogous to those described above for λ.

3. Phage Pl in Myxococcus xanthus

A derivative of coliphage Pl carrying Tn*5* has been used to generate auxotrophic mutations in *M. xanthus* (Kuner and Kaiser, 1981). Pl can adsorb to the surface of this organism and can inject its DNA. However, the phage cannot grow lytically or be propagated as a lysogen. Thus kanamycin-resistant colonies can form only after transposition of Tn*5* into the chromosome.

C. Temperature-sensitive plasmid vectors

Elimination of a transposon-carrying plasmid with a temperature-sensitive mutation in a gene controlling replication can be used to select transposition into the chromosome or other replicons present in the cell. The *ts* plasmid is maintained by growth at the permissive temperature. Dilutions of cultures grown at this temperature are plated on agar incorporating the antibiotic to which the transposon confers resistance. The plates are incubated at the temperature restrictive for maintenance of the plasmid. The number of colonies growing should exceed that obtained when other (non-transposable) plasmid markers are selected. The putative transposition colonies should be scored for loss of other plasmid markers because stable inheritance of the transposon could be achieved by reversion of the mutation conferring temperature sensitivity or by integration of the entire plasmid into the chromosome. The appearance of auxotrophs at a frequency of about 1% is indicative of successful transposition.

Several *ts* plasmid vectors have been described: F′$_{ts114}$*lac*-Tn*10* delivers Tn*10* (Kleckner *et al.*, 1977); plasmid pMR5, a *ts* mutant of RPl (Robinson *et al.*, 1980), and pSC304, a derivative of pSC101 (Kretschmer and Cohen, 1979), both donate Tn*A*; plasmid pRN3091, a derivative of the penicillinase plasmid pI258 of *Staphylococcus aureus*, donates the erythromycin resistance transposon Tn*551* (Novick *et al.*, 1979). Plasmid pMR5 is of particular interest because of its wide host range. In principle, transpositions of Tn*A* can be selected in any of the diverse hosts in which IncP plasmids can be propagated, provided that the cells grow at the restrictive temperature. Plasmid pRN3091 could possibly be transferred into other Gram-positive species (e.g. *Bacillus subtilis*) and used to generate mutations. The range of elements transposed by this method could be extended by constructing *ts* plasmid derivatives incorporating other transposons.

D. Suicide plasmids

Derivatives of broad host range plasmids belonging to incompatibility group P (Chapter 2) which incorporate bacteriophage Mu have been constructed. The survival of these plasmid derivatives is prevented in some Gram-negative bacteria. A restriction–modification system specifically directed against Mu DNA sequences reduces plasmid inheritance by 10^3. In addition, expression of an unidentified Mu gene product prevents Mu DNA sequences becoming established. Thus, only derivatives with extensive deletions of the Mu sequences can be stably inherited as plasmids. This "suicide" of Mu-carrying plasmids can be used to select for transposition of any transposon. Survivors expressing the antibiotic resistance encoded by the transposon should occur at a higher frequency than those expressing the other plasmid markers. The success of the method depends on the frequency of transposition being at least as high as the background of plasmid survival. Suicide plasmids have been used successfully to generate chromosomal mutations in *Rhizobium* species and *Agrobacterium tumifaciens*. RP4::Mu::Tn*7* was used to generate chromosomal mutations in *A. tumifaciens* (van Vliet *et al.*, 1978) and in *R. meliloti* (Casey *et al.*, 1981). Plasmid pPHl.J.1, which carries Mu and Tn*5*, will generate chromosomal mutations in *R. leguminosarum*, *R. trifoli* and *R. phaeseoli* (Beringer *et al.*, 1978). RP4::Mu will transpose Tn*1* into the *R. meliloti* chromosome but auxotrophs were not detected (Casadesus *et al.*, 1980).

E. Plasmid incompatibility

The phenomenon of plasmid incompatibility has been used to select for transposon insertions in the host chromosome (Foster *et al.*, 1975). Two incompatible plasmids are introduced into the same strain, preferably a Rec⁻ strain in order to prevent plasmid–plasmid recombination. Selection is imposed for the antibiotic resistance of the transposon on the first plasmid and for a resistance marker on the second plasmid. Derivatives are selected where the two markers are stably inherited. This can be achieved by alternate cycles of growth on antibiotic-containing and drug-free media. Once the element has transposed to another replicon in the cell, the donor plasmid carrying the transposon may be lost because of incompatibility. Among the survivors will be insertions into the bacterial chromosome or into another plasmid carried by the cell.

F. Selection by conjugational transfer

This approach is widely used in Gram-negative bacteria for the insertion of transposons into conjugative plasmids. Chromosomal genes located on F′ elements as well as plasmid genes can be mutagenized. The transposon is located in the chromosome of the donor, or is linked to a non-conjugative replicon in the donor cell, which also carries the conjugative plasmid. Transposition into the conjugative plasmid prior to conjugation may then result in the transfer of the transposon into the recipient cell. These recombinant plasmids can be selected using the phenotype encoded by the transposon. Mutants of the vector plasmid can be identified among the transconjugant progeny. A variety of techniques to reduce or eliminate transfer of the transposon by any means other than linkage by transposition to the conjugative plasmid are discussed below. The success of the method depends on the transfer frequency of the conjugative vector plasmid being sufficiently high to detect vector::Tn recombinants above any background transfer.

1. Transposition from the chromosome

Transfer of antibiotic resistance from a donor strain that has a transposon integrated in the chromosome and carries an autonomous conjugative plasmid will be effected primarily by integration of the transposon into the plasmid prior to conjugation. However, some plasmids (e.g. F and R100) can integrate into the host chromosome to form Hfr strains. This could result in the transfer of chromosomal DNA, including the transposon, thus interfering with the detection of transpositions. This problem can be eliminated by using a recA donor strain to prevent plasmid integration, or by using a donor that has a deletion of chromosomal genes corresponding to the DNA carried by the F′ element so that plasmid integration into the chromosome by homologous recombination is prevented. In addition, a recA recipient should be used to prevent rescue of chromosomal fragments by recombination into the chromosome of the recipient.

   This approach has been used to isolate Tn10 insertions in F′lac (Foster,

1977), in an R100-1 derivative (Foster and Willetts, 1977) and in the *Klebsiella pneumoniae nif* genes on an R'*nif* element in *E. coli* (Merrick *et al.*, 1978).

2. Transposition from a non-conjugative plasmid

A common source of transposons in enteric bacteria is small non-conjugative plasmids. The strategy is simple. A conjugative plasmid is introduced into the cell harbouring the non-conjugative plasmid that carries the transposon. The double plasmid strain is then out-crossed with an appropriate recipient strain and progeny which have acquired the phenotype conferred by the transposon are selected. The hope is that these cells will carry transposon derivatives of the conjugative plasmid, but care must be exercised. Many natural, non-conjugative plasmids e.g. ColE1, can be mobilized at high frequency by conjugative plasmids (Chapter 3) in a way that does not involve recombination, so the use of a *recA* host will not prevent it. These plasmids are, in general, not particularly suitable as transposon donors. However, mutants that cannot be mobilized by conjugative plasmids can be isolated (Mob⁻ mutants); e.g. many cloning vectors (Chapter 9) are Mob⁻, and these plasmids make suitable transposon donors. Alternatively, some small non-conjugative plasmids, e.g. ColE1, require DNA polymerase I activity to replicate and so cannot be maintained in DNA polymerase I-deficient strains (*polA*). Hence, markers originally carried on such a plasmid, if stably established in a *polA* strain, must have recombined, probably by transposition into the conjugative plasmid. In this case, however, there is strong selective pressure for recombination events other than true transpositions, and recombinants may not be all they seem to be. Donor plasmid markers may sometimes be transferred into the recipient in the form of unresolved transposition cointegrates (Fig. 2), which undergo further rearrangements to stabilize the cointegrate structure. Such events tend to occur at low frequency, but if transpositions also occur at low frequency these secondary rearrangements could become significant.

In general, transposition cointegrates transferred to the recipient will resolve normally to yield the desired transposition product together with a copy of the donor plasmid. The latter will be lost if it cannot be maintained in the new host. Some transposons, e.g. Tn*1* (Arthur and Sherratt, 1979), encode functions that ensure the cointegrates resolve, even in a *recA* host. Other transposons rely on host *recA*-controlled homologous recombination for cointegrate resolution. Retransfer experiments will be necessary to ensure that only the transposon is linked to the conjugative plasmid (Chapter 11).

The mobilization of plasmid ColE1 and its derivatives can be prevented by using as recipient an *E. coli* strain deficient in DNA polymerase I (*polA* mutants; Kingsbury and Helinski, 1970). This has been used in procedures to select for transposition of Tn*A* from ColE1::Tn*A* onto conjugative plasmids such as F (Heffron *et al.*, 1977; So *et al.*, 1978).

Insertion sequences have not been used extensively as mutagenic probes because they do not encode a selectable phenotype. However, there is one technique for selecting insertions of an IS into a non-mobilizable non-conjugative plasmid such as pBR322. F factor carrying cells promote the transfer of pBR322 at a low frequency (10^{-6}) due to the insertion of the $\gamma\delta$ insertion sequence (Tn*1000*) into pBR322 to provide homology between F and pBR322 for recombination to occur (Guyer, 1978). The F::pBR322::$\gamma\delta$ cointegrate is then transferred by conjugation into the recipient where it dissociates into F and pBR322::$\gamma\delta$. This dissociation occurs in Rec$^+$ or Rec$^-$ cells. More than 99% of the pBR322-carrying exconjugants contain the pBR322::$\gamma\delta$ derivative. In some cases $\gamma\delta$ has inserted in a pBR322 structural gene to cause a mutation. This technique has been used to generate insertion mutations in the *uvrA* and *uvrB* genes cloned in pBR322 (Sancar and Rupp, 1979; Sancar *et al.*, 1981a, b).

3. Transposition from a low frequency transferring conjugative plasmid

It is possible to select for transpositions from a conjugative plasmid that transfers at a low frequency (e.g. RP1) to a plasmid that transfers at high frequency, provided that the difference in transfer frequencies is great enough. This technique was used to transpose Tn*A* from RP4 to R64 in the initial characterization of Tn*A* (Hedges and Jacob, 1974), and in Tn*A* mutagenesis of the *mer* genes of R100-1 (Foster *et al.*, 1979). The CAM-OCT plasmid represses the fertility of RP1 in *Pseudomonas aeruginosa*, a feature that has been used to select transpositions of Tn*7* from RP1::Tn*7* to CAM-OCT (Fennewald and Shapiro, 1979).

G. Selection by transformation and transduction

In some situations the conjugational transfer transposition selection system described above will not be suitable for detecting plasmid-linked insertions, in which case the putative plasmid::Tn recombinants can be either transduced or transformed into a new host.

1. Selection of plasmid-linked insertions by transformation

Plasmid DNA is isolated from a strain harbouring a suitable plasmid vector and a transposon in the chromosome. It may not be necessary to purify the plasmid DNA by dye-buoyant density gradient centrifugation, particularly if the plasmid exists in multiple copies. It is usually sufficient to use phenol-extracted cleared lysates, which predominantly contain covalently closed circular plasmid DNA molecules (Chapter 4). Fragments of chromosome carrying the transposon are inherited at a very low frequency. Transformants are selected by plating on the antibiotic to which the transposon confers resistance.

It is appropriate to mention here an extremely effective method for generating Tn5 insertions in DNA sequences cloned on chimeric plasmids. The transposition of Tn5 from a λ vector is selected in an Su⁻ host carrying the plasmid (details of the procedure are described in Section II.A.1). Kanamycin-resistant colonies (> 1000) are pooled in buffer and plasmid DNA isolated by a small-scale cleared lysate procedure. The DNA is extracted with phenol and used to transform a competent recipient. Plasmid-linked Kmʳ transformants form a high proportion of the total plasmid transformants (1:20–1:50). Mutations in the region of interest can usually be found at a frequency of 1–10% of Kmʳ colonies.

2. Selection of plasmid-linked insertions by transduction

Propagation of transducing phage φ80a on a plasmid-containing strain of Staphylococcus aureus which has a transposon in the chromosome, followed by selection of transductants that express the antibiotic resistance determined by the transposon has been used to generate insertions of Tn551 in a plasmid (Novick et al., 1979). This technique could be applied to other species where a transformation system is not available.

3. Transduction used to select chromosomal insertions

Ultra-violet (u.v.) light irradiation of generalized transducing phage lysates prepared from a strain carrying a plasmid can be used to select for insertions of a transposon into the chromosome of the recipient. For example, a S. aureus phage φ80a lysate, prepared from a cell line carrying plasmid p1258 (Tn551), was treated with sufficient u.v. light to cause lethal mutations to the plasmid. Erythromycin-resistant transductants were still recovered and carried Tn551 inserted in the chromosome of the recipient (Novick et al., 1979).

III. Factors affecting the frequency of transposition

An important factor to be considered in planning plasmid mutagenesis and tagging experiments is the frequency of transposition of the element concerned. The factors discussed below may influence the successful outcome of such experiments.

A. The host strain

The frequency of transposition may vary from one species to another and from strain to strain within the same species. Transposon Tn*10* transposes from a λ vector into the chromosome of *E. coli* C derivatives at a 10- to 100-fold higher frequency than into the chromosome of *E. coli* K12 (Beacham and Garrett, 1979). There are no data available for other transposons in *E. coli* strains or for the behaviour of transposons in different species.

B. Selection of antibiotic resistance

When using the λ vector method for transposing Tn*10* into the bacterial chromosome it has been found that 12.5 μg ml^{-1} of Tc is the optimal concentration for selecting resistant colonies rather than the commonly used concentration of 20–25 μg ml^{-1} (Beacham and Garrett, 1979). Incorporation of sodium pyrophosphate (2.5 mM) into the Tc agar plates reduces the background growth of Tc^s cells and also prevents those cells in which transposition events have occurred being infected with phages on the surface of the plate (Kleckner *et al.*, 1978). If Tn*10* is inserted into a multicopy plasmid it should be noted that the level of Tc^r expressed by the transposon in the multicopy state is reduced by a factor of 10–20 (Coleman and Foster, 1981). In this case a concentration of tetracycline of no greater than 5 μg ml^{-1} should be used.

C. The transposition selection method

Transposition of Tn*5* occurs at a much higher frequency immediately after the transposon enters a new cell (Biek and Roth, 1980). If the cell already carries a copy of the transposon the frequency is lower. This is interpreted to mean that Tn*5* transposition is repressed in cells in which the transposon is established but can be derepressed by a form of zygotic induction. This interpretation is supported by the finding that transposition of Tn*5* from the chromosome to a small multicopy plasmid (i.e. in established cells) occurred at a 10- to 100-fold lower frequency than transposition from a λ-Tn*5* donor phage (T. J. Foster, unpublished data). It is possible that other transposons behave in a similar fashion.

In addition, the nature of the donor and recipient replicons may influence the transposition efficiency. Thus it has been reported that the ampicillin resistance transposon Tn*3* transposes from plasmid to plasmid at a 10^3 to 10^4-fold higher frequency than from plasmid to chromosome (Kretschmer and Cohen, 1977).

D. Temperature

The temperature of incubation of cultures may be important in determining the frequency of transposition. Thus, Tn3 transposes at a much higher frequency when the cells are incubated at 30°C than at 37°C or 42°C (Kretschmer and Cohen, 1979). The temperature characteristics of other transposons have not been reported.

IV. Specificity of insertion

One of the factors that might influence the choice of a transposon as a mutagen is its specificity of insertion. Transposon insertion may appear to be relatively non-specific when the distribution of insertions in a large genome like the chromosome is examined. Tn10 and Tn5 insertions in the chromosome of E. coli or S. typhimurium generate auxotrophic mutations at a frequency of about 1% (Kleckner et al., 1977). Most auxotrophic requirements will be represented in a collection of 200–500 independent mutants. However, some requirements may occur more frequently than others, which indicates that the transposon may insert preferentially in certain genes. Regions of preferred insertion are more apparent when smaller targets are studied.

A detailed comparative study involving fine-structure genetic and physical analysis (including DNA sequencing) has been performed using insertions of Tn9, Tn10 and Tn5 in the lac operon of E. coli (Miller et al., 1980; Galas et al., 1980). An analogous study was performed with TnA insertions in the small plasmid pTU4 (Tu and Cohen, 1980). One common feature that emerged from these experiments was that each of the transposons studied appeared to insert preferentially into AT-rich regions. This phenomenon is called regional specificity. Thus, the distal part of the lacZ gene and the entire lacY gene were 50 times more likely to receive a transposon than the proximal part of the lacZ gene. However, the transposons varied in their insertion behaviour when multiple insertions within a small region were examined. Thus, Tn10 inserted preferentially at a small number of sites. These are called hot spots for insertion, a concept first recognized by genetic mapping of Tn10 insertions in the S. typhimurium his operon (Kleckner et al., 1975, 1977). Tn9 is much less specific than Tn10, but several sites where multiple insertions had occurred were identified. Many insertions were clustered in a 16 bp region which has homology with the outer ends of IS1, the Tn9 terminal repeat sequence. Thus, hot spots may be determined by homology between the transposon and the target in an AT-rich region of the chromosome.

The pattern of TnA insertions within the small plasmid pTU4 was similar in that insertions occurred preferentially in AT-rich regions (Tu and Cohen, 1980). One region which had DNA sequence homology with the ends of Tn*A* contained several hot spots. Regional specificity was also reported following studies of Tn*A* insertions in plasmid R6–5 (Kretschmer and Cohen, 1977), in phage P22 (Weinstock *et al.*, 1979) and in plasmid pUB307 and its derivatives (Grinsted *et al.*, 1978).

The first report of Tn7 insertion specificity revealed a single site for insertion of the transposon in the *E. coli* chromosome (Barth *et al.*, 1976). However, multiple insertions occurred in plasmid RP4 without any apparent specificity (Barth and Grinter, 1977), but all in the same orientation. Tn7 insertion mutations in the *nif* genes of *Klebsiella pneumoniae* (Merrick *et al.*, 1978), in the CAM-OCT plasmid of *Pseudomonas putida* (Fennewald and Shapiro, 1979) and in the chromosome of *Rhizobium meliloti* (Casey *et al.*, 1981) have been reported.

V. Analysis of plasmid structure and function

The analysis of transposon insertions is a powerful method of probing plasmid structure and function. The principle of these experiments is outlined below. First a number of independent insertions in the plasmid are collected and scored for defects in known plasmid-encoded functions. The insertion mutant derivatives are then mapped physically (Section VI). Thus, the positions of the various functions can be placed on the plasmid map. It is likely that mutations with similar defects will cluster, although this need not be the case; some phenotypes may be determined by widely separated genes (e.g. the *tra* genes of RP4: Barth and Grinter, 1977; Barth *et al.*, 1978). Silent regions of the plasmid may be identified by mapping insertions which do not change any known plasmid property. Forbidden regions for insertion may also be provisionally identified as regions in which no insertions occur. These could represent genes for plasmid replication and partition functions, where insertions would prevent or jeopardize plasmid survival.

There are numerous examples of plasmid structure and function being elucidated by a combination of transposon and deletion analysis. Thus, Tn*A* has been used to analyse ColE1 (Dougan and Sherratt, 1977) and RSF1010 (Heffron *et al.*, 1975). Tn7 was used in the structural analysis of RP4 (Barth and Grinter, 1977) and a Ti plasmid of *Agrobacterium tumifaciens* (van Vliet *et al.*, 1978). Similarly, Tn5 was used to probe pKM101 (Langer *et al.*, 1981).

Transposon analysis can also help in studies of the genetic structure of a particular plasmid-encoded property. This applies to natural plasmid functions as well as chromosomal genes cloned into plasmid vectors. A number of independent insertion mutations in the genes of interest are isolated. Physical mapping of these insertions provides a minimum estimation of the coordinates for the genes involved. Examination of proteins expressed by these mutant plasmids in minicells (Chapter 12) will enable gene products to be identified. The insertion will disrupt the gene and so destroy the structure of the protein encoded by that gene. The insertion may also eliminate expression of distal genes in an operon through polarity. Thus, if a single protein band is missing in the mutant strain it will be a good candidate for the gene product. The direction of transcription may be elucidated by comparing different insertions in the same gene and comparing the size of the truncated protein fragment. The more distal the insertion in the gene, the larger the fragment. Similarly, an operon might be identified if the number of missing proteins in different mutants can be correlated with the physical map position. This type of logic was used to postulate an operon of three genes required for the synthesis of the K88 adhesion antigen of enteropathogenic *E. coli* (Kehoe *et al.*, 1981)

VI. Physical mapping of transposon insertions in plasmids

Two techniques can be used to map transposon insertions: electron microscope heteroduplex analysis (Chapter 7) and restriction endonuclease analysis (Chapters 8 and 9). Nowadays restriction enzyme techniques are more widely used, primarily because they are cheap, quick and give accurate results, and they do not require sophisticated equipment.

A. Restriction enzyme analysis

Mapping transposon insertions by restriction enzyme analysis requires knowledge of the restriction map of the plasmid and of the transposon. It involves measuring the size of the DNA fragments that contain the junctions between the transposon and the plasmid by gel electrophoresis. The accuracy of the mapping will depend on the sizes the junction fragments. This in turn is dependent on the distance of the transposon from a reference restriction site in the plasmid and also on the distance of the transposon's restriction sites from its outer ends. Two methods are available for restriction mapping of transposon insertions.

1. Restriction sites within the transposon's inverted repeats

This approach is usually applicable only to those transposons having long inverted repeats which contain restriction sites for commonly used enzymes. Sites present in the inverted repeats will be located the same distance from either end of the transposon. There are two particular advantages to this technique: (a) sites that are close to the outer ends will generally generate smaller junction fragments, the size of which can be accurately measured; (b) the orientation of the transposon need not be known because the transposon restriction sites are symmetrically located. Transposon Tn5 is an excellent choice for mapping by this method because a number of different restriction sites have been mapped in the inverted repeats, including some very close to the ends (Jorgensen *et al.*, 1979).

The principle of the method is best illustrated by considering a hypothetical example (Fig. 3). A restriction enzyme (A) cleaves the region of interest on the plasmid into three fragments A1, A2 and A3. The same enzyme cleaves the transposon within the inverted repeats at sites x kb from its outer ends. Cleavage of the recombinant plasmid with the enzyme will reveal that fragment A1 of the parental plasmid is missing and is replaced by several additional bands. One (or more) of these new bands will be internal to the transposon (y in Fig. 3). This will be constant for each different insertion mutant studied and can, therefore, be readily identified. The junction fragments will be recognizable because different insertions will generate different sized fragments. The sizes of the junction fragments in the example are A1a + x and A1b + x kb. Subtraction from each fragment of the transposon contribution (x kb) will give the sizes of A1a and A1b. Occasionally a junction fragment will be the same size as the parental fragment (e.g. A1 = A1a + x). This, in practice, rarely presents a problem

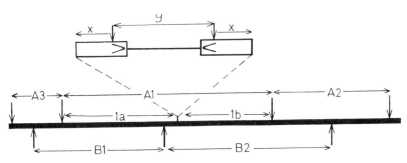

Fig. 3.   Mapping the location of a transposable element by restriction enzyme analysis. The heavy line represents the region of a DNA molecule in which the transposable element has inserted. The arrows above the line indicate the cleavage sites for restriction enzyme A which cuts the region into three fragments A1, A2 and A3. The arrows below the line show the position of the cleavage sites for restriction enzyme B which generates fragments B1 and B2. The upper part of the diagram shows the transposon with cleavage sites for enzyme A (indicated by the vertical arrows) located in its inverted repeats. The transposon has inserted at a site within fragments A1 and B2 as shown by the dashed line. 1a, 1b, y and x are distances referred to in the text.

because the required information can be obtained from the other junction fragment.

There is not sufficient information in this example to know if the transposon is inserted b kb from the right of the fragment A1 (as pictured) or the same distance from the left. The simplest way to resolve this is to digest with another restriction enzyme which in this case need not cleave the transposon. Thus enzyme B cuts within the fragment A1 but not within the transposon. Fragment B2 is missing from the gel and is replaced by a new band $2x + y$ kb larger (Fig. 3) thus mapping the insertion to the right of fragment A1.

There are published examples of this technique for analysing insertions in the *Klebsiella nif* genes (Reidel *et al.*, 1979), in the cloned R100 *tet* genes (Coleman and Foster, 1981) and in plasmid pKM101 (Langer *et al.*, 1981).

2. Restriction sites not in the inverted repeats

Mapping insertions by reference to asymmetrically located restriction sites within the transposon is often necessary and is most likely to be undertaken with those elements that have short inverted repeats (e.g. Tn*A*), but may be necessary also for elements with long inverted repeats like Tn*10*. The technique is slightly more complicated than that described above and is also likely to be less accurate. Furthermore, it is usually important to know the correct orientation of the inserted transposon. To this end additional restriction mapping experiments must be performed. The rationale of such experiments has been discussed in detail by Barth and Grinter (1977).

Consider the hypothetical example in Fig. 4. An 8 kb transposon has inserted in a plasmid. Cleavage with a restriction enzyme reveals that the 12 kb plasmid fragment is replaced by two bands of 7 kb and 13 kb. The transposon has a single cleavage site for this enzyme located 3 kb and 5 kb from its ends. In principle there are four possible sites where the transposon could insert so as to generate fusion fragments of 13 and 7 kb (Fig. 4). The possibilities are reduced to two if the orientation of the transposon is known. Additional restriction digests are needed to distinguish between these possibilities.

Examples of transposon mapping by this approach include mapping Tn*10* insertions in the *tra* genes of R100–1 (Kehoe and Foster, 1979a, b), Tn*7* insertions in RP4 (Barth and Grinter, 1977) and Tn*801* insertions in the *mer* region of R100–1 (Foster *et al.*, 1979).

B. Electron microscope heteroduplex analysis

Heteroduplexes (Chapter 7) formed between a single strand of DNA of a plasmid carrying a transposon insertion and the complementary strand of the

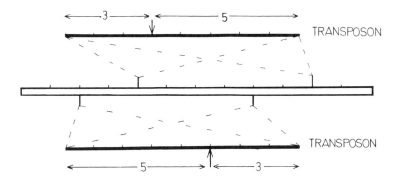

Fig. 4. Mapping the location of a transposable element by restriction enzyme analysis. The open horizontal box in the middle of the diagram is a 12 kb restriction fragment in which a transposon has inserted. The enzyme which generated the 12 kb fragment also cleaves within the transposon at a site shown by the vertical arrow in the upper and lower heavy horizontal lines. The four possible insertion sites which would generate new fragments of 7 and 13 kb are shown.

parental plasmid reveal the insertion as a characteristic single-stranded loop, usually with a double-stranded stem generated by intramolecular base pairing of the inverted repeats, marking the point of insertion. The position of the transposon insertion can be estimated by measuring the distance between the stem–loop structure and fixed reference points elsewhere in the heteroduplex.

Early studies with transposons used this method to probe the structure and function of small plasmids ColE1 (Dougan and Sherratt, 1977) and RSF1010 (Heffron *et al.*, 1975). Both plasmids have a single *Eco*R1 restriction site while the transposon Tn*A* is not cleaved with this enzyme. Heteroduplexes were formed between the parental plasmid and the Tn*A* insertion derivative both of which were cleaved with *Eco*R1. The heteroduplexes were, therefore, linear structures. The distance of the transposon from the restriction site, i.e. the ends of the linear molecules was measured. However, definitive mapping of the transposon to one particular side of the restriction site required an additional reference point. This was provided in heteroduplexes with other plasmids which had a different DNA insertion at a known position relative to the *Eco*R1 site.

Restriction sites cannot be used as reference points on most large plasmids because the majority of these will be cleaved many times by the enzyme. In the case of Tn7 insertions in the Ti plasmid of *Agrobacterium tumifaciens*, heteroduplex reference points were obtained by comparing pTi::RP4::Tn7 plasmids (i.e. pTi-RP4 hybrids also carrying Tn7 at different positions in the pTi part of the molecule) with a known pTi::Tn7 recombinant plasmid without the RP4 insertion (Hernalsteens *et al.*, 1978). The RP4 and the previously mapped Tn7 insertion provided two insertion loops of different sizes located at fixed positions for mapping the Tn7 mutations in pTi::RP4::Tn7 recombinants.

VII. Genetic mapping of transposon insertion mutations in plasmid genes

A. Properties of insertion mutations

Insertion mutations caused by transposons are very useful in genetic analysis of chromosomal genes (Kleckner et al., 1977) and have also been used to analyse genetically functions on plasmids. Insertion mutations are absolute non-leaky lesions that may revert to wild type by precise excision at a low frequency. The insertion disrupts gene continuity and this destroys protein structure, which can, in turn, aid identification of gene products in minicells. Transposon insertions in operons are usually strongly polar.

B. Polarity and the analysis of operons

1. Measurement of polarity

All transposable elements exert strong polarity when they insert in the proximal gene in an operon (Table I). In all cases studied, except IS2 and TnA, this applies to both possible orientations of insertion. This knowledge can be used to investigate the structure of operons and to locate weak promoters within operons. The strength of the polar effect can be measured in several ways.

(a) *Measurement of the activity of an enzyme* in vitro. Thiogalactoside trans-acetylase is the product of the lacA gene of the E. coli lac operon. Most proximal Tn5 insertions in lac reduced transacetylase to 0.2–0.3% of the induced wild type level. However, some mutations allowed expression of a slightly higher level, 1.2–1.3% of wild type. The increased enzyme levels were due to the activity of a low-level promoter associated with Tn5 (Berg et al., 1980).

(b) *Expression of a phenotype*. Insertions of TnA are polar in one orientation only. Insertions of TnA in the sulphonamide resistance gene of the small streptomycin–sulphonamide resistance plasmid RSF1010 eliminated expression of the Sm^r gene when in one orientation (P) whereas recombinant plasmids with insertions in the opposite orientation (M) still expressed Sm^r (Rubens et al., 1976), albeit at a lower level. This was quantitated by measuring the Sm resistance levels of cultures. This study also showed that the Sm^r and Su^r genes were co-ordinately expressed. Distal gene expression in orientation M, i.e. expression of Sm^r, may be due to read-through from the *bla* gene promoter.

The activity of the second gene in the *lac* operon, *lac*Y (codes for lactose permease), can be monitored by the growth of cells on melibiose at 41 C, simply by determining colony size on minimal melibiose agar or by the production of a red colour on MacConkey melibiose medium. These simple tests have been used to assess polarity of Tn*10* and Tn*5* insertions in the proximal *lac*Z gene (Foster, 1977; Berg *et al.*, 1980).

(c) *Expression of polypeptides in minicells.* Plasmid-directed protein synthesis in minicells (Chapter 12) is particularly applicable to systems where there is no enzyme assay available for the proteins under investigation and where the wild type phenotype is not easy to quantitate in a complementation test (see below). For example, an analysis of the K88 adhesion antigen of enteropathogenic *E. coli* revealed that four polypeptides were expressed from genes located in two operons. This was deduced primarily from the synthesis of polypeptides in minicells directed by recombinant plasmids with Tn*5* insertion in the cloned K88 genes (Kehoe *et al.*, 1981).

(d) *Complementation tests.* Complementation tests performed between plasmids carrying insertion mutations and non-polar point mutations provide information about the polar effects of the transposon. This is discussed in more detail below.

C. Complementation tests

1. Construction of heterozygous cells

Most of the problems that occur when attempting complementation tests with plasmid mutants involve the construction of heterozygous cells. Two mutant derivatives of the same plasmid will be incompatible (Chapter 2) and may not possess differential selective markers. This will prevent the construction of a stable heterozygous cell. In practice, the problems may be overcome as illustrated by the following approaches.

(a) *Transient heterozygotes.* The construction of transient heterozygotes, i.e. cells carrying the two mutant plasmids unstably, followed by an assessment of the degree of complementation before segregation could occur was used to analyse *tra* mutants of F'*lac* (Achtman *et al.*, 1972).

(b) *Selection for the phenotype generated by complementation.* If the phenotype formed by complementation generates a selective marker, this can be used to select for the heterozygote. For example, selection of mercuric ion resistant colonies allowed the detection of complementation between different Tn*A* insertion mutations in the *mer* region of otherwise isogenic R100-1 plasmid derivatives (Foster *et al.*, 1979).

(c) *Construction of stable heterozygous cells.* This may apply to the complementation analysis of functions which cannot be used as selective markers. In these cases it is better to attempt complementation analysis with two distinguishable compatible plasmids that can be used in strain construction. However, complementation tests between naturally occurring plasmids in different incompatibility groups may be impracticable because the genes concerned may have diverged too much to allow complementation between mutants. Hence the genes of interest may be transferred to another compatible plasmid by gene-cloning techniques. Mutations may then be generated both in the parent plasmid and in the cloned genes and complementation tests performed. Mutant alleles may also be switched from the parental plasmid into a cloning vector before attempting complementation.

2. Complementation tests with two transposon insertion mutants

Complementation between two insertion mutations caused by a transposon known to be polar in both orientations can only occur if the insertions are located in genes in different operons. In this way two operons involved in the expression of mercuric ion resistance were identified (Foster *et al.*, 1979).

3. Complementation tests between transposon insertion mutants and point mutants

More information about operon structure and gene order will be obtained if complementation tests are performed between a series of point mutants with lesions representing different cistrons and the insertion mutants. Thus the transposon mutation can be assigned to a particular cistron and the order of cistrons within an operon can be deduced. In a hypothetical example (Fig. 5) mutations in four genes in a single operon were tested for complementation in all pairwise combinations. In each cross one of the pair of mutations is a nonpolar point lesion (e.g. missense) and the other is a polar insertion. Complementation will occur if the insertion is located in a cistron distal to the missense lesion, whereas no complementation can occur when the insertion is in a more proximal gene. In the latter case, the gene distal to the insertion, whose product is needed to complement the missense lesion, will not be

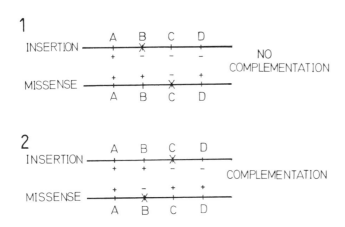

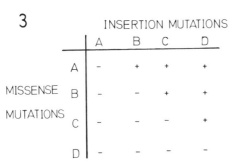

Fig. 5. Complementation between non-polar point mutations and polar insertion mutations. Sections 1 and 2 depict the interactions between two mutants with lesions in different cistrons in an operon. In each complementation test one of the mutations is caused by a transposable element while the other is a non-polar point mutation. The four cistrons in the operon are A, B, C and D. Expression of the cistrons is shown by + or − between the horizontal lines. The sites of the lesions are indicated by ×. Section 3 shows the overall pattern of complementation between non-polar and polar insertion mutations in the four cistrons when all possible pairwise combinations are tested.

expressed due to polarity. The pattern of complementation is represented in Fig. 5. The first negative in each vertical line represents the cistron inactivated by the insertion. In practice, some expression of genes distal to the insertion is usually detected. This could be due either to recombination or to incomplete polarity. This type of complementation analysis has led to the recognition of weak internal promoters within the *S. typhimurium his* operon (Kleckner *et al.*, 1975); it has revealed also the order of genes in the *tra* operon of R100–1 (Foster and Willetts, 1977) and the operon structure of the *Klebsiella pneumoniae nif* genes (Merrick *et al.*, 1978, 1980).

D. Recombination

Transposon insertion mutations behave as point lesions in genetic crosses. Thus, the site of insertion can be mapped genetically by marker rescue recombination analysis with a suitable series of deletion mutants. Tn*10* and Tn*5* insertions in the *E. coli lac* genes located on F'*lac* episomes were mapped in this way (Miller *et al.*, 1980). Similar fine-structure genetic analysis was performed with *his*::Tn*10* mutants of *S. typhimurium* (Kleckner *et al.*, 1975, 1978).

When the insertion and deletion mutations are both located on incompatible conjugative plasmids (e.g. F episomes), the crosses should be performed with one plasmid-carrying strain in exponential growth acting as the donor while the other strain, the recipient, should be in stationary phase so as to minimize any surface exclusion (Chapter 2). The crosses should be performed in both directions. Recombinant colonies should exceed the number of revertant colonies generated in self-cross control matings (Foster, 1977; Miller *et al.*, 1980). In this type of experiment the recipient cell should be Rec$^+$.

VIII. Other uses of transposons

A. Generation of deletions *in vivo*

Several transposons promote the formation of deletions. The deletion may or may not be accompanied by the loss of the transposon, but those involving loss of antibiotic resistance genes are easier to detect. Some transposons (e.g. Tn*A* and Tn*7*) promote deletions as a consequence of transposition and these show up when insertion into a conjugative plasmid is selected by conjugational transfer techniques (Foster *et al.*, 1979; Miller *et al.*, 1980; Wang *et al.*, 1980; Merrick *et al.*, 1978).

Detailed studies of Tn*10*-promoted deletions in the *S. typhimurium his* region and in bacteriophage λ have been reported (Kleckner *et al.*, 1979a, b; Ross *et al.*, 1979). Similar deletions have been isolated in the R100–1 *tra* genes (Kehoe and Foster, 1977, 1979). Tn*10* is particularly convenient for generating deletions because the frequency of deletion formation is high (about 10^{-4}) and because Tc^s cells can be easily enriched by the penicillin screening technique (Kleckner *et al.*, 1977) or by direct selection (Bochner *et al.*, 1980). Structurally the deletion extends from the inside end of one Tn*10* inverted repeat and removes the rest of the transposon and adjacent sequences. One copy of IS*10* remains behind.

B. Generation of deletions *in vitro*

The kanamycin resistance transposon Tn5 has been used as a mobile set of restriction enzyme sites for generating deletions in plasmids *in vitro*. A series of such deletions has been used for the structural analysis of pKM101 (Langer *et al.*, 1981) and a set of overlapping deletions within the cloned R100–1 *tet* genes have been used in fine-structure genetic analysis (Coleman *et al.*, 1983). A series of Tn5 insertions in different sites in the region of interest is obtained. A restriction enzyme that cleaves in the transposon at least once and also cleaves once in the adjacent plasmid sequences is chosen. A site in the inverted repeat sequence will ensure that a Km^s phenotype is caused irrespective of the orientation of the transposon. The DNA is cleaved with the enzyme, ligated and used to transform *E. coli*. Km^s transformants are identified by screening. A precisely mapped deletion extending from the site of Tn insertion to the adjacent restriction site is thus generated. The power of this technique lies with the fact that the end points of the deletions are precisely mapped by physical parameters, and they can be used in marker rescue recombination experiments with point mutations. Thus, point mutations can be placed on the physical map as well as on the genetic map of the region.

C. Generation of non-polar derivatives of transposon insertion mutations *in vitro*

A transposon insertion mutation which exerts strong polarity on a distal gene may be converted to a non-polar single-site mutation by restriction enzyme cleavage and ligation (Pannekoek *et al.*, 1980). The plasmid DNA is cleaved with an enzyme that cuts in the transposon inverted repeats but not elsewhere in the plasmid. The cleaved DNA is ligated and used to transform *E. coli*. Derivatives which express distal gene function(s) are sought. These will be mostly non-polar derivatives which retain a mutational lesion at the original transposon insertion site. Some precise excision revertants may also occur.

References

Achtman, M., Willetts, N. S. and Clark, A. J. (1972). *J. Bacteriol.* **10**, 831–842.
Arthur, A. and Sherratt, D. (1979). *Mol. Gen Genet.* **175**, 267–274.
Barth, P. T. and Grinter, N. J. (1977). *J. Mol. Biol.* **113**, 455–474.
Barth, P. T., Datta, N., Hedges, R. W. and Grinter, N. J. (1976). *J. Bacteriol.* **125**, 800–810.
Barth, P. T., Grinter, N. J. and Bradley, D. E. (1978). *J. Bacteriol.* **133**, 45–52.
Beacham, I. R. and Garrett, S. (1979). *FEMS Microbiol. Lett.* **6**, 341–342.

Berg, D. E., Davies, J., Allet, B. and Rochaix, J. D. (1975). *Proc. Natl. Acad. Sci. U.S.A.* **72**, 3628–3632.

Berg, D. E., Weiss, A. and Crossland, L. (1980). *J. Bacteriol.* **142**, 439–446.

Beringer, J. E., Beynon, J. L., Buchanan-Wollaston, A. V. and Johnston, A. W. B. (1978). *Nature (London)* **276**, 633–634.

Biek, D. and Roth, J. R. (1980). *Proc. Natl. Acad. Sci. U.S.A.* **77**, 6047–6051.

Bochner, B. R., Huang, H. C., Schieven, G. L. and Ames, B. N. (1980). *J. Bacteriol.* **143**, 926–933.

Calos, M. P. and Miller, J. H. (1980). *Cell* **20**, 579–595.

Casadesus, J., Ianez, E. and Olivares, J. (1980). *Mol. Gen. Genet.* **180**, 405–410.

Casey, C., Bolton, E. and O'Gara, F. (1981). *The Society for General Microbiology Quarterly* **8**, 94–95.

Cohen, S. N. (1976). *Nature (London)* **263**, 731–738.

Coleman, D. C. and Foster, T. J. (1981). *Mol. Gen. Genet.* **182**, 171–177.

Coleman, D. C., Chopra, I., Shales, S. W., Howe, T. G. B. and Foster, T. J. (1983). *J. Bacteriol.* **153**, 921–929.

Davis, R. W., Botstein, D. and Roth, J. R. (1980). "A Manual for Genetic Engineering. Advanced Bacterial Genetics". Cold Spring Harbor, New York.

Dougan, G. and Sherratt, D. (1977). *Mol. Gen. Genet.* **151**, 151–160.

Fennewald, M. A. and Shapiro, J. A. (1979). *J. Bacteriol.* **139**, 264–269.

Foster, T. J. (1977). *Mol. Gen. Genet.* **154**, 305–309.

Foster, T. J. and Willetts, N. S. (1977). *Mol. Gen. Genet.* **156**, 107–114.

Foster, T. J., Howe, T. G. B. and Richmond, K. M. V. (1975). *J. Bacteriol.* **124**, 1153–1158.

Foster, T. J., Nakahara, H., Weiss, A. A. and Silver, S. (1979). *J. Bacteriol.* **140**, 167–181.

Galas, D. J. and Chandler, M. (1981). *Proc. Natl. Acad. Sci. U.S.A.* **78**, 4858–4862.

Galas, D. J., Calos, M. P. and Miller, J. H. (1980). *J. Mol. Biol.* **144**, 19–41.

Gottesman, M. M. and Rosner, J. L. (1975). *Proc. Natl. Acad. Sci. U.S.A.* **72**, 5041–5045.

Grindley, N. and Sherratt, D. J. (1978). *Cold Spring Harbor Symp. Quant. Biol.* **43**, 1257–1261.

Grinsted, J., Bennett, P. M., Higginson, S. and Richmond, M. H. (1978). *Mol. Gen. Genet.* **166**, 313–320.

Guyer, M. S. (1978). *J. Mol. Biol.* **126**, 347–365.

Harshey, R. M. and Bukhari, A. I. (1981). *Proc. Natl. Acad. Sci. U.S.A.* **78**, 1090–1094.

Hedges, R. W. and Jacob, A. E. (1974). *Mol. Gen. Genet.* **132**, 31–40.

Heffron, F., Rubens, C. and Falkow, S. (1975a). *Proc. Natl. Acad. Sci. U.S.A.* **72**, 3623–3627.

Heffron, F., Sublett, R., Hedges, R. W., Jacob, A. E. and Falkow, S. (1975b). *J. Bacteriol.* **122**, 250–256.

Heffron, F., Bedinger, P., Champoux, J. J. and Falkow, S. (1977). *Proc. Natl. Acad. Sci. U.S.A.* **74**, 702–706.

Heffron, F., McCarthy, B. J., Ohtsubo, H. and Ohtsubo, E. (1979). *Cell* **28**, 1153–1163.

Herrmann, R., Neugebauer, K., Zentgraf, H., and Schaller, H. (1978). *Mol. Gen. Genet.* **159**, 171–178.

Hernalsteens, J. P., de Greve, H., van Montagu, M. and Schell, J. (1978). *Plasmid* **1**, 218–225.

Iida, S. and Arber, W. (1977). *Mol. Gen. Genet.* **153**, 259–269.

Jorgensen, R. and Reznikoff, W. S. (1979). *J. Bacteriol.* **138**, 705–714.

Jorgensen, R. A., Rothstein, S. J. and Reznikoff, W. S. (1979). *Mol. Gen. Genet.* **177**, 65–72.

Kehoe, M. A. and Foster, T. J. (1977). *Mol. Gen. Genet.* **157**, 109–118.

Kehoe, M. A. and Foster, T. J. (1979). *Mol. Gen. Genet.* **176**, 113–120.

Kehoe, M. A., Sellwood, R., Shipley, P. and Dougan, G. (1981). *Nature (London)* **291**, 122–126.

Kingsbury, D. T. and Helinski, D. R. (1970). *Biochem. Biophys. Res. Commun.* **41**, 1538–1544.

Kleckner, N. (1977) *Cell* **11**, 11–23.

Kleckner, N. (1981). *Annu. Rev. Genet.* **15**, 341–404.

Kleckner, N., Chan, R. K., Tye, B. K. and Botstein, D. (1975). *J. Mol. Biol.* **97**, 561–575.

Kleckner, N., Roth, J. and Botstein, D. (1977). *J. Mol. Biol.* **116**, 125–159.

Kleckner, N., Barker, D. F., Ross, D. G. and Botstein, D. (1978). *Genetics* **90**, 427–461.

Kleckner, N., Reichardt, K. and Botstein, D. (1979a). *J. Mol. Biol.* **127**, 89–115.

Kleckner, N., Steele, D., Reichardt, K. and Botstein, D. (1979b) *Genetics* **92**, 1023–1046.

Kretschmer, P. J. and Cohen, S. N. (1977). *J. Bacteriol.* **130**, 888–899.

Kretschmer, P. J. and Cohen, S. N. (1979). *J. Bacteriol.* **139**, 515–519.

Kuner, J. M. and Kaiser, D. (1981). *Proc. Natl. Acad. Sci. U.S.A.* **78**, 425–429.

Langer, P. J., Shanabruch, W. G. and Walker, G. C. (1981). *J. Bacteriol.* **145**, 1310–1316.

Merrick, M., Filser, M., Kennedy, C. and Dixon, R. (1978). *Mol. Gen. Genet.* **165**, 103–111.

Merrick, M., Filser, M., Dixon, R., Elmerich, C. and Houmard, J. (1980). *J. Gen. Microbiol.* **117**, 509–520.

Miller, J. H., Calos, M. P., Galas, D., Hofer, M., Buchel, D. E. and Muller-Hill, B. (1980). *J. Mol. Biol.* **144**, 1–18.

Nevers, P. and Saedler, H. (1977). *Nature (London)* **268**, 109–114.

Nomura, N., Yamagishi, H. and Oka, A. (1978). *Gene* **3**, 39–51.

Novick, R. P., Edelman, I., Schwesinger, M. D., Gruss, A. D., Swanson, E. C. and Pattee, P. A. (1979). *Proc. Natl. Acad. Sci. U.S.A.* **76**, 400–404.

Pannekoek, H., Hille, J. and Noordermeer, I. (1980). *Gene* **12**, 51–61.

Reidel, G. E., Ausubel, F. M. and Cannon, F. C. (1979). *Proc. Natl. Acad. Sci. U.S.A.* **76**, 2866–2870.

Robinson, M., Bennett, P. M., Falkow, S. and Dodd, H. M. (1980). *Plasmid* **3**, 343–347.

Rosner, J. L. and Gottesman, M. M. (1977). *In* "DNA Insertion Elements, Plasmids and Episomes", pp. 213–218. Cold Spring Harbor, New York.

Ross, D. G., Swann, J. and Kleckner, N. (1979). *Cell* **16**, 721–731.

Rubens, C., Heffron, F. and Falkow, S. (1976). *J. Bacteriol.* **128**, 425–434.

Sancar, A. and Rupp, W. D. (1979). *Biochem. Biophys. Res. Commun.* **90**, 123–129.

Sancar, A., Clarke, N. D., Griswold, J., Kennedy, W. J. and Rupp, W. D. (1981a). *J. Mol. Biol.* **148**, 63–76.

Sancar, A., Wharton R. P., Seltzer, S., Kacinski, B. M., Clarke, N. D. and Rupp, W. D. (1981b). *J. Mol. Biol.* **148**, 45–62.

Shapiro, J. A. (1979). *Proc. Natl. Acad. Sci. U.S.A.* **75**, 1933–1937.

Shapiro, J. A. and Sporn, P. (1977). *J. Bacteriol.* **129**, 1632–1635.

So, M., Heffron, F. and Falkow, S. (1978). *J. Bacteriol.* **133**, 1520–1523.

Starlinger, P. (1980). *Plasmid* **3**, 241–259.

Tu, C.-P. D. and Cohen, S. N. (1980). *Cell* **19**, 151–160.
van Vliet, F., Silva, B., van Montagu, M. and Schell, J. (1978). *Plasmid* **1**, 446–455.
Wang, A., Dai, X. and Lu, D. (1980). *Cell* **21**, 251–255.
Weinstock, G., Susskind, M. and Botstein, D. (1979). *Genetics* **92**, 685–710.

Note added in proof
The article by de Bruijn and Lupski (1984) is an invaluable source of information concerning the use of Tn5 to analyse plasmid DNA.

de Bruijn, F. J. and Lupski, J. R. (1984). *Gene* **27**, 131–149.

11
Detection of Transposable Elements on Plasmids

P. M. BENNETT

Department of Microbiology, University of Bristol, Medical School, Bristol, UK

Bacterial plasmids confer a rich variety of cell phenotypes (Chapter 2). Many of the genes that encode these functions are carried on elements called transposons (Chapter 10). It follows that the characterization of a newly isolated plasmid should include tests to discover if transposable elements comprise part of the plasmid.

The procedures used to demonstrate the presence of a transposable element do not differ significantly from those employed when using transposons to tag or mutate particular DNA molecules (Chapter 10). Tests to demonstrate the existence of a transposable element employ the same basic strategy, namely, transposition from one replicon to another. Various combinations have been used (plasmid to plasmid, plasmid to chromosome, plasmid to phage); which combination will be most suitable in a particular situation is usually a case of trial and error.

The simplest tests for transposition involve plasmid–plasmid combinations because the experiments usually rely on bacterial matings (Chapter 3) to separate the transposition products from the original donor and recipient plasmid molecules. Many plasmids isolated from nature transfer poorly, or not at all, by conjugation. This deficiency can be exploited to search for transposable sequences carried by these plasmids. The plasmid of interest is transferred into a suitable *Escherichia coli* K12 *recA* strain (by conjugation, transformation or transduction, as convenient, see the appropriate chapters). A second plasmid, which transfers by conjugation at a respectable frequency ($10^{-3} - 1$ transconjugants per donor), is then transferred (by conjugation) into the same cell. As the conjugative plasmid, we use routinely the IncW plasmid R388 (markers Tp^{r}Su^r, Ward and Grinsted, 1981) or the IncP plasmid pUB307 (markers Km^{r}Tc^r, Bennett *et al.*, 1977). Once the potential donor and recipient plasmids are resident in the same cell we store the culture on Dorset Egg slopes for one to two weeks at room temperature. This strategy is followed because transposition events can be shown to accumulate over a period of a few days. We find that it is not necessary to follow this procedure with all transposons, but we advise it in the case of an uncharacterized one.

A typical experiment would involve the following steps.

METHODS IN MICROBIOLOGY
VOLUME 17   ISBN 0–12–521517–7

Protocol 1
1. Streak a wire-loopful of the plasmidless recipient strain on nutrient agar. We use, for example, JC6310 (Bennett and Richmond, 1976), which is Str^r, *recA* and requires histidine, lysine and trytophan.
2. Streak the donor cell line (which contains both the test plasmid, and R388, for example) at right angles across the first streak.
3. Incubate the plate at 37°C for 18 h.
4. Collect the bacterial growth where the streaks intersect (with a wire loop) and suspend it in 1 ml of nutrient broth.
5. Prepare a 1 in 10 dilution series (to 10^{-4}) of the suspension in nutrient broth.
6. Spread 0.1-ml aliquots of the undiluted suspension and the various dilutions on an appropriate selective agar: with JC6310 used as the recipient this could be nutrient agar containing streptomycin (100–200 μg ml^{-1}) and an antibiotic appropriate for the putative transposable resistance determinant. Alternatively, an appropriate minimal medium could be used, if auxotrophic counterselection is appropriate (i.e. if the donor and recipient were different auxotrophs or if the donor was auxotrophic and the recipient was a prototroph). For example, with JC6310 as recipient, a minimal salts agar containing glucose (0.2%), tryptophan, histidine and lysine (all at 20 μg ml^{-1}) and the antibiotic selective for the putative transposon would be appropriate.
7. Incubate plates for 24–48 h at 37°C.
8. Transconjugants are tested to establish that they contain transposon-carrying derivatives of the potential recipient plasmid (R388 in this case). This can be determined by demonstrating genetic linkage of the putative transposon marker to the plasmid markers; e.g. the putative recombinant plasmid is transferred to another strain and transconjugants are selected for acquisition of one of the original plasmid markers (Tp^r or Su^r for R388). These transconjugants are then tested to see if they have also acquired the putative transposon marker. If this marker is transferred, unselected, at the same frequency as the selected marker then the two markers are genetically linked and transposition has probably occurred. Physical analysis of the plasmid DNA is then undertaken to confirm the genetic analysis (Chapter 6).

This form of experiment is straightforward and variations can be introduced to enhance the rigour of the selection. One such variation is to use an interspecies cross, instead of a cross between strains of the same bacterial species. Many plasmids display a relatively narrow host range; in contrast, plasmids such as pUB307 (Bennett *et al.*, 1977) have an extended host range. This difference can be exploited successfully to isolate new transposons. The protocol of the experiment is similar to that outlined above. In summary, a plasmid such as pUB307 is transferred (by conjugation) to the strain carrying the test plasmid; the resulting strain is, in turn, mated with another bacterial strain to which the test plasmid will not transfer, but to which pUB307 will transfer (previously established). Transconjugants are selected on an agar supplemented appropriately for growth of the recipient organism and containing, in addition, a reagent selective for the putative transposon-encoded phenotype. Any transconjugants obtained are examined genetically and physically to establish linkage of a transposon to the mobilizing plasmid (e.g. pUB307).

In the course of this type of experiment it may be found that all the markers of both plasmids (test and recipient) have been transferred to the recipient strain. Thus, although the basis of the above type of experiment is that the test plasmid is not transferred during the mating, transposable elements can mediate mobilization of a non-conjugative plasmid by a conjugative plasmid. This mobilization is due to physical linkage between the test plasmid and the conjugative plasmid. Such "cointegrates" are usually formed by the process of transposition (Chapter 10). Mobilization of normally non-conjugative plasmids is *prima facie* evidence for the presence of a transposable element. It should be noted that mobilization can be used to detect an element that does not carry a selectable phenotypic marker (for instance, insertion elements).

In *E. coli* a simple experiment can be performed to exploit this phenomenon and the following example illustrates the point. Plasmid pACYC184 is a small non-conjugative plasmid that encodes resistance to chloramphenicol and tetracycline (Chang and Cohen, 1978). It was constructed *in vitro* and during this process lost the genetic information that would permit comobilization by a conjugative plasmid (Chapter 3). Hence transfer of this plasmid requires covalent linkage to the mobilizing system at the time of transfer, i.e. it must be part of a cointegrate.

Protocol 2
1. Plasmids pUB307::Tn*A* and pACYC184 are introduced into the same cell, e.g. JC6310, the former by conjugation and the latter by transformation.
2. Strain JC6310 (pUB307::Tn*A*, pACYC184) is crossed with an appropriate recipient and Cm^r transconjugants are selected (i.e. mobilization of pACYC184 is selected).
3. Cm^r transconjugants are found to be, in general, CmApKmTc.
4. Plasmid DNA is isolated from the transconjugants and used to transform another strain of *E. coli* to Cm^r.
5. Transformants are found to be, in general, CmTcAp.
6. A physical examination demonstrates that the transformants contain pACYC184::Tn*A* recombinant plasmids, i.e. Tn*A* has transposed from pUB307::Tn*A* to pACYC184.

In this example, pACYC184 is transferred as a cointegrate which resolves in the recipient to give the original donor plasmid (pUB307::Tn*A*) and a derivative of pACYC184 carrying Tn*A*. This resolution is effected by a site-specific recombination system encoded by the element itself (Chapter 10). However not all transposons encode such a system, in which case the cointegrate may survive in a *recA* cell line. Resolution can be demonstrated, in these cases, in a Rec$^+$ background, although the process may be slow.

The example illustrates how to detect a transposon on a conjugative plasmid. The strategy can also be employed to identify transposons on non-conjugative plasmids. In this case pACYC184 is replaced by the test plasmid, and pUB307::Tn*A* is replaced by, say, R388 (or even pUB307).

Finally, a brief mention of a system that may be appropriate if all others fail. As the number of copies of a particular gene in a cell increases, the overall level of gene expression increases, often proportionately. In terms of drug resistance this can mean that a particular determinant confers a higher level of resistance when the gene(s) is carried on a high copy number plasmid than when it is on a low copy number plasmid. This difference can be used, in these cases, to select for transpositions.

Protocol 3

1. A small multicopy plasmid such as ColE1, pBR322 or pACYC184 is introduced (usually by transformation) into the same cell as the test plasmid.
2. The cell line containing both plasmids is spread on agar containing in addition to growth requirements the antibiotic to which the putative transposon confers resistance at a concentration two to three times that needed to prevent colony formation of the strain that carries only the test plasmid. An inoculum of 10^8–10^9 cells is used.
3. Plates are incubated under normal conditions.
4. Colonies which grow potentially contain transposon-carrying derivatives of the multicopy plasmid. These can be recovered by plasmid isolation and transformation, as indicated in Protocol 2. The transformants are selected with normal levels of the antibiotic, not the raised level used in Step 2.
5. To maximize the chances of recovery of plasmid–transposon recombinants, the colonies obtained after Step 3 can be pooled for plasmid isolation prior to transformation, rather than isolating plasmid DNA from individual cultures grown from single colonies, since the object is simply to demonstrate transposition and not to estimate transposition frequency.

The strategy has been used successfully to demonstrate transposition of Tn*A* elements (Wallace *et al.*, 1981; Dodd and Bennett, 1983). With some transposons the approach would be inappropriate (e.g. Tn10, Chapter 10). Therefore, although in principle this approach can be successful, in particular instances it may be inappropriate. Unfortunately we can offer no advice as to how to judge if this type of approach is likely to be successful. It is very much a case of try it and see.

The various techniques outlined in this chapter, together with others discussed in a different context in Chapter 10 provide sufficient variety that one or more should be applicable in most experimental situations. It may be necessary to change the identity of the potential recipient replicon to take account of the marker on the potential transposon. The examples given above are taken from studies using *E. coli*, because that is the system with which we are most familiar, and is also the system which has been used most extensively. The logic behind each procedure is, however, widely applicable, given suitable recipient replicons and a reasonably efficient transfer system (conjugation, transformation or transduction). In our experience, the most suitable system will be a matter for trial and error. What works effectively for one transposon cannot be guaranteed to work for an entirely different element.

References

Bennett, P. M. and Richmond, M. H. (1976). *J. Bacteriol.* **126**, 1–6.
Bennett, P. M., Grinsted, J. and Richmond, M. H. (1977). *Mol. Gen. Genet.* **154**, 205–211.
Chang, A. C. Y. and Cohen, S. N. (1978). *J. Bacteriol.* **134**, 1141–1156.
Dodd, H. M. and Bennett, P. M. (1983). *Plasmid* **9**, 247–261.
Wallace, L. J., Ward, J. M. and Richmond, M. H. (1981). *Mol. Gen. Genet.* **184**, 87–91.
Ward, J. M. and Grinsted, J. (1981). *Gene* **3**, 87–95.

12

The Minicell System as a Method for Studying Expression from Plasmid DNA

G. DOUGAN* AND M. KEHOE†

Microbiology Department, Trinity College, Dublin, Ireland

I. Introduction

The major difficulty encountered when analysing plasmid or phage encoded mRNA and polypeptides in whole (normal) bacterial cells is that the majority of these products are masked by those encoded by the host cell's chromosome. This difficulty often remains even when the genes of interest have been

Present addresses. * Department of Bacteriology, Wellcome Research Labs., Beckenham, Kent, England. † Department of Microbiology, The University of Newcastle-upon-Tyne, NE1 7RU, England.

METHODS IN MICROBIOLOGY
VOLUME 17   ISBN 0–12–521517–7

amplified by cloning into multicopy vectors. In relatively few cases does a very high rate of expression or the availability of a specific assay (e.g. zymogram staining or a specific antisera) allow the experimenter to distinguish between the plasmid and chromosome-encoded products. It is usually necessary to label specifically the plasmid-encoded products in the absence of significant expression from the host cell's chromosome. In recent years a number of techniques have been developed which allow this to be achieved. These include the use of bacterial minicells (Frazer and Curtiss, 1975; Reeve, 1979), the maxicell system (Sancur *et al.*, 1979), cell-free (*in vitro*) synthesis (Zubay *et al.*, 1970), selective expression from ColE1-type plasmids after prolonged chloramphenicol treatment (Neidhardt *et al.*, 1980), and induction of selective expression from colicin plasmids by mitomycin C (Tyler and Sherratt, 1975). All of these techniques have been designed to maximize expression from plasmid DNA while minimizing the level of background expression from the host chromosome or, in the case of the *in vitro* system, from mis-transcription or mis-translation. The systems have been developed mainly using *Escherichia coli* K12 and to a lesser extent *Bacillus subtilis*, but it is likely that in the near future the methodology will be improved and extended to other procaryotes.

In this chapter the bacterial minicell system will be described in detail and the other systems will be discussed briefly. The chapter is not intended to be a review of bacterial minicells *per se*; for that the reader is referred to Frazer and Curtiss (1975). Instead we concentrate on the properties of minicells and the methodology relevant to the use of the bacterial minicell system.

II. Properties of bacterial minicells

A. Minicell-producing mutants

Minicells are small ($< 1.0~\mu$m), spherically shaped, anucleated bodies that are produced at the polar ends of certain mutant strains of rod shaped bacteria (Fig. 1). Minicell-producing mutants have been isolated from *E. coli* (Adler *et al.*, 1967), *B. subtilis* (Van Alstyne and Simon, 1971; Reeve *et al.*, 1973), *Vibrio cholera* (Gardner, 1930), *Haemophilus influenzae* (Setlow *et al.*, 1973), *Erwina amylovora* (Voros and Goodman, 1965), *Shigella flexneri* 2a and *S. dysenteriae* (Gemski and Griffin, 1980) and a variety of *Salmonella* species (Epps and Idziak, 1970; Tankersley, 1971; Tankersley and Woodward, 1973). In addition to normal cell division these mutants can undergo an aberrant cell division where a septum is produced close to either pole of the cell, resulting in the formation of a minicell. These minicells contain little or no chromosomal DNA and cannot divide. However they do remain metabolically active for long periods after their formation (Black, 1976; Reeve, 1979) and can transcribe and translate DNA which has been introduced into them.

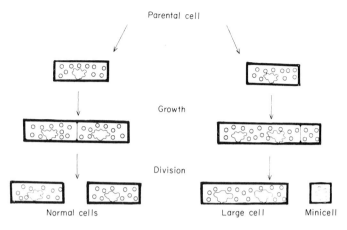

Fig. 1a. Mechanism of minicell formation

Most minicell-producing mutants were isolated fortuitously by microscopic screening of mutagenized or irradiated cells. The original *E. coli* K12 minicell-producing mutant, P678–54, was isolated by Adler *et al.* (1967). A single colony isolate (named χ925) of P678–54 was subsequently selected for its high minicell yield. These original mutants have a complex and not completely defined genotype, possessing a number of mutations affecting galactose utilization and possibly a number of suppressor and hidden mutations (Frazer and Curtiss, 1975). Most *E. coli* K12 minicell-producing strains in use today, some of which are listed in Table I, are derivatives of these original Adler mutants. The minicell strain which we use, termed DS410, was isolated by selecting Gal$^+$ Sm^r recombinants after mating P678–54 with the Hfr donor CSH74 (Dougan and Sherratt, 1977a). Strain DS410 is non-suppressing and gives a high-minicell yield.

The genetic basis of minicell production is poorly understood. Mutations at both of two independent loci are required for minicell production in *E. coli* K12. These are *min*A, which maps between *lac* and *pur*E at 9 to 12 min, and *min*B, which maps between *pyr*C and *trp* at 24 to 27 min on the map of Bachmann and Low (1980). In *B. subtilis* mutations at either of two loci, *div*IV-B1 (mapping close to *phe*A) or *div*IV-A1 (mapping close to *ura*), result in minicell production (Reeve *et al.*, 1973). The *div*IV-B1 mutants give higher minicell yields than the *div*IV-A1 mutants and are, therefore, preferred for analysis of plasmid- or phage-encoded products. The products encoded by the *min*A and *min*B determinants of *E. coli* or the *div*IV-B1 and *div*IV-A1 determinants of *B. subtilis* have not been identified nor assigned a specific function. Little is known about the genetic basis of minicell production in other species.

TABLE I

Minicell strains used in studies on gene expression from plasmid and phage DNA

Name	Genotype/Phenotype	Comment	Source
E. Coli K12 P678–54	*thr ara leu azi*^{r} *tonA lacY* T6^s *minA gal minB* Str^r *malA xyl mtl thi sup*	The original *E. coli* minicell strain, also known as χ925	Adler *et al.* (1967) Frazer and Curtiss (1975)
DS410	*lac* Str^r *minA minB*	Non-suppressing minicell derivative of P678–54 Prototroph	Dougan and Sherratt (1977 a, b)
DS830	Su$^-$ rho$^-$ *thi*	Defective in transcription termination	D. J. Sherratt
DS835	As P678–54 but Rif^r *polA1*	Defective in DNA polymerase 1 activity	D. J. Sherratt
DS910 DS410 (Mal)	As P678–54 but Su$^-$ *recA1* As DS410	Recombination deficient Derivative of DS410 capable of using maltose as sole carbon source. Useful for phage infection experiments	D. J. Sherratt Reeve (1977)
M2141 χ1081	*minA minB* Str^r *sup*$^+$ (Δ*lac-pro*) *thr lac proC* T6^r *minA purE* λ^- *minB his* Str^r T3^r *xyl ilv cycA*^{r} *cycB*^{r} *met*	Derivative of DS410	Thompson and Achtman (1978) Frazer and Curtiss (1975)
CU403	*thyA thyB metB divIV*-B1	Grows in minimal medium with glucose, thymine and methionine. Commonly used in phage and plasmid experiments.	Reeve (1979)

B. Characteristics of plasmids and phages in minicells

It was recognized early on that if plasmids were introduced into a minicell-producing strain the plasmids could segregate into the minicells (Inselberg, 1970; Levy, 1970; Roozen et al., 1970). Segregation into minicells is usually more efficient for small multicopy plasmids, such as ColE1, ColE2 and CloDF13 (Dougan and Sherratt, 1977a; Hallewell and Sherratt, 1976; Kool et al., 1972) than for large plasmids. However, many low copy number conjugative plasmids, including the F-factor, R1, R64 and ColV, segregate into minicells (Roozen et al., 1971a; Cohen et al., 1971; Levy and McMurray, 1974). Plasmid DNA can be introduced into minicells directly, since purified minicells can act as genetic recipients in conjugation, but most of the DNA introduced in this way remains in the single-stranded form (Cohen et al., 1967, 1968). Purified minicells harbouring conjugative plasmids can also act as genetic donors in matings with whole cells (Kass and Yarmolinsky, 1970; Levy and Norman, 1970).

The nucleic acid of a wide range of double-stranded DNA phage can be introduced into minicells by directly infecting purified minicells with the phage (Reeve, 1979). Attempts to infect purified minicells with the single-stranded filamentous phage M13 resulted in no detectable disassembly of the virion or conversion of the single-stranded DNA to the double-stranded replicative form (RF) (Smits et al., 1978). However, when the minicell-producing strain is infected with M13, the RF form of M13DNA can segregate into minicells in the same manner as a plasmid (Smits et al., 1978; Reeve, 1979). When minicells are infected with a virulent phage there is no burst of phage-directed lysis as there is in whole cells. Instead, phage-encoded polypeptides continue to be produced for several hours after infection (Reeve, 1979). This suggests that the normal regulation of phage expression may be disrupted in minicells and that caution should be exercised when attempting to draw conclusions on regulation based on minicell data alone.

Some small plasmids can replicate in minicells (Inselberg, 1970) but this replication is not efficient and a number of replicative forms have been isolated from ColE1 harbouring minicells (Fuke and Inselberg, 1972). Although some incorporation of ^{3}H-thymidine into E. coli minicells harbouring ColV (Roozen et al., 1971) and into B. subtilis minicells harbouring phage (Amann and Reeve, 1978) has been observed, replication of large plasmids or phage in minicells has not been confirmed.

Even though replication of plasmids and phage in minicells either does not occur or is very inefficient, transcription and translation does occur with reasonable efficiency. However, a number of observations have suggested that the rate of gene expression in minicells is slower than in whole cells. Hence, actively translating minicells have been shown to accumulate guanosine tetraphosphate and guanosine pentaphosphate, suggesting that ribosome stalling may occur during protein synthesis (Nothling and Reeve, 1980); also the rate of removal of the signal sequence from a number of exported polypeptides is slower in minicells (Dougan *et al.*, 1979).

C. Uses of bacterial minicells

Since minicells contain little or no chromosomal DNA, but may transcribe and translate for long periods after their formation, they provide an excellent system in which plasmid- or phage-encoded products can be labelled in the absence of significant background expression. The plasmid is first introduced into the minicell-producing strain by conjugation or transformation (Chapters 3 and 4). The minicells harbouring the plasmid, which has segregated into them, are then separated (purified) from the whole bacterial cells as described in Section III. If phage-encoded products are to be analysed the minicells are usually purified first and then infected directly with the phage. The purified minicells, harbouring the plasmid or phage, are then incubated in a suitable medium and the plasmid or phage products are labelled with radioactive precursors, usually ^{35}S-methionine or ^{14}C-labelled amino acid hydrolysate for polypeptides and ^{3}H-uridine for mRNA. After cell lysis and electrophoresis to separate total minicell polypeptides or mRNA, the plasmid-encoded products are detected and identified by autoradiography or fluorography. In this system only the plasmid- or phage-encoded products should be strongly labelled. In Section III the methodology involved in using the bacterial minicell system is described.

III. Methods

A. Storage and growth of minicell-producing strains

Minicell-producing strains should be stored in glycerol (20% v/v) at -20°C, but can be stored at room temperatures on dorset egg slopes or for routine purposes at 4°C on nutrient agar plates. Growth of minicell-producing strains is slower than that of normal bacterial strains and therefore revertants are at a selective advantage. Before each experiment the yield of minicells should be checked and it may be necessary from time to time to reisolate a high minicell yielding "cell line" from a single colony. The minicell yield can be checked microscopically. Minicells appear as dots near the ends of whole cells at $\times 40$ magnification under phase contrast. The majority of minicell-producing strains form filamenting cells and the absence of filaments usually indicates a decrease in, or loss of, minicell production. If the minicell-producing strain harbours a plasmid, it should be grown on selective medium to ensure the plasmid is maintained. We have found that plasmid-harbouring minicell-producing strains often give rise to poor minicell-producing variants following storage on slopes. Accordingly, it may be advisable to reintroduce the plasmid into the minicell-producing strain before each experiment or to use glycerol stocks routinely (see above).

Minicells are produced throughout the growth cycle and in all media in which the minicell-producing strain can grow, but the yield of *E. coli* minicells is highest at fast growth rates (Frazer and Curtiss, 1975). Therefore, growth in a rich medium, such as Brain Heart Infusion Broth (Difco), and vigorous aeration is recommended. However, a medium which only supports slow growth is recommended when purifying *B. subtilis* minicells because, although slow growth rates result in poorer minicell production (Reeve *et al.*, 1973), minicells are difficult to purify from whole cells following growth at faster rates. *B. subtilis* minicells are produced in highest yields in the late logarithmic or early stationary phase (Reeve *et al.*, 1973; Mendelson and Reeve, 1973). Minicell-producing strains of *E. coli* continue to produce minicells for several hours into the stationary phase (Frazer and Curtiss, 1975). When purifying *E. coli* minicells we find it convenient to inoculate 200 ml of broth with a single colony and to incubate at 37°C overnight (12–14 h).

B. Purification of minicells

A number of procedures for separating bacterial minicells from whole cells have been described, including differential centrifugation, filtration, differential sedimentation through sucrose gradients and selective lysis of whole cells with cycloserine or penicillin (Appendix III, Frazer and Curtiss, 1975). The objective is to obtain minicells as free from contaminating whole cells as possible. The procedure now most commonly employed is outlined in Fig. 1b. This involves an initial differential centrifugation step, which removes the majority of the whole cells, followed by at least two (and sometimes three) differential sedimentation spins through sucrose gradients to separate the minicells from the remaining whole cells. The parameters of the procedure can be varied to optimize conditions for a particular strain but it is essential that, in the final preparation, there be less than one contaminating whole cell per 10^7 purified minicells, otherwise the level of background labelling will be too high.

Up to six different strains can be handled simultaneously, with ease, using the procedure outlined in Fig. 1b but the more adventurous can attempt more. If a large quantity of minicells is required, for example for phage infection or membrane purification, then 1.2 litres of culture is divided into 6×200 ml lots and the minicells are pooled after purification. For each strain the following materials are required: a fresh overnight 200 ml culture; two sterile 250-ml

Introduction of plasmid DNA into minicell producing strain, purification of single colony.
↓
Growth overnight for 12–15 h in rich medium (200–1 200 ml)
↓
Low speed differential centrifugation to remove large whole cells
↓
Sedimentation through two or three sucrose gradients to purify minicells
↓
Labelling of minicells with radioactive precursor
↓
Analysis by autoradiography of SDS-polyacrylamide gels of whole minicells or fractionated extracts

Fig. 1b. Experimental steps involved in minicell analysis of expression from plasmid DNA.

centrifuge buckets; three sterile 15- to 50-ml centrifuge tubes; three sterile Pasteur pipettes; about 20 ml of sterile BSG (0.85% w/v NaCl, 0.03% w/v KH_2PO_4, 0.06% w/v Na_2HPO_4, 100 mg ml^{-1} of gelatine); two (possibly 3) 25-ml sucrose gradients. A 20% (w/v) sucrose solution in sterile BSG and sterile 30-ml glass centrifuge tubes (e.g. Corex tubes) are required for the gradients. Satisfactory gradients can be made by dispensing 25 ml of the 20% (w/v) sucrose solution into the 30-ml glass centrifuge tubes, freezing these at $-20°C$ and then thawing them slowly (4°C, overnight). Alternatively, the gradients can be made immediately before use, using a gradient maker and 5% (w/v) and 20% (w/v) sucrose solutions.

First, the fresh overnight culture (200 ml) is subjected to low-speed differential centrifugation (1000–2000 × **g**, 5 min, 4°C). Sterile centrifuge tubes are used and the minicells are kept at 4°C throughout the purification procedure. The differential centrifugation step removes about 80% of the whole cells and leaves 50–80% of the minicells in the supernatant. This supernatant is decanted into a second sterile 250-ml centrifuge tube, taking care to avoid scuffing of the loose whole cell pellet, and the minicells and remaining whole cells are pelleted (12 000–15 000 × **g**, 10 min, 4°C). The pellet is resuspended in 2 ml of sterile BSG, mixing vigorously to disrupt cell aggregates which can cause loss of minicells. The resuspended minicells are carefully layered on the top of a 25-ml sucrose gradient and centrifuged in a swing-out rotor at 4000 × **g** for 20 min, 4°C. A typical minicell sucrose gradient is shown in Fig. 2. The minicells form a rather broad band in the top half of the gradient, with a broad whole cell band below and a pellet of larger whole cells or whole cell filaments at the bottom of the tube. Minicells are

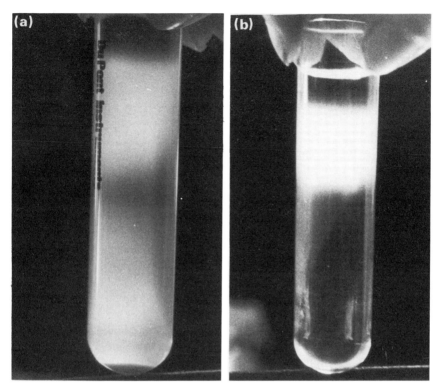

Fig. 2. Banding patterns of cells and minicells after (a) the first sedimentation through sucrose and (b) the second sedimentation through sucrose.

usually present in excess, so it is not necessary to recover all of the minicell band. Indeed, the lower part of the minicell band should be avoided, since this is more likely to be contaminated with small whole cells. Therefore, 2 to 3 ml are recovered from the top of the minicell band, transferred to a sterile 1.5-ml (eppendorf) or 15-ml centrifuge tube and centrifuged at 12 000–15 000 × **g** for 10 min at 4°C to pellet the minicells. The pellet is resuspended in 2 ml of sterile BSG and the minicells are sedimented through a second 25-ml sucrose gradient. The second gradient should contain considerably fewer whole cells than the first (Fig. 2) and at this stage the minicells may be sufficiently purified. However, it is usually necessary to use a third sucrose gradient, and if this is the case the pelleted minicells from the second gradient are resuspended in 1 ml of sterile BSG and sedimented through a third 25-ml gradient.

After the final gradient the minicells are washed with 10 ml of sterile BSG and the pellet is resuspended in a suitable labelling medium or, if bulk quantities of minicells are being prepared for subsequent phage infection, the pellet can be stored at −70°C or in liquid nitrogen (Reeve, 1979).

C. Labelling plasmid-encoded products in minicells

After purification, the minicells are resuspended in a suitable labelling medium at a concentration of approximately $2–4 \times 10^9$ minicells per millilitre. The labelling medium is usually an M9-based minimal medium (Miller, 1972), supplemented with vitamins and all of the amino acids and nucleotides, other than the labelled precursor. If ^{35}S-methionine is being used to label polypeptides, it may be more convenient to supplement the minicell medium with Methionine assay medium (Difco) rather than each of the other 19 amino acids. Before adding the label, the minicells are preincubated at 37°C, with shaking, for 20 min to allow them to reach maximum metabolic activity. The labelling conditions depend on the nature of the experiment, but normally 20 μCi of ^{35}S-methionine or 5 μCi of ^{14}C-labelled amino acid hydrolysate are used to label polypeptides, while 100 μCi of ^{3}H-uridine is used to label mRNA. Labelling is carried out for 30 min at 37°C, and can be followed by a 45 min chase in five times excess of nutrient broth. The chase prevents non-specific labelling of charged tRNAs, which appears as a smear at the bottom of the autoradiogram after ^{14}C-labelled amino acid hydrolysate labelling (Dougan and Sherratt, 1977b).

If polypeptides are to be analysed, the labelled minicells are pelleted by centrifugation (12 000–15 000 × $\mathbf{g}$, 10 min, 4°C), washed with approximately 10 ml of nutrient broth and resuspended in approximately 100 μl of final sample buffer for SDS-polyacrylamide gel electrophoresis or in a suitable buffer for subsequent fractionation, as described in Section IV. The resuspended minicells in final sample buffer are boiled for 2 min. The SDS present in the buffer lyses the minicells and denatures the polypeptides on heating. Samples (10–20 μl) are then run on unidirectional SDS-polyacrylamide gels (Laemmli, 1970) or, if necessary, a two-dimensional system (O'Farrell, 1975) can be used. Total minicell polypeptides will be visible on staining, but only labelled (i.e. plasmid-encoded) polypeptides will be detected by autoradiography (Dougan and Sherratt, 1977a) or fluorography (Bonner and Laskey, 1974). When labelling mRNA in minicells it is necessary to add an inhibitor such as NaN_3 or NaF, immediately after labelling to inhibit degradation of unstable mRNA molecules. Labelled mRNA can be extracted from minicells with SDS-phenol at 60°C as described by van Den Elzen et al. (1980) and analysed on SDS–urea–polyacrylamide gels as described by Rivera et al. (1978).

D. Problems

In this section some of the problems commonly encountered when first using minicells, and suggestions for avoiding them, are described.

1. Stable chromosomally-encoded mRNAs in minicells

If plasmidless or phage-free minicells are labelled with ^{35}S-methionine or ^{14}C-labelled amino acid hydrolysate a number of discrete polypeptides can be detected, particularly if the minicells have been purified from early stationary phase cultures. Levy (1975) demonstrated that these polypeptides are encoded by stable, chromosomally-directed mRNAs, which segregate into the mini-cells during their formation. These stable mRNAs are known to encode a number of outer membrane proteins, including Omp I, Omp II* and lipo-protein (Levy, 1975). These proteins run at characteristic positions on SDS-polyacrylamide gels and, rather than being a problem, can sometimes act as useful internal markers on the autoradiograms. The levels of these proteins can be decreased, or totally abolished, by preincubating the minicells for 60 min before labelling (Reeve, 1979) or by purifying minicells from late stationary phase cultures.

2. Heavy background labelling

The main reason for heavy background labelling is usually the presence of whole cell contaminants. The minicells recovered from the final sucrose gradient can be checked microscopically for the presence of whole cells. A moderate to large whole cell pellet at the bottom of the gradient usually indicates that whole cell contamination of the minicell band is still high. If no whole cells can be detected in a single microscope field at $\times 40$ magnification, the minicell preparation is satisfactory. However, if whole cells are detected, then a further sucrose gradient will be necessary. Heavy background may also result if minicells are purified from early log phase cultures, because of the presence of stable mRNAs (see above).

3. Low minicell yields

The most common reason for low minicell yields is that the original single colony inoculum was a poor minicell-producing variant. If this occurs it will be necessary to reisolate a high minicell-producing strain from a single colony before repeating the experiment. Minicells can also be lost during purification, for example by centrifuging too hard or for too long during the initial differential centrifugation step, or by failing to break up cell aggregates when resuspending pellets.

4. Inefficient labelling

If labelling of purified minicells is inefficient it may be that the minicells are not metabolically active. Metabolic activity will be lost if the minicells are not kept at 4°C throughout the purification procedure or if they are not sufficiently aerated, both during labelling and during the growth of the original culture. Labelling will also be inefficient if the radioactive precursor is too old or has not been stored properly. This is particularly true for ^{35}S-methionine, which should be stored at $-70°$C.

5. Caution

Regulation of expression or localization of polypeptides need not necessarily be identical in minicells and whole cells, since minicells are not normal cells. This possibility should be considered when interpreting minicell data.

IV. Analysis of plasmid products in minicells

Almost all of the published studies of plasmid- or phage-encoded products in minicells have involved the E. coli minicell system and, to a lesser extent, the B. subtilis minicell system. In this section no attempt at a complete review of the literature will be made, but selected examples, which should demonstrate the value of the minicell system, will be described.

A. Analysis of RNA in minicells

Early work on ^{3}H-uridine incorporation into purified minicells demonstrated that RNA can readily be synthesized in minicells harbouring plasmid or phage DNA (Frazer and Curtiss, 1975). Practically all of this RNA is encoded by the plasmid or phage. Kool et al. (1974) showed that less than 2.0% of the RNA labelled in minicells harbouring the plasmid CloDF13 could hybridize to E. coli chromosomal DNA and Smits et al. (1978) could detect no hybridization between chromosomal DNA and RNA synthesized in minicells carrying the RF form of the M13 phage. Thus, minicells provide an excellent system in which to study plasmid- or phage-encoded mRNA molecules.

A good example of transcriptional analysis in minicells has been published by van Den Elzen et al. (1980). These workers detected 25 different RNA species after gel electrophoresis of labelled RNA isolated from minicells harbouring the cloacinogenic plasmid CloDF13. Three of these RNAs, a 2400 b, a 2200 b and a 100 b species, were produced in large amounts. By analysing the RNA molecules produced by a number of transposon insertion mutants of CloDF13 and combining these data with information from hybridization and RNA polymerase binding experiments, a transcriptional map of CloDF13 was constructed. The 2400 b and 2200 b RNA species were shown to be overlapping transcripts which orginate from the same promotor. These were assigned to the region of CloDF13 encoding the cloacin and cloacin immunity determinants.

B. Analysis of polypeptides in minicells

The minicell system has been used extensively to study polypeptides encoded by a wide variety of plasmids and phage. Large conjugative plasmids such as R100, R64 and R6-3*drd*12 (Levy, 1973; Levy and McMurray, 1974; Cohen *et al.*, 1971b) and small non-conjugative plasmids like ColE1 and ColE2 (Dougan and Sherratt, 1977a; Hallewell and Sherratt, 1976) have been studied in minicells. Large conjugative plasmids are difficult to study because their segregation into minicells is inefficient and because they encode a large number of gene products. Nevertheless, a number of polypeptides encoded by large plasmids have been identified in minicells. For example, the 36000 mol. wt Tet protein was first identified by the fact that its expression could be induced in minicells harbouring tetracycline-resistant (Tet^r) plasmids but not in minicells carrying Tet^s plasmids (Levy and McMurray, 1974).

Small plasmids are easier to study in minicells because of their efficient segregation into minicells and their genetic simplicity. The polypeptides encoded by a number of commonly used vector plasmids have been very well characterized in minicells. These include ColE1 (Dougan and Sherratt, 1977a), pSC101 (Tait and Boyer, 1978), pACYC184 (Chang and Cohen, 1978), pBR322 and pBR325 (Covarrubias, 1981) and ColE1-Trp plasmids (Hallewell and Emtage, 1980). TEM β-lactamase encoded by pBR322 and related plasmids is expressed in minicells as three different related polypeptides of mol. wt 30000, 28000 and 26000. The 28000 mol. wt polypeptide is the active β-lactamase protein (Dougan and Sherratt, 1977a), while the 30000 mol. wt polypeptide is a precursor form carrying the signal sequence (Achtman *et al.*, 1979) and the 27000 mol. wt polypeptide is a breakdown product which cross-reacts with anti-β-lactamase sera (Dougan *et al.*, 1979). The precursor form of β-lactamase is unusually stable in minicells and this is also the case with the precursor forms of a number of other exported polypeptides (G. Dougan, unpublished data). Thus, minicell studies may help to identify precursor polypeptides.

The products of bacterial genes encoded by large plasmids or by the chromosome can readily be studied in minicells if the genes of interest are first cloned into a small vector plasmid. By isolating specific mutants of the cloned determinants the polypeptides encoded by individual cistrons can be identified in minicells, even in the absence of any other assay. Deletion mutants or transposon insertion mutants (Chapter 10) are particularly useful because

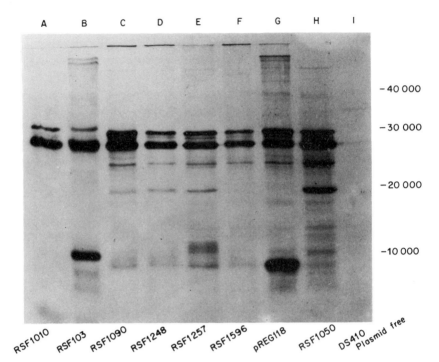

Fig. 3. Patterns of polypeptides expressed in minicells harbouring plasmids encoding wild type and mutant Tn*3* elements. Track H shows expression from wild type Tn*3* (three forms of β-lactamase and 19 000 mol. wt repressor visible); tracks C, D and E show expression from Tn*3* element defective in transposase (108 000 mol. wt); tracks B and G show expression from Tn*3* element defective in repressor (transposase visible); track F shows expression from Tn*3* defective in transposase and repressor. The Tn*3* element of RSF103 contains a deletion in the β-lactamase gene and is carried on RSF1010. All other transposon mutants (tracks C to G) are derivatives of RSF1050 (pMB8::Tn*3*). The polypeptides of below 10 000 mol. wt visible in tracks B and G are truncated forms of the repressor which normally autoregulates its own expression (from Dougan *et al.*, 1979).

they may result in truncated polypeptide fragments which can be detected in minicells. This often aids the determination of the transcriptional orientation of a particular gene. This approach has been successfully used to identify gene products which would otherwise be difficult or impossible to identify. The power of this approach should be apparent from the examples described below.

Polypeptides involved in the transposition of Tn*3* have been identified by studying mutants of Tn*3* in minicells (Fig. 3). Transposon Tn*3* encodes a 19 000 mol. wt polypeptide which represses transposition of Tn*3* and is involved in resolving cointegrate intermediates during Tn*3* transposition

(Dougan *et al.*, 1979; Gill *et al.*, 1979; Arthur and Sherratt, 1979). In addition, a 100000 mol. wt Tn*3* polypeptide, which is detected only in minicells harbouring the 19000 mol. wt repressor-defective mutants, is thought to be required for transposition and has been referred to as a "transposase" (Gill *et al.*, 1979; Chou *et al.*, 1979). Similar studies on mutants of Tn*5* have allowed four polypeptides, which are encoded by the inverted repeats of Tn*5*, to be identified (Rothstein *et al.*, 1980).

A number of virulence determinants of enterotoxigenic *E. coli* (ETEC) have been analysed, by studying mutants of cloned determinants, in minicells. The structure of the heat-labile (LT) toxin, which had proved very difficult to purify by conventional means, was elucidated with the aid of cloning and minicell analysis (Dallas and Falkow, 1979; Dallas *et al.*, 1979). The LT toxin could be precipitated from lysed minicells with anti-cholera-toxin sera, showing that the two toxins are structurally related. Subsequent DNA sequencing studies confirmed the data obtained from earlier minicell studies (Spicer *et al.*, 1981). Another virulence factor of ETEC strains which has been studied with the aid of minicell analysis is the K88 adhesion antigen (Kehoe *et al.*, 1981). By studying both deletion and Tn*5* insertion mutants of a cloned K88 determinant in minicells five cistrons involved in the expression of K88 have been identified and mapped and the polypeptide products of four of these cistrons have been identified. Only one of these polypeptides, the 23500 mol. wt K88 antigen subunit, can be detected after staining SDS-polyacrylamide gels of total whole cell protein or of total minicell protein. The other three polypeptides can only be detected by labelling in minicells (Shipley *et al.*, 1981; M. Kehoe and G. Dougan, 1981; Dougan, Dowd and Kehoe, 1983).

Another example where minicells allowed the identification of polypeptides, for which no other assay was available, is the products of the conjugal transfer (*tra*) cistrons of the F-factor. Kennedy *et al.* (1977) studied mutants of cloned *tra* cistrons in minicells and by *in vitro* transcription, and identified the products of 13 of the *tra* cistrons. Furthermore, these workers detected a number of additional polypeptides which could be assigned to the transfer operon but not to individual *tra* cistrons. These polypeptides were subsequently shown to be encoded by other *tra* cistrons, some of which had not been identified at the time of the original study (Thompson and Achtman, 1979; Manning *et al.*, 1980; Willetts and Maule, 1979; Willetts and Skurray, 1980). To date, 18 of the F *tra* cistron products have been identified and the products of only four of the known *tra* cistrons, *tra*V, *tra*W, *tra*U and *tra*N, have yet to be identified. Further, analysis of fractionated minicells (see below) allowed the localization of many of the *tra* cistron products in minicells (Achtman *et al.*, 1979). Of the 18 *tra* cistron products identified, only *tra*R, *tra*T and *tra*J products can be detected by staining SDS-polyacrylamide gels of whole cell protein.

C. Fractionation of minicells

The studies described above involve the analysis of polypeptides expressed in whole minicells by SDS-polyacrylamide gel electrophoresis and auto-radiography. Having identified polypeptides encoded by particular cistrons, it may be necessary to localize the polypeptides to a particular minicell fraction or to carry out immunological or enzymic analysis of a particular product. To do this minicells have to be lysed and fractionated. Minicells can be lysed by sonication or french pressing, but they are more resistant to both of these treatments than are whole cells (Curtiss and Frazer, 1975). Whitholt *et al.* (1976) described a lysing procedure designed for stationary phase whole cells of *E. coli*, involving the initial formation of spheroplasts and lysis of the spheroplasts by osmotic shock. We have found that minicells are efficiently lysed by this procedure. Thus, it is a relatively simple task to localize a polypeptide to either the cytoplasmic or envelope fraction of minicells (Kennedy *et al.*, 1977; Levy and McMurray, 1974).

A number of attempts have been made to prepare inner and outer membrane fractions of minicells (Goodall *et al.*, 1974; Levy, 1975). The best characterized and most successful attempt to date is the attempt to localize *tra* cistron products (Achtman *et al.*, 1979), involving an adaptation of the technique of Osborn *et al.* (1972). Achtman *et al.* (1979) separated different fractions of minicell envelopes on sucrose gradients and obtained five main peaks. The two heaviest peaks were enriched for outer membrane polypep-tides, the central peak appeared to consist of a mixture of both inner and outer membranes (possibly membrane adhesion sites) and the two lighter peaks were enriched for inner membranes. Although the separation was not as efficient as can be obtained with whole cell envelopes, the workers were able to assign a number of the *tra* cistron products to either the inner or outer membrane fractions.

Selective solubilization of cell or minicell envelopes with Triton X-100 and Sarkosyl has often been used to obtain preliminary data on membrane

Fig. 4. Fractionation of whole minicells using the cold-shock procedure. W is whole minicells; S is supernatant from shocked minicells; R is shocked cell residue. DS410 is the plasmid-free minicell strain and pMK005 are minicells harbouring the pBR322–K88 hybrid plasmid. The β-lactamase polypeptides (28) and the 17 000 mol. wt polypeptides (17) are released from shocked cells and are presumed to be periplasmic proteins. Only low levels of the K88 pili subunit (23 000 mol. wt) are released. The polypeptides labelled in the DS410 track are expressed from stable mRNAs which have segregated into the minicells before isolation.

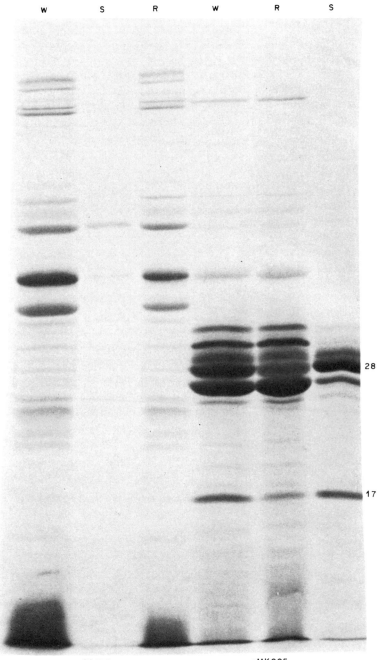

localization of polypeptides, but this technique is not reliable when used alone. Although 1% (w/v) Sarkosyl is considered to solubilize only inner membrane proteins, it has been reported that proteins which have been shown to be located predominantly in the outer membrane by other methods were up to 70% soluble in Sarkosyl (Ferrazza and Levy, 1980).

Periplasmic polypeptides can readily be located in minicells using the cold shock technique developed by Hazelbauer and Harayama (1979). The labelled minicells are resuspended in 20% (w/v) sucrose and incubated on ice for 10 min before pelleting. The pellet is resuspended in cold distilled water and after a further 10 min incubation on ice the minicells are pelleted. The periplasmic proteins which have been released into the supernatant are concentrated by TCA precipitation and detected by SDS-polyacrylamide gel electrophoresis and autoradiography. We have recently used this procedure to locate the product of one of the K88 adhesion cistrons (the 17000 mol. wt $adhC$ product) in the periplasmic fraction of minicells (Fig. 4). In this case β- lactamase, which is expressed by the vector part of the K88 hybrid plasmid, acts as a useful internal control (Dougan, Dowd and Kehoe, 1983).

D. Direct assays for polypeptides expressed in minicells

Besides identifying and localizing polypeptides in minicells and assigning them to particular cistrons by studying specific mutants, some polypeptides labelled in minicells can be directly identified if a specific assay is available. This can be a useful supplement to minicell analysis in that it shows that a particular polypeptide detected in minicells is a previously known antigen or possesses a particular enzymic activity.

The immunological techniques developed by Kessler (1975), involving the selective precipitation of antibody–antigen complexes using *Staphylococcus aureus* protein A, have been adapted to identify specific antigens expressed in minicells (Maegher *et al.*, 1977). Labelled polypeptides can be precipitated from lysed minicells provided they have not been inserted into the membrane. The precipitated *S. aureus* protein A–antibody–antigen complex is resuspended in final sample buffer and run alongside total minicell proteins (for comparison) of an SDS-polyacrylamide gel. Since the antigen has been labelled in minicells it can readily be distinguished and identified upon autoradiography. Specific antigens which have been identified by this method include the three forms of β-lactamase expressed in minicells harbouring pBR322 (Section IV.B) and the K88 adhesion subunit (Shipley *et al.*, 1981; Fig. 5). Many polypeptides retain antigenicity even after denaturation by boiling and electrophoresis on SDS-polyacrylamide gels. Such polypeptides can be identified *in situ* in the SDS-polyacrylamide gel by a simple agarose gel–antibody overlay technique (Reeve *et al.*, 1981; Kehoe *et al.*, 1981) or by

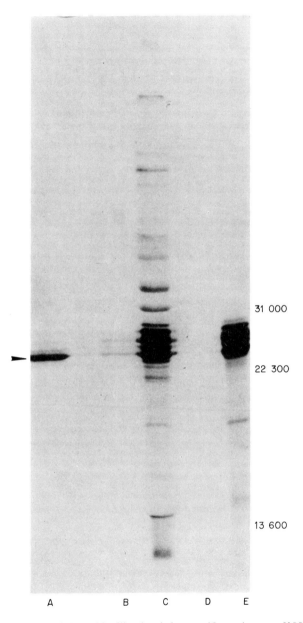

Fig. 5. Precipitation of the K88 pili subunit by specific antisera to K88 pili and *S. aureus* protein A from lysed minicells harbouring pMK005 (pBR322–K88 hybrid plasmid). Track A, + antibody; track C, minicell lysate; track D. − antibody; track E, whole minicells harbouring pMK005.

Western blotting. Polypeptides labelled in minicells which have been analysed by these methods include the K88 antigen pili subunit (Kehoe *et al.*, 1981), the product of the *ban* cistron of phage P1 (Reeve *et al.*, 1981), and the group A streptococcal toxin, SLO (Kehoe and Timmis, 1984).

Zymogram staining can sometimes be used to identify a particular enzyme activity possessed by a polypeptide detected in minicells. Of the three forms of β-lactamase expressed in minicells harbouring pBR322 (Section IV.B) the 28000 mol. wt polypeptide was shown to possess β-lactamase activity by zymogram staining. In this case the products released by lysed minicells were first separated on a non-denaturing gel and the gel was zymographically stained for β-lactamase activity. The stained band detected was cut out, macerated and the macerated material was run alongside total minicell proteins on an SDS-polyacrylamide gel. A single 28000 mol. wt polypeptide was detected in this track upon autoradiography (Dougan and Sherratt, 1977a).

E. Expression of foreign DNA in minicells

As would be expected, DNA from bacteria which are closely related to *E. coli*, including *Salmonella typhimurium* (Kodin *et al.*, 1980), is expressed well in *E. coli* minicells. Little information is available on the expression of DNA from other sources in minicells. Cloned chromosomal DNA from *Bordetella pertussis* and *Neisseria gonorrhoeae* appear to be expressed well in *E. coli* minicells (S. Falkow, personal communication). Production of a 20 000 mol. wt polypeptide from a cryptic *Streptococcus mutans* plasmid which had been linked to pBR322 has also been detected in *E. coli* minicells (Hansen *et al.*, 1981). Three polypeptides encoded by cloned fragments of *Agrobacterium tumafaciens* Ti plasmid are expressed in *E. coli* minicells, but expression is poor and probably initiated from vector promotors (Schweitzer *et al.*, 1980).

Maegher *et al.* (1977) studied expression of DNA from a variety of eucaryotic sources in minicells, but were unable to detect expression of normal eucaryotic proteins. A number of polypeptides were produced in minicells harbouring hybrid plasmids carrying cauliflower mosaic virus DNA, but these were not related to any normal viral proteins. A case where eucaryotic DNA is expressed in *E. coli* minicells has been published by Gatenby *et al.* (1981). These workers studied cloned wheat chloroplast DNA in minicells and detected the expression of a number of polypeptides from the cloned fragment, one of which was identified, by immunoprecipitation (Section IV.D), as the large subunit of ribulose diphosphate carboxylase. These polypeptides were expressed when the chloroplast DNA fragment was cloned in both orientations in the vector, suggesting that expression was initiated from a site within the chloroplast DNA. Other workers have recently detected expression from cloned *Trypanosome brucei* kinetoplast DNA in minicells (Brunel *et al.*, 1980). It is unlikely that very many cloned eucaryotic DNA genes will be expressed from promotor sites within the cloned fragment, but minicells may prove useful in studying hybrid polypeptides expressed from fused procaryotic–eucaryotic genes.

F. *Bacillus subtilis* minicell system

Bacillus subtilis minicells are purified and labelled in a similar manner to *E. coli* minicells, with some modifications as described in Section III. The *B. subtilis* minicell system has not been used very extensively. The majority of studies using this system have involved the analysis of phage products and have been the subject of a review by Reeve (1979). A number of *S. aureus* drug-resistant plasmids have been studied in *B. subtilis* minicells and were found to express significant levels of a number of polypeptides (Shivakumar *et al.*, 1979, 1980). Five polypeptides were detected in minicells harbouring a copy mutant of the erythromycin resistance plasmid, pE194, and one of these (a 29000 mol. wt polypeptide) was shown to be inducible with erythromycin (Shivakumar *et al.*, 1979, 1980). With the advent of a cloning system in *B. subtilis* it is likely that *B. subtilis* minicells will prove extremely useful in the future for analysing the products of recombinant plasmids.

V. Other methods for analysing plasmid products

In this section a number of other methods developed to study plasmid-encoded products are described briefly. For a more detailed description of these methods the reader is referred to the papers cited.

A. The maxicell system

Sancar *et al.* (1979) described a simple system, commonly called the maxicell system, whereby plasmid products expressed in whole bacterial cells can be selectively labelled. The multicopy plasmid (or phage) is introduced into an *E. coli* strain which is defective in repairing DNA damaged by ultra-violet light (u.v.). Strains commonly used include AD2480 (*recA*13, *uvr*A6, *pro*, *thi*) and CSR600 (*recA*1, *uvr*A6, *phr*-1). The latter strain offers the advantage of being defective in the photoreactivation repair system. The strain harbouring the plasmid is grown to late logarithmic phase and exposed to a carefully controlled dose of u.v.-irradiation. This should effectively destroy the ability of the chromosomal DNA to direct protein synthesis, but, with the plasmid being smaller and present in multiple copies, should result in a higher percentage of plasmid genes escaping u.v. damage. To achieve the correct balance between chromosome damage and plasmid damage the u.v. dose must be very carefully controlled. The irradiated culture is then incubated overnight at 37°C in the dark in the presence of cycloserine which lyses cells which are still able to divide. Unlysed cells are recovered, labelled with radioactive precursors and the labelled products are analysed by SDS-polyacrylamide gel electrophoresis and autoradiography.

The level of background polypeptide synthesis can vary using this technique and it is critical to control carefully the u.v. dose if good expression from plasmid DNA is to be obtained. However, this system has been successfully used by a number of workers (Christiansen and Petersen, 1981; Platz and Sjoberg, 1980; Bendiak and Friesen, 1981) and is likely to become more popular in the future. It offers the advantage over minicells that expression occurs in whole cells, although it is not clear how high levels of u.v. damage affect regulation of expression in this system.

B. Protein synthesis *in vitro*

The cell-free protein-synthesizing system described by Zubay (1970) involves a complicated mix of components which allows polypeptides to be synthesized *in vitro* using purified DNA as a template. The system has been used extensively for a number of years to study expression from both wild type and hybrid plasmids (Kennedy *et al.*, 1977; Collins, 1979). The major disadvantage of the system is that it is expensive and difficult to set up from scratch in a new laboratory, often requiring advice from someone already familiar with the system. However, once the system has been established it is a valuable method and offers several advantages over the other techniques used to analyse plasmid-encoded products. For example, regulation can be studied by adding or leaving out a putative regulatory component. Exported polypeptides are expressed in the precursor form, so allowing signal sequence to be studied by comparison with the processed product. Indeed, processing *in vitro* can be achieved by adding purified membrane vesicles.

C. Chloramphenicol amplification and mitomycin C induction

Some multicopy plasmids (e.g. ColE1) can continue to replicate in the presence of high concentrations of chloramphenicol, which inhibits protein synthesis and thus cell division. Up to 1000 copies of such plasmids can be found in chloramphenicol-treated cells after 6 h at 37°C. If these cells are washed free of chloramphenicol it has been found that protein synthesis resumes slowly and is predominantly plasmid directed (Neidhardt *et al.*, 1980), thereby allowing the plasmid-encoded polypeptides to be selectively labelled in whole cells. It is worth noting that a number of commonly used vector plasmids can be amplified by chloramphenicol and that this approach may be useful in studying expression from cloned fragments in such vectors.

Treatment of cells harbouring certain colicin plasmids, such as ColE2 and CloDF13, with mitomycin C results in high levels of expression of the colicin and immunity proteins and significant repression of expression from the bacterial chromosome (Tyler and Sherratt, 1975; Dougan and Sherratt, 1977b). The mechanism of repression of chromosome expression in these cells is unknown, although the product of the CloDF13 H gene, which maps adjacent to the cloacin and immunity determinants on this plasmid, may be responsible in this case for shutting down chromosomal expression (Van Tiel-Menkweld et al., 1981). It is possible that this repression may be developed as a system for studying the products of cloned DNA fragments in the future.

Acknowledgements

We thank Valerie Phipps for typing the manuscript and Gerrard Dowd for photography. The work was supported by a Wellcome Trust grant to Gordon Dougan.

References

Achtman, M., Manning, P. A., Edelbluth, C. and Herrlich, P. (1979). Proc. Natl. Acad. Sci. U.S.A. 76, 4837–4841.
Adler, H. I., Fisher, W. D., Cohen, A. and Hardigree, A. A. (1967). Proc. Natl. Acad. Sci. U.S.A. 57, 321–326.
Amman, E. and Reeve, J. N. (1978). Biochim. Biophys. Acta 520, 82–84.
Arthur, A. and Sherratt, D. J. (1979). Mol. Gen. Genet. 175, 267–274.
Backmann, B. J. and Lowe, K. B. (1980). Bacteriol. Rev. 44, 1–56.
Bendiak, D. S. and Friesen, J. D. (1981). Mol. Gen. Genet. 181, 356–362.
Black, J. W. (1976). Masters Thesis, University of Tennessee.
Bonner, W. M. and Laskey, R. H. (1974). Eur. J. Biochem. 46, 83–88.
Brunel, F., Davison, J., Thia, H. V. and Merchez, M. (1980). Gene 12, 223–234.
Chang, A. C. Y. and Cohen, S. N. (1978). J. Bacteriol. 134, 1141–1156.
Christiansen, L. and Pedersen, S. (1981). Mol. Gen. Genet. 181, 548–551.
Cohen, A., Allison, D. P., Adler, H. I. and Curtiss, R. (1967). Genetics 56, 550–551.
Cohen, A., Fisher, W. D., Curtiss, R. and Adler, H. I. (1968). Proc. Natl. Acad. Sci. U.S.A. 61, 61–68.
Cohen, S. N., Silver, R. P., McCoubrey, A. E. and Sharp, P. A. (1971a). Nature (London) New Biol. 231, 249–252.
Cohen, S. N., Silver, R. P., McCoubrey, A. E. and Sharp, P. A. (1971b). Ann. N.Y. Acad. Sci. 182, 172–187.
Collins, J. (1979). Gene 6, 29–42.

Chou, J., Lannaux, P. G., Casadaban, M. J. and Cohen S. N. (1979). *Nature* (*London*) **282**, 801–806.

Covarrubias, L., Cervantes, L., Covarrubias, A., Soberon, X., Vichido, I., Blanco, A., Kuperztoch-Portnoy, Y. N. and Bolivar, F. (1981). *Gene* **13**, 25–35.

Dallas, W. S. and Falkow, S. (1979). *Nature* (*London*) **277**, 406–408.

Dallas, W. S., Gill, D. M. and Falkow, S. (1979). *J. Bacteriol.* **139**, 850–858.

Dougan, G. and Sherratt, D. J. (1977a). *Mol. Gen. Genet.* **151**, 151–160.

Dougan, G. and Sherratt, D. J. (1977b). *J. Bacteriol.* **130**, 846–851.

Dougan, G., Saul, M., Twigg, A., Gill, R. and Sherratt, D. J. (1979). *J. Bacteriol.* **138**, 48–54.

Dougan, G., Dowd, G. and Kehoe, M. (1983). *J. Bacteriol.* **153**, 364–370.

Epps, N. A. and Idziak, E. S. (1970). *Appl. Microbiol.* **19**, 338–344.

Ferrazza, D. and Levy, S. (1980). *J. Bacteriol.* **144**, 149–151.

Frazer, A. C. and Curtiss, R. (1975). *Curr. Top. Microbiol. Immunol.* **69**, 1–84.

Fuke, M. and Inselberg, J. (1972). *Proc. Natl. Acad. Sci. U.S.A.* **69**, 89–92.

Gardner, A. D. (1930). *In* "A System of Bacteriology in Relation to Medicine" (P. Fildes and J. C. G. Ledingham, Eds), Vol. 1, pp. 159–170. H.M.S.O., London.

Gatenby, A. A., Castleton, J. A. and Saul, M. W. (1981). *Nature* (*London*) **291**, 117–121.

Gemski, P. and Griffin, D. E. (1980). *Infect. Immun.* **30**, 297–302.

Gill, R., Heffron, F. and Falkow, S. (1979). *Nature* (*London*) **282**, 797–801.

Goodall, E. W., Schwarz, V. and Teather, R. M. (1974). *Eur. J. Biochem.* **47**, 567–572.

Hallewell, R. A. and Emtage, S. (1980). *Gene* **9**, 27–46.

Hallewell, R. A. and Sherratt, D. J. (1976). *Mol. Gen. Genet.* **146**, 239–245.

Hansen, J. B., Abiko, Y. and Curtiss, R. (1981). *Infect. Immun.* **31**, 1034–1043.

Hazelbauer, G. L. and Harayama, S. (1979). *Cell* **16**, 617–625.

Inselberg, J. (1970). *J. Bacteriol.* **102**, 642–647.

Kass, L. R. and Yarmolinsky, M. B. (1970). *Proc. Natl. Acad. Sci. U.S.A.* **66**, 815–822.

Kehoe, M., Sellwood, R., Shipley, P. and Dougan, G. (1981). *Nature* (*London*) **291**, 122–126.

Kehoe, M. and Timmis, K. (1984). *Infect. Immun.* **43**, 804–810.

Kennedy, N., Beutin, L., Achtman, M., Skurray, R., Rahmsdorf, V. and Herrlich, P. (1977). *Nature* (*London*) **270**, 580–585.

Kessler, J. (1975). *J. Immunol.* **115**, 1617–1624.

Koduri, R. K., Bedwell, D. M. and Brenchley, J. E. (1980). *Gene* **11**, 227–237.

Kool, A. J., Pranger, H. and Nijkamp, N. J. J. (1972). *Mol. Gen. Genet.* **115**, 314–323.

Kool, A. J., Van Zeben, M. S. and Nijkamp, J. J. (1974). *J. Bacteriol.* **118**, 213–224.

Laemmli, U. K. (1970). *Nature* (*London*) **227**, 680–685.

Levy, S. B. (1970). *Prox Xth. Intern. Congr. Microbiol.* p. 60.

Levy, S. B. (1973). *Bacteriol. Proc.* **62**.

Levy, S. B. (1975). *Proc. Natl. Acad. Sci. U.S.A.* **72**, 2900–2904.

Levy, S. B. and McMurray, L. (1974). *Biochem. Biophys. Res. Commun.* **56**, 1060–1068.

Levy, S. B. and Norman, P. (1970). *Nature* (*London*) **227**, 606–607.

Maegher, R. B., Tait, R. G., Betlach, M. and Boyer, H. M. (1977). *Cell* **10**, 521–536.

Manning, P. A. and Achtman, M. (1979). *In* "Bacterial Outer Membranes" (M. Inouye, Ed.), pp. 409–447. Wiley, New York.

Manning, P. A., Morelli, G. and Achtman, M. (1980). *Proc. Nat. Acad. Sci. USA* **78**, 7487–7491.

Mendelson, N. H. and Reeve, J. N. (1973). *Nature (London) New Biol.* **243**, 62–64.

Miller, J. (1972). "Experiments in Molecular Genetics". Cold Spring Harbor, New York.

Neidhardt, R. C., Wirth, R., Smith, M. W. and Van Bogelen, R. A. (1980). *J. Bacteriol.* **143**, 535–537.

Nothling, R. and Reeve, J. N. (1980). *J. Bacteriol.* **143**, 1060–1062.

O'Farrell, P. H. (1975). *J. Biol. Chem.* **250**, 4007–4021.

Osborn, M. J., Gander, J. E., Parisi, E. and Carson, J. (1972). *J. Biol. Chem.* **247**, 3962–3972.

Platz, A. and Sjoberg, B. M. (1980). *J. Bacteriol.* **143**, 561–568.

Reeve, J. N. (1972). *In* "Methods in Enzymology" (R. Wu, Ed.), Vol. 68, pp. 493–503. Academic Press, New York and London.

Reeve, J. N., Mendelson, N. H., Coyne, S. I., Hallock, L. L. and Cole, R. M. (1973). *J. Bacteriol.* **114**, 860–866.

Reeve, J. N., Lanka, E. and Schuster, H. (1980). *Mol. Gen. Genet.* **177**, 193–197.

Rivera, M. J., Smits, M. A., Quint, W., Schoenkamers, J. G. G. and Konings, R. N. H. (1978). *Nucleic Acids Res.* **5**, 2895–2912.

Roozen, K. J., Fenwick, R. G., Levy, S. B. and Curtiss, R. (1970). *Genetics* **64**, 554–556.

Roozen, K. J., Fenwick, R. G. and Curtiss, R. (1971). *In* "Informative Molecules in Biological Systems" (L. G. H. Ledoux, Ed.), pp. 249–264. North-Holland Publ., Amsterdam.

Rothstein, S. J., Jorgenson, R. A., Postler, K. and Reznikoff, W. S. (1980). *Cell* **19**, 795–805.

Sancar, A., Hack, A. M. and Rupp, W. D. (1979). *J. Bacteriol.* **137**, 692–693.

Schweitzer, S., Blohm, D. and Geilder, K. (1980). *Plasmid* **4**, 196–204.

Setlow, J. K., Boling, M. E., Allison, D. P. and Beattie, K. L. (1973). *J. Bacteriol.* **115**, 153–161.

Shipley, P., Dougan, G. and Falkow, S. (1981). *J. Bacteriol.* **145**, 920–925.

Shivakumar, A. G., Hahn, J. and Dubnau, D. (1979). *Plasmid* **2**, 279–289.

Shivakumar, A. G., Gryozan, J. J., Kozlov, Y. I. and Dubnau, D. (1980). *Mol. Gen. Genet.* **179**, 241–252.

Smits, M. A., Simons, G., Konings, R. N. Y. and Schoenmakers, J. G. G. (1978). *Biochim. Biophys. Acta* **521**, 27–44.

Spicer, E. K., Kavanaugh, W. M., Dallas, W. S., Falkow, S., Konigsberg, W. H. and Shafer, D. E. (1981). *Proc. Natl. Acad. Sci. U.S.A.* **78**, 50–54.

Tait, R. C. and Boyer, H. W. (1978). *Cell* **13**, 73–81.

Tankersley, W. G. (1970). Masters Thesis, University of Tennessee.

Tankersley, W. G. and Woodward, J. M. (1973). *Bacteriol. Proc.* **97**.

Thompson, R. and Achtman, M. (1978). *Mol. Gen. Genet.* **165**, 295–304.

Tyler, J. and Sherratt, D. J. (1975). *Mol. Gen. Genet.* **140**, 349–353.

Van Alstyne, D. and Simon, M. I. (1971). *J. Bacteriol.* **108**, 1366–1379.

van den Elzen, P. J. M., Konings B. N. H., Veltkamp, E. and Nijkamp, N. J. N. (1980). *J. Bacteriol.* **144**, 579–591.

Van Tiel-Menkweld, J. G., Velkamp, E. and De Graaf, F. K. (1981). *J. Bacteriol.* **141**, 41–48.

Voros, J. and Goodman, R. N. (1965). *Phytopathology* **55**, 876–879.

Whitholt, B., Boekhout, M., Brock, M., Kingman, J., Van Heerikhuisen, H. and deLey, L. (1976). *Anal. Biochem.* **4**, 160–170.

Willetts, N. S. and Maule, J. (1980). *Mol. Gen. Genet.* **178**, 675–680.

Willetts, N. S. and Skurray, R. (1980). *Annu. Rev. Genet.* **14**, 41–76.

Zubay, G., Chambers, D. A. and Cheong, L. C. (1970). *In* "The Lactose Operon", pp. 375–391. Cold Spring Harbor, New York.

Note added to proof

Since this manuscript was written (1981) a number of papers have been published which indicate the usefulness of the *E. coli* minicell system for studying expression of cloned DNA sequences from both gram-negative and gram-positive bacterial species, other than *E. coli*. Because of limits to changes at proof stage, citation of recent papers has been kept to a minimum. It should also be noted that ^{35}S-cysteine is now commercially available (Amersham, U.K.).

13

DNA Sequencing

N. L. BROWN

Department of Biochemistry, University of Bristol, Bristol, UK

I. Introduction

Several revolutionary contributions to an understanding of the mechanisms of gene expression have arisen directly from DNA sequence analysis. What was until recently a specialized technique is now a standard and routine procedure in many laboratories; indeed, DNA sequencing may be the first analytical procedure applied to a newly isolated and ill-understood genetic element.

METHODS IN MICROBIOLOGY
VOLUME 17   ISBN 0–12–521517–7

The purpose of this chapter is to allow any competent molecular biologist to become adept at DNA sequencing. It is not intended that this be a comprehensive review of methods and potential pitfalls, as new examples of both are continually being discovered. Instead, working methods are described, and the reader is encouraged to look to the original literature for other methods. It is axiomatic that significant advances in methodology will be made during the gestation of this chapter. The truism bears repeating, that it is easier to determine the wrong DNA sequence than to determine the correct one.

A. Historical aspects

The first successful attempts to determine the primary structures of nucleic acids were made in 1961, when compositional analysis of oligopyrimidine and oligopurine tracts was performed on DNA. These crude techniques of depurination and depyrimidination may very occasionally be used today to resolve sequence ambiguities. Methods for RNA sequence analysis were developed at about this time. Degradative methods requiring ^{32}P-labelled RNA, and utilizing base-specific ribonucleases and two-dimensional analytical techniques, made RNA sequence analysis a powerful, if slow, method for determining the primary structure of nucleic acids. These methods are reviewed in detail by Brownlee (1972).

Degradative methods were similarly applied to sequencing DNA, but were hindered by the relatively large size of the smallest known DNA molecules and by the lack of base-specific deoxyribonucleases. These methods have been described and reviewed (Brown, 1979; Murray, 1974; Salser, 1974). The breakthrough in DNA sequencing methods was both conceptual, in the initial use of synthetic rather than degradative methods, and technical, in the development of a gel electrophoresis system capable of resolving oligonucleotides differing in length by one nucleotide (Sanger and Coulson, 1975). Subsequently, the availability of many different type II restriction endonucleases allowed degradative methods to be used (Maxam and Gilbert, 1977). The first rapid gel method—the "plus and minus" method (Sanger and Coulson, 1975)—has now been superseded by the chain-termination method (Sanger et al., 1977b) and this together with the chemical method are the main techniques currently used.

The discovery of a large number of type II restriction endonucleases allowed for the first time the fragmentation of large DNA molecules into smaller specific pieces which are readily purified and are amenable to sequence analysis. This, coupled with the associated development of genetic engineering methods, allows the isolation and purification of DNA from genomes too complex, or otherwise unsuitable, for direct sequence analysis.

B. Principle of rapid gel methods

All rapid DNA sequencing methods (and the analogous, but rarely used, rapid RNA sequencing methods) follow the same principle.

A nested series of ^{32}P-labelled single-stranded DNA fragments is generated such that one end is common to all fragments, and the other end is generated in a base-specific manner (Fig. 1). A number (usually four) of nested series is generated, each series having the same common end, but with a different base or bases at the other end.

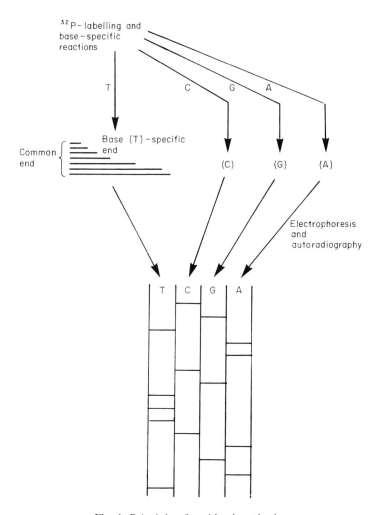

Fig. 1. Principle of rapid gel methods.

The (four) different base-specific series of fragments are analysed in parallel by slab-gel electrophoresis, under conditions in which the DNA is denatured and its migration determined primarily by the length of the oligonucleotide chain. The gel system used is capable of resolving oligonucleotides differing in length by one nucleotide.

The ^{32}P-labelled fragments are detected by autoradiography, and the relative order of radioactive DNA fragments in each base-specific series of fragments reading up the autoradiogram gives the relative order of the specific bases from the common end, that is, the DNA sequence. It follows that if the common end is a 5′ end the sequence will be read in the 5′ to 3′ direction, and if it is a 3′ end the sequence will be 3′ to 5′. Depending on the exact conditions used, it is possible to read sequences up to about 400 nucleotides from the common end. The rapid accumulation of sequence data is therefore possible.

C. Outline of the methods

1. Plus and minus method

This method of Sanger and Coulson (1975) is of historical importance in that it was the first of the rapid gel methods, and was used to obtain the first sequence of a DNA genome, that of bacteriophage ϕX174 (Sanger et al., 1977a). This method has been totally superseded by the faster and more reliable chain-termination method (Sanger et al., 1977b) and will not be discussed further.

2. Chemical method

This method of Maxam and Gilbert (1977) has been the most widely used of the DNA sequencing methods, primarily because of its applicability to double- as well as single-stranded DNA, its reliance on chemical rather than enzymic procedures in the base-specific reactions and the availability of well-annotated and carefully written protocol sheets. Although working procedures for this method are described in this chapter, time, space and the author's experience preclude discussion of the method with the detail given by Maxam and Gilbert (1980). Readers are encouraged to read their article, which is available as a loose-bound reprint from New England Nuclear when purchasing a DNA sequencing kit (Section VI.D).

In the chemical method, a double- or single-stranded DNA fragment is end-labelled with ^{32}P-phosphate. The DNA can be labelled at the 5′ end by using polynucleotide kinase and (γ-^{32}P)ATP; or at the 3′ end by using terminal transferase with (α-^{32}P)ATP or with cordycepin (α-^{32}P) triphosphate; or, for double-stranded DNA only, at the 3′ end using DNA polymerase and deoxyribonucleoside (α-^{32}P) triphosphate. A double-stranded DNA fragment must then be manipulated to separate the labelled ends, either by strand separation or by secondary cleavage with a restriction enzyme and separation of the subfragments (Fig. 2). Whatever combination of labelling and separation methods is used, the result is a single DNA fragment labelled at one end only and in one strand only. The labelled end constitutes the common end described in Section I.B.

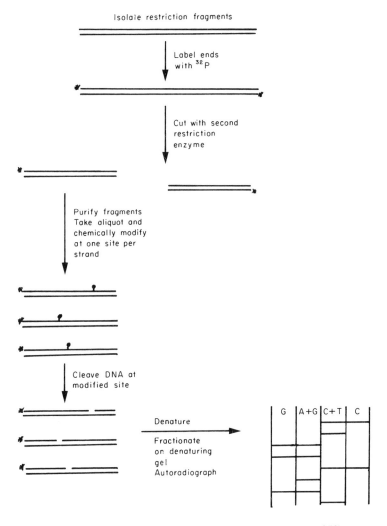

Fig. 2. Principle of the chemical method (from Brown, 1979).

End-labelled DNA is then subject to base-specific chemical cleavage. Typically the DNA is divided into four aliquots and four chemical reactions are used which allow differentiation between the four bases. The reaction may be specific for more than one base, and involves three steps: modification of the base, removal of the modified base from the sugar-phosphate backbone and scission of the backbone at that site (Fig. 2). The first step must be base-specific and occurs under conditions which allow modification of only one base per strand in the region to be sequenced (which may be shorter than the complete DNA strand). The remaining steps must be quantitative, otherwise DNA fragments with anomalous electrophoretic mobilities may result.

Typically the four sets of chemical reactions are specific for C, C + T, G and A + G, respectively. A number of other base-specific reactions are available (e.g. T, A > G, G > A, A > C) and some of these reactions are listed in Section II.B. In recent protocols the base-removal and strand-scission reactions are performed simultaneously by using piperidine. This causes removal of the modified base, then catalyses β-elimination of phosphates from the sugar. Piperidine is volatile and can easily be removed from the DNA to leave a salt-free product which can be analysed on thin acrylamide gels (Section IV.A).

3. M13-cloning/chain-termination method

The chain-termination method (Sanger et al., 1977b) was originally applied to the sequence analysis of single-stranded bacteriophage DNA (Sanger et al., 1978; Godson et al., 1978). The method depends on the in vitro copying of a single-stranded DNA template by primed synthesis using DNA polymerase I (Fig. 3). Single-stranded template DNA can be obtained from almost any DNA by cloning double-stranded fragments of DNA into the replicative form (RF) DNA of bacteriophage M13. A series of bacteriophage M13 derivatives have been constructed specifically for this purpose (Table I; Fig. 4).

Bacteriophage M13 (Ray, 1977) is a filamentous single-stranded DNA phage which infects only male (F^+) Escherichia coli in a chronic non-lytic mode. There is no strict geometric constraint on the size of single-stranded DNA that can be packaged in the virion. The replicative form DNA is present in infected cells in high copy number and can easily be isolated as a covalently closed, double-stranded DNA (RFI DNA). Although infected cells are viable, they grow more slowly than uninfected cells and continually extrude bacteriophage; M13 thus forms plaques of retarded growth when plated on a lawn of cells by the overlay method.

The bacteriophage vector M13mp2 (Gronenborn and Messing, 1978) carries in a non-essential region of its genome part of the E. coli lac operon; this is the regulatory region and the coding sequence for the first 145 amino acids of the β-galactosidase (the α-peptide). In vitro mutagenesis was used to

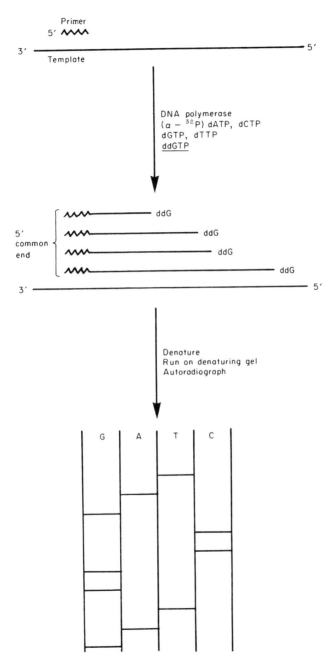

Fig. 3. Principle of the chain-termination method.

TABLE I

Bacteriophage M13mp vectors

Bacteriophage	Target sites	Insert fragments[a]	Fragment termini
M13mp2	*Eco*RI	*Eco*RI	5′–AATTC– –
			G– –
M13mp5	*Hind*III	*Hind*III	5′–AGCTT– –
			A– –
M13mp7	*Eco*RI	*Eco*RI	5′–AATTC– –
			G– –
	*Pst*I	*Pst*I	G– –
			3′–ACGTC– –
	*Bam*HI	*Bam*HI, *Bcl*I, *Bgl*II,	5′–GATCN– –
		*Mbo*I, *Sau*3AI, *Xho*II	N– –
	*Sal*GI[b]	*Sal*GI, *Xho*II	5′– TCGAN– –
			N– –
	*Acc*I[b]	*Acy*I, *Asu*II, *Cla*I,	5′CGN– –
		*Hpa*II, *Nar*I, *Sci*NI,	N– –
		*Taq*I	
	*Hind*II[b]	Any fully-base-paired	5′–N– –
		terminus	3′–N– –
M13mp8[c] M13mp9[c]	All sites in M13mp7, plus		
	*Sma*I[d]	Any fully base-paired	5′–N–
		terminus	3′–N–
	*Xma*I[d]	*Xma*I	5′–CCGGG–
			C–
	*Hind*III	*Hind*III	5′–AGCTT– –
			A– –

[a] Enzymes recognizing related sequences (degenerate sites) of which only some would give the desired termini are not included in the table (e.g. not all *Acc*I fragments can be cloned into the *Acc*I site of M13mp7).
[b] The sequence 5′-GTCGAC-3′ is recognized by *Sal*GI, *Acc*I and *Hind*II.
[c] M13mp8 and M13mp9 carry identical 39 nucleotide sequences containing the target sites for cloning, and these are in opposite orientations in the two strains (Fig. 6).
[d] The sequence 5′-CCCGGG-3′ is recognized by *Sma*I and *Xma*I.

introduce a unique *Eco*RI site within the α-peptide coding region. A series of derivatives of M13mp2 have been constructed (Table I; Fig. 4; Messing *et al.*, 1981; Messing and Vieira, 1982) which carry synthetic oligonucleotide insertions at the *Eco*RI site. These insertions together with mutagenesis of other regions of the M13 genome have introduced unique target sites for a number of other restriction enzymes within the α-peptide coding sequence. All these M13 derivatives synthesize the α-peptide under the control of the *lac* regulatory region. In a suitable host (e.g. *E. coli* K12 71–18; Table II), which produces the corresponding C-terminal fragment of the *lac* β-galactosidase

M13mp2
```
        1   2   3   4   5   6   7   8
        T   M   I   T   N   S   L   A
     ATGACCATGATTACGAATTCACTGGCC
                    EcoRI    HaeIII
```

M13mp7
```
                                1   2   3   4   5   6   7   8   9  10 11 12 13 14
                1   2   3   4   5   S   P   D   P   S   T   C   R   S   T   D   P   G   N   6   7   8
                T   M   I   T   N                                                           S   L   A
     ATGACCATGATTACGAATTCCCCGGATCCGTCGACCTGCAGGTCGACGGATCCGGGGAATTCACTGGCC
                    EcoRI    BamHI  ─────  PstI ─────  BamHI     EcoRI    HaeIII
                                     AccI          AccI
```

M13mp8
```
                                1   2   3   4   5   6   7   8   9  10 11
                1   2   3   4   5   6   R   G   S   V   D   L   Q   P   S   L   A   7   8
                T   M   I   T   N   S                                           L   A
     ATGACCATGATTACGAATTCCCGGGGATCCGTCGACCTGCAGCCAAGCTTGGCACTGGCC
                    EcoRI────────BamHI─────  PstI  HindIII     HaeIII
                          SmaI        AccI
```

M13mp9
```
                                1   2   3   4   5   6   7   8   9  10 11
                1   2   3   4   P   S   L   A   A   G   R   R   I   P   G   5   6   7   8
                T   M   I   T                                           N   S   L   A
     ATGACCATGATTACGCCAAGCTTGGCTGCAGGTCGACGGATCCCCGGGAATTCACTGGCC
                    HindIII    PstI ─────BamHI─────EcoRI    HaeIII
                                     AccI      SmaI
```

Fig. 4. DNA sequences at the cloning sites in M13mp vectors. The N-terminal sequence of the β-galactosidase α-peptide is shown in each case using the single letter amino acid code (Messing et al., 1981; Messing and Vieira, 1982). Note that the universal primer primes from right to left in this orientation. The reference HaeIII site is that shown in the primer sequence (Fig. 6). The AccI sites are also cleaved by SalGI and HincII; the SmaI sites are also cleaved by XmaI.

(the ω-peptide), α-complementation occurs to give an active β-galactosidase protein. The β-galactosidase activity can be detected in vivo by using the chromogenic substrate 5-bromo-4-chloro-3-indolyl-β-D-galactopyranoside. This colourless substrate, also known as X-gal, is hydrolysed to give a dark blue product. Figure 5 illustrates this process.

If DNA fragments are cloned into the unique restriction sites in the α-peptide coding sequence of M13mp2 or its derivatives, and the resulting recombinant molecules are used to transfect the indicator host, then the recombinant bacteriophage will form plaques on a lawn of indicator host. However, the infected cells will not contain active β-galactosidase due to the disruption of the α-peptide coding sequence, and plaques due to the recombinants will be colourless on the chromogenic indicator, X-gal.

It is then a simple procedure to grow 1-ml cultures of infected cells from each colourless plaque, to remove the cells by centrifugation and to precipitate the virions with polyethylene glycol. Sufficient single-stranded DNA for

TABLE II

E. coli host strains for bacteriophage M13mp vectors

Strain	Genotype	Reference and notes
71–18	K12Δ(*lac*, *pro*), *sup*E, *thi* (F′ *pro*AB lacIq, ZΔM15)	Messing *et al.* (1977).
JM101	K12Δ(*lac*, *pro*), *sup*E, *thi* (F′ *pro*AB, *lac*Iq, ZΔM15, *tra*D36)	Messing (1979) Transfer-deficient F′-factor and therefore "safer vector"
JM103	K12Δ (*lac*, *pro*), *sup*E, *thi* *str*A, *end*A, *sbc*B15, *hsd*R4 (F′ *pro*AB, *lac*Iq, ZΔM15, *tra*D36)	Messing *et al.* (1980) Lacks nuclease activity of *Eco*K restriction/modification system

about ten sequence determinations can be made by phenol extraction of the bacteriophage pellet. A large number of M13 recombinants can be processed at one time.

The M13-cloning procedure is most commonly used to produce random subclones of the DNA to be sequenced, such that the sequence is obtained in a

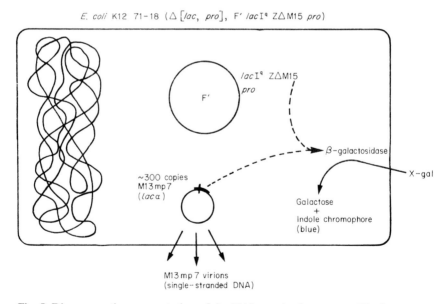

E. coli K12 71–18 (Δ [*lac*, *pro*], F′ *lac*Iq ZΔM15 *pro*)

M13mp 7 virions (single-stranded DNA)

Fig. 5. Diagrammatic representation of the M13mp selection system. The *lac* operon DNA in M13mp7 is shown as a thick black line; cloning at the site indicated by the bar prevents β-galactosidase activity, but does not prevent virion production.

random fashion and is gradually compiled. All the subclones produced have an identical (*lacZ* gene) sequence to the 3′ side of the inserted DNA. A universal primer can be annealed to this common flanking sequence for primed-synthesis copying of the insert DNA in the chain-termination reactions (Fig. 6). The primer may be a double-stranded restriction fragment. In this case, the strand which is non-complementary to the template competes with the template for the complementary (priming) strand, but does not otherwise interfere with the sequencing reactions. Even with single-stranded (e.g. synthetic) primers and single-stranded templates, the DNA should be heat-denatured before annealing in order to melt out any internal secondary structure in either DNA. The annealed primer-template mixture is divided into four aliquots, one for each specific base. These are incubated with *E. coli* DNA polymerase I (large fragment), (α-^{32}P) dATP, dCTP, dTTP, dGTP and a chain-terminating compound specific for one base. *E. coli* DNA polymerase I (large fragment) is often called Klenow polymerase, and is produced by limited protease treatment and chromatography of *E. coli* DNA polymerase I. This removes the 5′ exonuclease activity normally present in DNA polymerase I, which would otherwise act on the 5′ end of the primer fragment. If, as is usually the case, the primer fragment is not removed by restriction endonuclease cleavage after primed synthesis (or if a short primer is used and removal attempted), then the prerequisite condition

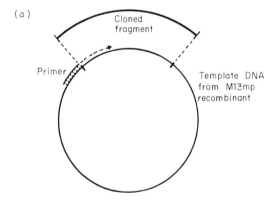

Fig. 6. (a) Use of the universal primer to sequence a DNA fragment cloned in a M13mp vector. (b) DNA sequence of the 96 bp universal primer. The *Hae*III site shown is that shown in Fig. 4. (Note that the orientation is opposite to that shown in Fig. 4.)

that all the DNA fragments have a common end as well as a base-specific end (Section I.B) will not be met if a 5′ exonuclease is present.

The DNA is internally labelled during primed synthesis; (α-^{32}P)dATP is normally used in the author's laboratory, but one of the other triphosphates can be used with minor variations in the subsequent protocol (Section III.B.2(b)). The specific chain-terminating compound used is usually the appropriate 2′,3′-dideoxyribonucleoside 5-triphosphate, but may be the arabinoside 5′-triphosphate. In the G-specific reaction, for example, a ratio of 2′,3′-dideoxyguanosine 5′-triphosphate (ddGTP) to 2′-deoxyguanosine 5′-triphosphate (dGTP) would be chosen such that a C residue in the template strand would direct the incorporation of a 2′-deoxyguanosine residue about 99% of the time and elongation of the ^{32}P-labelled DNA strand would continue; the remaining 1% of the time a 2′,3′-dideoxyguanosine residue would be incorporated*. As the dideoxyguanosine residue has no 3′ hydroxyl group, it cannot further participate in phosphodiester bond formation, and chain elongation stops. The incorporated dideoxynucleoside residue is only very slowly removed by the 3′ exonuclease activity of DNA polymerase I (Atkinson *et al.*, 1969). The net result is a nested series of DNA fragments with identical 5′ ends, and variable base-specific 3′ ends. The mechanism of chain termination by arabinoside triphosphates is more obscure, but is probably due to the low affinity of the primer terminus binding site of DNA polymerase I for a 3′ end containing an arabinoside residue. Now that all four dideoxyribonucleoside triphosphates are commercially available the arabinosides are little used.

4. Gel electrophoresis and autoradiography

Many of the problems preventing the rapid accumulation of good sequence data are encountered in obtaining well-resolved specific band patterns in autoradiograms. In addition, the radioactive DNA products of the chemical method are chemically identical with those of the chain-termination method, except in that the former have an additional 3′ phosphate group. Most of the considerations of electrophoresis and autoradiography are therefore common to both methods. With both methods the DNA samples are denatured by heating in formamide before loading them onto the gel.

The gel system normally used is an acrylamide slab-gel with 1 in 20 cross-linking, in 7 M urea and 90 mM Tris-borate, pH 8.3, 2.5 mM EDTA (TBE) buffer (Peacock and Dingman, 1967). The total acrylamide concentration can be varied according to the experiment, from, say, 20% for sequences close to the common end, to 5% for sequences much further from the common end.

---

* The chemical ratio dGTP:ddGTP will be lower than 99:1, as dideoxynucleotides are much poorer substrates than deoxynucleotides.

The urea is present as a denaturing agent, but is a poor one for nucleic acids in that 7M urea reduces the melting temperature of DNA by only about 20°C. The high ionic strength of the buffer causes a high current to be drawn, and the gels run at a temperature of 60–70°C, thus minimizing the formation of intrastrand secondary structure in the DNA fragments. The simple practice of running the electrophoresis system for 30–60 min to heat up the gel before loading the sample circumvents a number of artefacts that may cause problems in interpreting the gel pattern. Other gel systems (e.g. formamide–urea, Section IV.C) may be used for special reasons.

The apparatus used for gel electrophoresis should give direct contact between gel and buffer, allowing high-voltage gradients to be used. Models similar to that described by Studier (1973) are commercially available. Thin (0.35-mm) acrylamide gels (Sanger and Coulson, 1978) are normally run with the chain-termination procedure, and these can also be used with those reactions in the chemical method which give a salt-free product. Thin gels have the advantage that the bands on the autoradiogram are very sharp as a simple geometric consequence of reducing the distance between the film and the "back" face of the gel. Thin gels must be cast between plates of high quality float glass, otherwise variations in gel thickness cause abnormal mobilities of DNA fragments and cause localized variations in heating. Very thin gels (0.1 mm) have also been used, and these require special techniques (Ansorge and De Maeyer, 1980; Garoff and Ansorge, 1981). A variety of autoradiographic techniques is used (Section IV). Unless sequences very close to the common end are being determined, the use of indirect autoradiography is to be avoided due to the band-broadening caused by the intensifying screen.

II. Procedures for the chemical method

Although the main procedures, and some recent modifications thereof, are outlined here, the reader is referred to the excellent treatise by Maxam and Gilbert (1980).

A. Preparation of DNA

Chapters 6, 8 and 9 describe methods of preparing plasmid DNA and of digesting this DNA with restriction endonucleases. The preparation of DNA fragments for sequence analysis by the chemical method can be done by the methods described there. For many DNA sequencing projects it is preferable to isolate large unlabelled restriction fragments in bulk in an initial step. This has the advantages that unnecessary DNA sequences (e.g. from a vector replicon) can be discarded before ^{32}P-labelling, that resolution of labelled

DNA fragments in the area of interest is easier, that experiments can be more readily designed to give the optimum distribution of restriction sites and that problem areas can be more easily defined.

Some steps in the chemical method are inhibited or otherwise made less efficient by common contaminants of DNA. For example, the kinase reaction will also label oligodeoxyribonucleotides (fragments of chromosomal DNA) which are not efficiently removed by CsCl isopycnic centrifugation; some restriction endonucleases are stored in phosphate buffer, which will inhibit the phosphatase reaction; linear acrylamide will readily elute from low percentage acrylamide gels during extraction of DNA fragments and may inhibit DNA polymerase end-labelling. Care must be taken to remove such contaminants during the bulk preparation of DNA fragments.

Subsequent digestion of large DNA fragments with other restriction endonucleases can initially be done with small amounts of DNA to determine the best enzymes to use to get a good distribution of fragments. Enzymes with small (tetranucleotide) recognition sites giving DNA fragments with 5′ terminal extensions (Table III) are preferable due to the number of fragments produced and the greater efficiency and ease of labelling such fragments. Enzymes with such sites include: *Hinf*I, *Hpa*II, *Sci*Ni, *Sau*3AI, *Taq*I and their isoschizomers; but enzymes with pentanucleotide or hexanucleotide recognition sequences are also frequently used, as are enzymes generating fragments without 5′ extensions (Roberts, 1982).

1. Bulk preparation of DNA fragments

Mix in a 1.5 ml centrifuge tube:
200 μg plasmid DNA
30 μl 10 × restriction enzyme buffer (see supplier's recommendation)
Water to a *final* volume of 300 μl.
Mix and add 40 units restriction endonuclease.
Mix and incubate for 10 h at recommended temperature.
(This provides a safety margin of two-fold overdigestion, which is sufficient for all except a few unstable enzymes.)
Add 200 μl phenol, vortex and centrifuge for 30 s.
Remove and discard lower phase.
Add 30 μl 3 M sodium acetate, vortex and add 750 μl ethanol.
Chill for 5–10 min in a dry ice–isopropanol bath.
Centrifuge for 5 min at 4°C.
Remove supernatant and wash pellet by adding 95% ethanol, centrifuging 1 min and discarding supernatant.
Dry under vacuum.
Resuspend DNA in 80 μl H$_2$O, 20 μl Native loading buffer (Section VI.A).
Load into slot (2 cm × 0.15 cm) of 40-cm long slab-gel (5% acrylamide; 30:1 cross-linking), and run in TBE buffer at 300–400 volts for 16 h. Exact running conditions may be varied, but lower voltages prevent heating and aid resolution.

TABLE III
Restriction endonucleases generating 5' extensions

Fragment terminus	End repair with	Enzyme[a]	(recognition site)
5'–A–; 5'–T–	dATP, dTTP	ApyI	(CC/$\frac{A}{T}$GG)
5'–C–; 5'–G–	dCTP, dGTP	CauII, NciI[b]	(CC/$\frac{C}{G}$GG)
5'–N–	All four dNTPs	Fnu4HI	(GC/NGC)
		Tth111I	(GACN/NNGTC)
5'–CG	dCTP, dGTP	AcyI	(GPu/CGPyC)
		AosII	(TT/CGAA)
		ClaI	(AT/CGAT)
		HpaII	(C/CGG)
		NarI	(GG/CGCC)
		SciNI	(G/CGC)
		TaqI	(T/CGA)
5'–AT–; 5'–AG– 5'–CG–; 5'–CT–	All four dNTPs	AccI	(GT/$\frac{AT}{CG}$AC)
5'–ANT–	All four dNTPs	HinfI	(G/ANTC)
5'–GAC–; 5'–GTC–	All four dNTPs	AvaII	(G/G$\frac{A}{T}$CC)
5'–GNC–	All four dNTPs	AsuI	(G/GNCC)
5'–TNA–	All four dNTPs	DdeI	(C/TNAG)
		SauI	(CC/TNAGG)
5'–AATT–	dATP, dTTP	EcoRI	(G/AATTC)
5'–AGCT–	All four dNTPs	HindIII	(A/AGCTT)
5'–CCGG–	dCTP, dGTP	XmaI	(C/CCGGG)
5'–CGCG–	dCTP, dGTP	MluI	(A/CGCGT)
5'–CTAG–	All four dNTPs	XbaI	(T/CTAGA)
5'–GATC–	All four dNTPs	BamHI	(G/GATCC)
		BclI	(T/GATCA)
		BglII	(A/GATCT)
		MboI	(/GATC)
		XhoII	(Pu/GATCPy)
5'–GGCC–	dCTP, dGTP	CfrI	(Py/GGCCPu)
		XmaIII	(C/GGCCG)
5'–TCGA–	All four dNTPs	SalGI	(G/TCGAC)
		XhoI	(C/TCGAG)
5'–TTAA–	dATP, dTTP	AflII	(C/TTAAG)
5'–CCGG– 5'–CCGA– 5'–TCGG– 5'–TCGA–	All four dNTPs	AvaI	(C/PyCGPuG)
5'–GCAC– 5'–GCGC– 5'–GTAC– 5'–GTGC–	All four dNTPs	HgiCI	(G/GPyPuCC)
5'–NNNN–	All four dNTPs	BbvI[c]	(GCAGC. 8/12)
		FokI[c]	(GGATG. 9/13)
5'–CCAGG– 5'–CCTGG–	All four dNTPs	EcoRII	(/CC$\frac{A}{T}$GG)
5'–GTNAC–	All four dNTPs	BstEII	(G/GTNACC)
5'–NNNNN–	All four dNTPs	HgaI[c]	(GACGC. 5/10)

[a] Only one enzyme is given where several enzymes recognise the same sequence and cleave it identically. The isoschizomers are listed in Roberts (1982).

[b] NciI cleaves leaving the 3' phosphate groups.

[c] BbvI, FokI and HgaI cut to the 3' side of the recognition site given; the numbers refer to the distance in nucleotides from the recognition sequence to the cleavage site in the same/ complementary strands.

To detect the unlabelled DNA fragments remove one gel plate and either

(i) Stain the gel in ethidium bromide (0.5 μg ml^{-1} in water for 5–10 min, and examine under u.v. light (300 nm or 340 nm). The ethidium can be removed later by phenol extraction.

or (ii) Place the gel on transparent film (e.g. Saran Wrap) and place this on a TLC plate impregnated with fluorescent indicator. The DNA will absorb short-wave (260 nm) u.v. light and appear as dark bands against a fluorescent background. The short-wave u.v. light may cause some nicking of the DNA.

Each DNA fragment of interest should be excised in the minimum volume of gel and put in a tightly-stoppered tube (e.g. Sarstedt 55.516, 13 mm × 100 mm). Crush the gel slice to a lumpy paste (too fine crushing causes too much acrylamide to be released). Add 4 ml Gel Elution Buffer (Section VI.A), cap the tube and agitate at 40–50°C for 16 h.

Centrifuge the tube, take the supernatant and filter it under pressure through a Millipore HA 0.45-μm filter (or equivalent) into a 20-ml centrifuge tube. The filtration is best done using a syringe and filter holder rather than by negative pressure, as there is SDS in the buffer. Wash the gel fragments in a further 1 ml of Gel Elution Buffer, vortex and centrifuge; filter and pool the supernatant with the earlier filtrate.

Add 10 ml 2-butanol. Vortex to mix the phases; centrifuge briefly and discard the top phase. Repeat until the lower aqueous phase is 200–500 μl. (If it disappears completely—add water to regenerate it.) Transfer the concentrated DNA solution to a 1.5-ml microfuge tube, and precipitate the DNA with three volumes ethanol at −70°C for 5 min. Centrifuge and resuspend the pellet in 300 μl of 0.3 M sodium acetate, add 600 μl ethanol and chill at −70°C. Centrifuge, wash the pellet in 95% ethanol and dry under vacuum.

Resuspend the pellet in 200 μl TE buffer (Section VI.A) and store at −20°C. Ignoring losses, 1 μl of this solution contains fragment DNA from 1 μg of plasmid DNA.

2. Preparation of labelled DNA

Digests of bulk-prepared DNA should be carried out on a small scale to determine which enzymes give the optimum number and location of cleavage sites. Enzymes generating fragments with 5′ terminal extensions are ideal in that such fragments can be 5′ or 3′ end-labelled with good efficiency. The ideal pattern is one with fragments between 200 and 800 nucleotide pairs, with no comigrating fragments.

Mix:
    10 μl bulk-prepared fragment
    2.5 μl 10 × RE buffer (see supplier's recommendation)
    10 μl water
    2.5–5 units restriction enzyme (in 2.5 μl).

Incubate for 3 h at the appropriate temperature.
Add 70 μl water, 5 μl 0.25 M EDTA and 50 μl phenol.
Vortex and centrifuge to separate the phases.
Discard the bottom layer.
Add 10 μl 3 M sodium acetate and 250 μl of ethanol.
Chill, centrifuge and discard supernatant.
Resuspend the precipitate in 50 μl 0.5 M sodium acetate and repeat the ethanol precipitation.
Ethanol-wash and dry the pellet as before.

The DNA is now ready for 5′ or 3′ end-labelling. It may be useful to resuspend the DNA in water and dry it down in aliquots containing 10 pmol of fragment ends. For 5′ end-labelling the number of pmol of fragment ends must be known. Simple formulae for this are: number of *pmol* fragment ends

$$= \frac{2x.n}{y}$$

or

$$= \frac{3\cdot4x.n}{z}$$

Where x is the number of *micrograms* of original of plasmid used; y is the size of the original plasmid in *megadaltons*; z is the size of the original plasmid in *kilobase* pairs and n is the number of fragments in the restriction digest to be labelled.

The calculations are approximate and ignore losses, giving a beneficial underestimate of the number of pmol of ends to be labelled.

(a) *5′ end-labelling (from Weaver and Weissmann, 1979)*

For an aliquot of 10 pmol of fragment ends:
Redissolve DNA in 17 μl water.
Add: 3 μl 10 × phosphatase buffer (Section VI.B)
10 μl calf intestinal phosphatase (Boehringer, diluted to four units per microlitre).
Incubate at 37 C for 60 min.
Heat at 65 C for 60 min to inactivate the enzyme.
Add 5 μl 10 × kinase buffer (Section VI.B).
Use this mixture to dissolve 100–150 μCi (γ-^{32}P) ATP (5000 Ci mmol^{-1}; 20–30 pmol) recently dried from ethanol (do not leave the label in the dry state for more than 30 min).
Add 5–10 units T4 polynucleotide kinase and water to 50 μl.
Incubate at 37 C for 10–60 min.
Add 150 μl water and 10 μl 0.25 M EDTA.
Either add 20 μl 3 M sodium acetate and 500 μl ethanol.

Chill, centrifuge, discard the (very radioactive!) supernatant, ethanol-wash the precipitate, and dry under vacuum.
Redissolve the DNA in 20 μl water.
Or phenol-extract (100 μl phenol) to remove the kinase and do two rounds of ethanol precipitation if a second restriction cleavage is to be performed prior to

separation of the labelled ends. [The specific radioactivity of the (γ-^{32}P)ATP used above is a good compromise between obtaining a high specific radioactivity of labelling and driving the reaction with a sufficiently high concentration of ATP to be above the K_m for the enzyme and to provide a sufficient excess molar ratio of ATP to ends.]

(b) *3' end-labelling*

The most straightforward procedure for labelling the 3' ends of double-stranded DNA fragments is the end-repair of 5' terminal extensions with (α-^{32}P)dNTPs and DNA polymerase I (large fragment). As a number of enzymes generating DNA fragments with 5' terminal extensions now exist (Table III), only this method will be described. Other methods are described by Maxam and Gilbert (1980) and Tu and Cohen (1980). DNA polymerase I (large fragment) is normally used for these end-repair labelling reactions as it contains no 5' exonuclease activity. T4 DNA polymerase (from bacteriophage T4-infected *E. coli*) can be used for similar reasons, and has the advantage of a relatively higher 3' exonuclease activity which will convert 3' terminal extensions into fully base-paired termini. Fully base-paired termini can be 3' end-labelled using the combined 3' exonuclease and polymerase activities of T4 DNA polymerase to replace the terminal nucleotide with its α-^{32}P-labelled equivalent. This turnover labelling gives much lower specific radioactivities than end-repair labelling.

The choice of labelled nucleotides depends on the termini to be labelled, e.g. only dCTP and dGTP are required to fill in termini generated by *Hpa*II or *Taq*I, and only dGTP is required to label a *Hae*III digest by turnover.

For an aliquot of 10 pmol of fragment ends:
Dry down 20 μCi of each (α-^{32}P)dNTP required (400–1000 Ci mmol^{-1}; 20–50 pmol).
Resuspend the radioactive label in 45 μl water.
Add this to the precipitated DNA.
Redissolve the DNA fragments.
Add 5 μl 10 × R buffer (Section VI.A) and one unit of DNA polymerase I (large fragment).
Incubate at 12–16 °C for 2 h.
Add 150 μl water and 5 μl 0.25 M EDTA (to stop the enzyme and to minimize precipitation of unincorporated triphosphates).
Either add 20 μl 3 M sodium acetate and 500 μl of ethanol.
Chill, centrifuge and discard the radioactive supernatant.
Ethanol-wash and dry the pellet.
Or phenol-extract (100 μl phenol) to remove the polymerase and do two rounds of ethanol precipitation if a second restriction enzyme cleavage is to be performed prior to separation of the labelled ends.

(c) *Isolation of DNA fragments labelled at one end*

The first step in this procedure is often the isolation of single fragments labelled at both ends. If the number of fragments is small and the fragments are well resolved, this first step can be omitted. The isolation of these fragments is performed as described in Section II.A.2.(c)(i) for the isolation of subfragments after secondary cleavage with a restriction enzyme.

The labelled ends of a fragment can be separated by secondary cleavage or strand separation. For smaller fragments (< 500 bp) strand separation should be attempted, as it has the advantage that overlapping sequence from both strands can be obtained, and about 90% of such fragments will strand-separate satisfactorily. Strand separation will often work on longer fragments.

Secondary cleavage with restriction enzymes is best performed by splitting the labelled DNA into two aliquots and cutting these with different enzymes, each cleaving near one end. This obviates the problem that secondary cleavage may remove a small central region of the fragment, which would not be labelled and may not therefore be included in the composite sequence of the fragment; and it also allows overlapping sequence from both strands to be obtained. Restriction endonucleases with hexanucleotide recognition sequences are less likely than those with tetranucleotide sequences to cleave the DNA fragment in several places and to generate central unlabelled fragments.

(i) **Isolation of subfragments after secondary cleavage (purification of single fragments)**

Redissolve labelled DNA in 20 μl water.

Add 5 μl Native loading buffer and mix well.

Load the sample into one slot (1 cm × 0.15 cm) on a 40-cm long slab-gel (5% acrylamide; 30:1 cross-linking) and run at 600 volts for 2–6 h in TBE buffer. (The run conditions can be based on earlier analytical digests.)

Remove one glass plate, leaving the gel on the other, and cover the gel with Saran Wrap transparent film. Label the gel with either luminous paint or radioactive ink markers sufficient to show in a short exposure time.

In the dark room put an X-ray film on the gel and leave, under pressure, for 2–20 min to expose (Section IV.B). A second exposure should be taken if a permanent record is required. Develop the film according to the manufacturer's instructions.

Identify the bands of interest and cut the photographic image from the film. Align the film with the luminous or radioactive markers and use it as a template to excise the DNA fragments in a small volume of gel. A much smaller amount of DNA is eluted here than in the bulk preparation of DNA fragments, and the protocol is therefore different.

Lightly crush the gel slice with a glass rod and elute the DNA at 37°C overnight in 0.6 ml Gel Elution Buffer in a stoppered tube.

Vortex the tube, and decant into a 1-ml plastic pipette tip plugged with siliconized glass wool, resting in a 12 mm × 75 mm polycarbonate or siliconized glass tube.

Briefly re-extract the gel paste with 0.2 ml Gel Elution Buffer, and add to the pipette tip. Recover all the buffer by brief centrifugation. A hand Geiger Monitor can be used to determine the efficiency of recovery.

Extract the eluate with 2-butanol (2 ml) to reduce the volume, centrifuge and discard the top phase. Transfer the bottom phase to a 1.5-ml microfuge tube, add 20 μg tRNA and three volumes ethanol, chill and centrifuge to precipitate the DNA.

Unless the next step is to be strand separation of purified DNA fragments, the precipitate should be redissolved in 50 μl of 0.3 M sodium acetate and precipitated with three volumes ethanol, washed in 95% ethanol and dried. Strand separation can follow a single precipitation.

(ii) Strand separation of DNA fragments

Redissolve labelled DNA in 25 μl TE buffer.

Add 25 μl 2 × Strand Separation Buffer (Section VI.B).

Heat at 90°C for 2 min.

Quickly chill to 0°C.

Without allowing the sample to warm up, load it into one slot (1 cm × 0.15 cm) in a 40-cm long strand separation gel (5% acrylamide, 0.083% bis-acrylamide in 0.55 × TBE; note that 60:1 cross-linking and 50 mM Tris-borate conditions are important).

Run gel at 200 volts (maximum) for 10–20 h.

The DNA is detected by autoradiography and eluted as described in Section II.A.2.(c)(i). Two ethanol precipitations should be performed.

Multiple loadings are required to separate the strands of fragments of different sizes. (Remember to load the largest fragments first!) On these gels xylene cyanol comigrates with strands approximately 200 nucleotides long.

The separate strands form intrastrand secondary structure under the conditions used, and separation is achieved according to small differences in secondary structure in each strand. Heating would denature the strands, and low voltage gradients and lower ionic strength buffer helps prevent this. Some renaturation of the double-stranded DNA may occur and be visible on the gel as a third band of different intensity to the other two. Note that the appearance of the sample entering the gel should not be cause for concern.

B. Modification and cleavage reactions

The procedures described here are those preferred at present. They are simple to perform in parallel, with the same incubation temperatures and many steps in common, and they give products which are salt-free and can easily be analysed on thin acrylamide gels. Other procedures are described in Maxam and Gilbert (1980) and are listed in Table IV. Details of buffers and solutions are given in Section VI.B.

TABLE IV

Alternative procedures for the chemical Method[a]

Cleavage	Base modification	Base displacement	Stand scission	Reference
G > A	Dimethyl sulphate	Heat, pH 7	NaOH	[b]
A > G	Dimethyl sulphate	Acid	NaOH	[b]
C + T	Hydrazine	Piperidine	Piperidine	[b]
C	Hydrazine + salt	Piperidine	Piperidine	[b]
G	Dimethyl sulphate	Piperidine	Piperidine	[10a]
G + A	Acid	Acid	Piperidine	[11a]
A > C	Sodium hydroxide	Piperidine	Piperidine	[14a]
G > A	Dimethyl sulphate	Heat, p H7	Piperidine	[15a]
G	Methylene blue	Piperidine	Piperidine	[c]
T	Osmium tetroxide	Piperidine	Piperidine	[c]

[a] Adapted from Maxam and Gilbert (1980). The numbers in the reference column refer to the procedure number in that paper.
[b] Original procedures from Maxam and Gilbert (1977).
[c] From Friedmann and Brown (1978).

Note that some of the reagents are dangerous and great care should be taken with them. All operations involving these reagents should be performed in a fume hood, and appropriate safety clothing should be worn.

Dimethyl sulphate is mutagenic, causes burns and is poisonous. It can be inactivated by excess sodium hydroxide.

Hydrazine is mutagenic, causes burns and is poisonous. It is a highly reactive reducing agent. It can be inactivated by saturation with ferric chloride.

Piperidine is poisonous and highly flammable.

1. Setting up the reactions

Resuspend the ^{32}P-labelled DNA in 40 μl water.
Label four 1.5-ml microfuge tubes "G", "A", "T" and "C".
Keep the tubes at 0 C and add to them:
  G: 5 μl ^{32}P-DNA + 200 μl DMS buffer
  A: 10 μl ^{32}P-DNA
  T: 10 μl ^{32}P-DNA + 15 μl water
  C: 5 μl ^{32}P-DNA + 20 μl 4 M sodium acetate
(The unused 10 μl ^{32}P-DNA can be kept at -20 C for use in case of accident!)
Fresh aliquots of the following solutions should be prepared each day:
1. Hydrazine and DMS is removed from the stock bottles and kept in the fume hood.
2. 88% formic acid is chilled to 0°C.
3. tRNA is added to the DMS stop solution and to the HZ stop solution (Section VI.B).

2. Base-specific modification reactions

These must be followed through without stopping. The reactions are identical from the first addition of ethanol.

Times marked (*) are approximate, and can be varied to suit the length of the sequence required and the efficacy of the reagents. Incubations at 20 °C should be done in a water bath to ensure rapid temperature equilibration.

"G" reaction

Add 1 μl of dimethyl sulphate to chilled tube "G" from 1. *Do this using a mechanical pipetting device in a fume hood.*
Cap the tube, mix gently by flicking the tube, and incubate at 20 °C for 6 min(*).
Return the tube to 0 °C and add 50 μl cold DMS Stop solution.
Cap the tube and vortex.
Add 750 μl ethanol.
Cap the tube and invert several times to mix.
Chill at − 70 °C for 5 min.
Centrifuge for 5 min at 4 °C in a Microfuge.
Remove the supernatant (and *carefully discard into 5 M sodium hydroxide* to destroy mutagenic dimethyl sulphate).
Resuspend the pellet by vortexing in 200 μl 0.3 M sodium acetate.
Add 600 μl ethanol.
Chill at − 70 °C for 5 min or longer.
(If desired, the reaction can be put at − 20 °C at this stage.)

"A" reaction (Actually A + G reaction; Skryabin et al., 1978)

Add 25 μl chilled (0 °C) 88% formic acid to chilled tube "A" from 1.
Cap the tube, mix gently by inverting the tube and incubate at 20 °C for 10 min(*).
Return the tube to 0 °C and add 200 μl HZ Stop solution.
Cap the tube and vortex.
Add 750 μl ethanol.
Cap the tube and invert several times to mix.
Chill at − 70 °C for 5 min.
Centrifuge for 5 min at 4 °C in a Microfuge.
Remove the supernatant (and discard: non-mutagenic).
Resuspend the pellet by vortexing in 200 μl 0.3 M sodium acetate.
Add 600 μl ethanol.
Chill at − 70 °C for 5 min or longer.
(If desired, the reaction can be put at − 20 °C at this stage.)

"T" and "C" reactions

These reactions (actually "T + C" and "C" reactions) differ only in the addition of sodium acetate (to "C" in Section II.B.1) to suppress the reaction of T residues. Sodium chloride was used in earlier protocols but tended to coprecipitate with the DNA.

Add 30 μl hydrazine to chilled tubes "T" and "C" from Section II.B.1. *Do this using a mechanical pipetting device in a fume hood.*
Cap the tube and mix gently by flicking the tube, and incubate at 20 °C for 10 min (*).

Return the tube to 0°C and add 200 μl cold HZ Stop solution.
Cap the tube and vortex.
Add 750 μl ethanol.
Cap the tube and invert several times to mix.
Chill at −70°C for 5 min.
Centrifuge for 5 min at 4°C in a Microfuge.
Remove the supernatant (and *carefully discard into 3 M ferric chloride* to destroy mutagenic hydrazine).
Resuspend the pellet by vortexing in 200 μl 0.3 M sodium acetate.
Add 600 μl ethanol.
Chill at −70°C for 5 min or longer.
(If desired, the reaction can be put at −20°C at this stage.)

3. Cleavage reactions

All four base-specific modification reactions can now be treated in parallel easily. A good vacuum pump (or a Speed-Vac system) is essential to the efficient removal of piperidine following these reactions.

Centrifuge the tubes for 5 min at 4°C in a Microfuge.
Carefully remove and discard the supernatant.
Gently add 0.5 ml ethanol without disturbing the pellet, centrifuge for 2 min and carefully remove and discard the supernatant.
Dry the pellet under vacuum.
Resuspend the DNA in 100 μl 1.0 M piperidine by vortexing.
Firmly cap each tube and almost fully immerse in a 90°C water bath.
Cover with a heavy weight (e.g. lead brick).
Incubate for 20 min.
Put the tubes at 0°C for 5 min.
Centrifuge briefly to collect condensate.
Poke holes in tube cap with heated needle (or cover with parafilm and puncture).
Freeze samples at −70°C.
Lyophilize samples to dryness.
Resuspend each sample in 100 μl water, vortex, freeze and lyophilize.
Resuspend each sample in 25 μl water, vortex, freeze and lyophilize.

The samples are now ready for suspension in the formamide–dye mix for electrophoresis. This is done immediately before heat denaturation of the sample and loading of the gel. If the samples are to be kept for a time before the gel is run, they should be stored dry at −20°C.

Conditions for forming, loading and running the sequencing gels are given in Section IV.

III. Procedures for the M13 cloning/chain-termination method

A. Cloning in bacteriophage M13 derivatives

1. Maintenance and growth of bacteria and bacteriophage

It is essential for the M13-cloning/chain-termination method that the M13mp derivatives used as vector produce the α-peptide of β-galactosidase and that the E. coli (F⁺) host strains produce the ω-peptide (Section I.B.3). The ω-peptide coding sequence is carried on an F′-plasmid which also carries the *pro* marker; this plasmid can be selected and used in a Δ(*pro, lac*) host. The first steps in a series of M13-cloning experiments are the testing of the bacteriophage and bacterial strains.

E. coli K12 strains 71–18, JM101 or JM103 can be maintained as stab-cultures or as lyophilized cultures. To select for cells containing the F′-episome, the strain is streaked out on Minimal A–glucose plates. Cells can be maintained on minimal medium for one to two weeks. (Details of media, buffers, and other solutions are given in Section VI.C.)

The F′-episome is readily lost from the strains, and cannot be reacquired by mating in liquid culture of strains JM101 and JM103 in which the episome is transfer-deficient. It is important that all liquid cultures are freshly inoculated with discrete colonies from the minimal medium.

All bacteriophage growth in liquid culture is done in 2 × YT medium. Solid media are 1 × YT. Top-agar for p.f.u. assays is used in 3-ml aliquots and the indicators for detecting the lac⁺ phenotype (IPTG and X-gal) are used at 30 μl of solution per 3 ml of top-agar.

Bacteriophage M13 does not lyse its host and is therefore very easy to maintain and grow. Stocks can be kept for long periods as a suspension in 2 × YT medium at 4°C. We normally remove cells and cell debris by centrifugation, and filter the lysate through a HAWP 0.45-μm membrane filter. Some workers freeze the M13 lysate at −20°C. The phage cannot be stored over chloroform. A stock of M13mp derivative bacteriophage is easily obtained by taking a single blue plaque from the lac-selective medium (IPTG + X-Gal), and incubating this plaque with shaking at 37°C for 6–8 h in 5 ml of 2 × YT medium. The infected cells will grow and a phage titre of approximately 10^{12} ml^{-1} will be achieved. The culture is then briefly centrifuged and filtered into a sterile bottle.

Throughout the procedures below, the use of the vector M13mp7 will be assumed to be used, and the procedures will apply to other M13mp derivatives unless specifically noted. The vectors M13mp8 and M13mp9 do offer a number of advantages (Section III.C), and are superseding M13mp7 as vectors of choice. (These and other vectors are described in Section I.B.3 and Table I.)

2. Vector DNA

(a) Preparation of vector DNA

Take a single colony of *E. coli* JM101 from minimal medium and grow it up in a small volume of $2 \times$ YT medium at 37°C with shaking until $A_{550} = 0.6$.

Dilute bacteriophage M13mp7 stock to approximately 10^3 p.f.u. ml^{-1} in YT medium.

To 3 ml molten YT-top-agar at 45°C add 0.2 ml *E. coli* JM101 ($A_{550} = 0.6$), 0.1 ml diluted phage, 30 μl IPTG solution and 30 μl X-gal solution. Mix and pour onto YT-agar plate, agitate so that plate is uniformly covered. Allow agar to set and incubate the plate inverted at 37°C until the colour has developed (about 9 h).

With a sterile toothpick, Pasteur pipette or similar sterile object, touch a blue plaque that is well-separated from others and transfer it to 1 ml $2 \times$ YT medium. Grow this at 37°C with shaking (300 r/min) for 6–8 h. Meanwhile grow up a 10-ml culture of *E. coli* JM101, from a single colony on minimal medium, until $A_{550} = 0.5$ approximately. Add the *E. coli* JM101 culture and the 1 ml of bacteriophage preparation to 500 ml of prewarmed $2 \times$ YT medium in a 2 l Ehrlenmeyer flask. Shake this vigorously at 37°C for 4 h.

Collect the cells by centrifugation and prepare RFI DNA by a cleared-lysis/dye-buoyant density centrifugation procedure suitable for small *E. coli* plasmids (Chapter 6). Two rounds of dye-buoyant density centrifugation are essential to remove all traces of contaminating chromosomal, single-stranded bacteriophage or other DNA. One litre of culture should yield about 500 μg M13mp7 RFI DNA. This is kept frozen in small aliquots in TE buffer at a concentration of 0.1–1.0 mg ml^{-1}.

(b) Cleavage and testing of vector DNA

Vector DNA must be tested prior to attempting to clone DNA fragments. The exact conditions for cleavage and testing depend on the vector and the restriction enzyme used. Table I lists the M13mp vectors so far available and the restriction enzymes that can be used to linearize the vector and to generate fragments for cloning.

Generally, sufficient linearized vector for a number of cloning experiments is prepared and tested. During subsequent cloning experiments the vector is tested each time to ensure that no spurious colourless plaques are generated in the ligation reactions.

(i) Sticky-end vector (e.g. using EcoRI)

Mix:
  2 μg M13mp7 RF DNA
  2 μl $10 \times$ EcoRI buffer
  water to give a final volume of 20 μl
  3 units EcoRI.
Incubate at 37°C for 1 h.
Heat at 70°C to inactivate the enzyme.
Add 180 μl water (to bring to DNA concentration of 10 ng μl^{-1}).
Store at 4°C.

Test this vector preparation by transformation of competent *E. coli* JM101 (Section III.A.4(c)) to ensure that it gives few plaques (less than 10 per nanogram); and by religation (Section III.A.4(a)) and transformation to ensure that it gives only blue plaques (300–400 per nanogram).

Religation of vector DNA can also be used to determine the correct amounts of T4 DNA ligase to use, if 1 μl of ten-fold serial dilutions of T4 DNA ligase in ligase dilution buffer are used in the assay.

(ii) Blunt-end vector. M13mp7 cleavage with *Hind*II (or *Hinc*II) to generate a vector for fragments with fully base-paired termini is unsatisfactory due to the high frequency ($\sim 10\%$) of colourless plaques formed on religation. All batches of *Hind*II, however carefully prepared, appear to contain a small amount of exonuclease activity.

Blunt-end ligation into an end-repaired *Eco*RI or other such site on M13mp7 has been used in some laboratories. The end-repair causes loss of the lac screen against plaques formed by religated vector, and such plaques are selected against by treating the vector DNA with calf intestinal phosphatase. Self-ligation of the vector should not then occur, and only in the presence of a DNA fragment with 5′ phosphate groups will circularization occur to give high-frequency transforming DNA molecules (Chapter 9). The use of end-repaired, phosphatase-treated vector will not be considered in detail here. Suitable conditions for phosphatase treatment of DNA are given in Section II.A.2(a). Care should be taken to titrate the phosphatase treatment to obtain minimal religation of vector with minimum phosphatase treatment.

The use of *Sma*I-cut M13mp8 or M13mp9 is superseding other methods for cloning blunt-end fragments. The cleavage and religation conditions are essentially the same as for sticky-end vector, but typically about five times the amount of DNA ligase is required.

3. Preparation of insert DNA

The manner of preparation of the insert DNA depends on the sequencing objective. A very small region or a large region of DNA to be sequenced may demand different approaches. Large sequences may be cloned in a vector of known sequence (e.g. pBR322), the whole chimeric plasmid subcloned in M13, and the subclones tested for homology with pBR322 by T-channel screening (Section III.B.3). Alternatively, and for smaller sequences, the DNA to be sequenced may be prepared in bulk as described in Section II.A.1.

DNA fragments can be prepared by restriction enzyme digestion; or by non-specific nuclease digestion (Anderson, 1981); or by sonication. Other treatments such as end-repair and/or the addition of oligonucleotide linkers may be desirable or necessary. The fragments may be fractionated by electrophoresis, by chromatography or by precipitation with polyethylene glycol (Lis, 1980). The number of possible permutations of methods is large. Some of the common methods are described below. References to other methods are given.

(a) *Restriction fragments*
Digest 1–3 μg of DNA according to supplier's recommendations. Usually the enzyme will not interfere with subsequent end-repair and end-labelling reactions, but routinely the reaction is heated at 70°C for 10 min to inactivate any contaminating phosphatases, etc.

If the fragments are to be cloned directly, phenol-extract and then ether-extract the DNA. Precipitate the DNA by adding 0.1 volume 3 M sodium acetate, 2.5 volumes ethanol, chill at −70°C for 5 min and centrifuge in a microfuge. Wash the pellet in ethanol and dry under vacuum. Resuspend the DNA in 20 μl water. Store at −20°C.

(b) *Restriction fragments, end-repaired*
Fragments with 5′ or 3′ terminal extensions which cannot be cloned directly into M13mp7, 8 or 9 (e.g. *Hinf* I- or *Hha*I-generated fragments) can be converted into blunt-ended fragments.

To 20 μl digest (1–3 μg DNA fragments) from Section (a), add:
2 μl dNTP mix (1.25 mM dCTP, 1.25 mM dTTP, 1.25 mM dGTP, 1.25 mM dATP in water).
0.2 unit T4 DNA polymerase (or Klenow polymerase).
Incubate at room temperature for 10 min.
Heat at 70°C for 10 min to inactivate the enzyme.
Extract with phenol.
Ethanol precipitate as described in Section III.A.3 (a).
Resuspend in 20 μl 0.3 M sodium acetate and ethanol-precipitate.
Ethanol-wash the pellet and dry under vacuum.
Resuspend the DNA in 20 μl water.
Store at −20°C.

Ethanol precipitation will not remove all the deoxyribonucleoside tri-phosphates, and these may inhibit the subsequent ligation reaction. This inhibition is not usually sufficient to cause problems, but if difficulty with ligations is encountered the triphosphates should be removed by chromatography on Sephadex (Section III.A.3(c)) as a precautionary measure.

End-repaired fragments can be cloned in *Sma*I-cut M13mp8 or 9. Care should be taken that two end-repaired fragments are not cloned together in the same vector molecule. Such artefactual joins are not easily recognized and eliminated; for example, the sequence 5′-GATTACTC-3′ may result from two end-repaired *Hinf* I fragments, or may exist in the original DNA (and is not a *Hinf* I site). End-to-end cloning problems can be eliminated by size-fractionation of the DNA; or minimized by adding linkers or by choosing conditions in which only low frequencies of recombinant formation occurs.

(c) *Restriction fragments plus linkers*
Newer vectors and methods have displaced the addition of linkers as the

routine method for generating insert DNA. However, this method is very useful for (i) batches of DNA ligase which do not catalyse blunt-end ligation at high efficiency under the conditions normally used and (ii) avoiding the problem of end-to-end cloning of end-repaired (or other) DNA fragments. The high molar concentration of oligonucleotide linkers drives the reaction in (i), and competes with end-to-end joining in (ii).

The DNA fragments may be radioactively labelled to allow easy identification during separation from the cut linkers at the end of the reactions. Fragments with 5′ terminal extensions can be labelled by including a suitable (α-^{32}P) dNTP in the end-repair reaction in Section III.A.3(b). Fragments with 3′ extensions or fully base-paired termini can be labelled by the exchange of the 3′ nucleotide by its α-^{32}P-labelled derivative as described in Section II.A.2(b). For both end-repair and exchange labelling, the appropriate deoxyribonucleoside triphosphate in the dNTP mix in Section III.A.3(b) should be replaced by 5 μCi (>400 Ci mmol^{-1}) of its α-^{32}P-labelled derivative. The DNA is then phenol-extracted, ether-extracted and ethanol-precipitated.

EcoRI octanucleotide linkers (GGAATTCC) or similar linkers are phosphorylated.

Mix:
    2 μl (1 μg; 0.02 unit) EcoRI linkers
    1 μl 500 mM Tris-Cl, pH 7.5, 100 mM MgCl$_2$
    1 μl 100 mM DTT
    1 μl 5 mM rATP
    4 μl water
    1 μl T4 polynucleotide kinase (4 units).
Incubate at 37°C for 60 min.
Store at -20°C.
Take up the precipitated DNA fragments from Section III.A.3(b) or from the labelling reaction in 4 μl linker mixture.
Add 1 μl 2 mM ATP, 0.7 mM spermidine
    0.1 unit T4 DNA ligase.
Incubate at 16°C for 16 h in a sealed glass capíllary.
Heat at 70°C for 10 min.
Add 15 μl water.
    2.5 μl 10 × RI buffer
    20 units EcoRI (approx 5 μl, or adjust buffer used).
Incubate at 37°C for 5–6 h.
Add 1 μl 0.25 M EDTA.
Phenol-extract, ether-extract twice and blow off excess ether on an air-line.

Either fractionate the fragments by size [Section III.A.3(e)]
or load the sample onto a column of Sephadex G-75 (0.3 cm × 20 cm in a 1-ml disposable pipette) pre-equilibrated with G-75 high salt buffer. Elute the sample in the same buffer, monitor the radioactive polynucleotide peak with a Geiger monitor and collect. Add 2.5 volumes ethanol to precipitate the DNA. Chill (-70°C) for 5 min and collect the precipitate by centrifugation in a microfuge. Ethanol-wash and dry the DNA under vacuum. Resuspend the DNA in 20 μl water. Store at -20°C.

(d) *Sonicated DNA*

Sonication offers advantages over restriction endonuclease digestion in that the fragments are truly random. It is important therefore that the fragments are sized before cloning in order to prevent errors due to cloning several small fragments in one replicon. The fragments are end-repaired to produce fully base-paired termini.

The sonication conditions required to give fragments of the desired size range must be determined empirically.

Take 2–4 μg DNA in 200 μl TE buffer at 0°C.

Sonicate for, say, two to eight times 5 s at 15 watts with intervening 10 s period of cooling.

Ethanol-precipitate the DNA (200 μl 3 M sodium acetate, 500 μl of ethanol, chill at −70°C and centrifuge).

End-repair the DNA as described in Section (b) above.

Size fractionate the DNA as described in Section (e).

(e) *Selection of DNA fragments*

In some experiments a specific fragment of DNA may be sequenced, in others DNA of a specific size range may be sequenced. In both cases the DNA can be fractionated by electrophoresis, identified and eluted. For size fractionation polyethylene glycol precipitation (Lis, 1980) can be used.

For large sequencing projects it is more efficient if large random DNA fragments are sequenced initially, and specific fragments are isolated to complete the sequence. Specific fragments may still need to be isolated even with the newer non-random kilobase sequencing methods (Hong, 1982; Barnes *et al.*, 1982).

(i) **Electrophoretic separation**

Resuspend the DNA in 50–100 μl TE buffer. Add 0.1 volume Native Loading buffer. For large DNA fragments:

Load the DNA into the well of a horizontal 2% agarose gel in ACE buffer. Ensure that the sample fills the well so that the maximum cross-sectional area of the gel is used. Electrophorese at 5–10 volts per centimetre, with a suitable restriction digest as a size marker in an adjacent channel.

Identify the fragment of interest or the appropriate size range of DNA by u.v. illumination. Excise the gel containing the DNA, and place in a dialysis sac with ACE buffer. Electrophorese at 100 volts until all the DNA has left the gel (check using u.v. lamp).

Reverse the polarity for 1–2 min. Remove the buffer.

Phenol extract (removes ethidium bromide).

Ethanol precipitate.

Resuspend the DNA in 100 μl 100 mM NaCl, 1 mM EDTA, 10 mM Tris-HCl at pH 7.9.

Load onto a pre-equilibrated DEAE column, approximately 0.3 ml packed volume in a Pasteur pipette (plugged with siliconized glass wool). Wash with several column volumes of buffer. Wash with 1.0 ml 400 mM NaCl, 1 mM EDTA, 10 mM Tris-HCl, pH 7.9, and elute the DNA with 600 mM NaCl, 1 mM EDTA, 10 mM Tris-HCl, pH 7.9.

Collect approximately 0.3 ml fractions and ethanol-precipitate the DNA.

(The fraction containing the DNA can be identified by gel electrophoresis of a small aliquot of each fraction. Experience subsequently allows the fraction to be predicted.)

For small DNA fragments:

Load the DNA onto an 8% acrylamide slab-gel (30:1 cross-linking) and run in TBE buffer at 5–15 volts per centimetre. (Below 6% acrylamide gel contaminants elute with the DNA and these may inhibit subsequent ligation or any DNA polymerase-dependent steps.)

Stain the gel (15 min) in 0.5 μg ml^{-1} ethidium bromide in water.

Excise the gel slice containing the fragment(s) of interest under u.v. illumination.

Crush and extract the DNA as described for end-labelled fragments in the chemical method (Section II.B.2).

Phenol-extract the DNA and ethanol-precipitate.

This method works well for fragments less than 400 nucleotides long.

(ii) Polyethylene-glycol precipitation

Polyethylene-glycol (PEG) precipitation can be used to precipitate DNA fragments in a given size range. The exact PEG concentrations to give DNA of the correct size range should be calculated from the data given by Lis (1980).

Resuspend the DNA in 20–60 μl 0.5 M NaCl, 10 mM Tris-HCl, pH 7.4, 10 mM EDTA (i.e. to approximately 50 μg ml^{-1}). Add 50% (w/w) polyethylene glycol 6000 in 0.5 M NaCl to the desired concentration to precipitate all DNA above a certain size. Incubate the mixture at 0°C for 12 h for DNA fragments greater than 500 bp, or for 1 h for fragments less than 500 bp.

Collect the precipitate by centrifugation for 5 min in a microfuge.

Remove the supernatant for further PEG precipitation if a narrow size range is required.

Recentrifuge the pellet containing DNA fragments of the desired size range and remove the last traces of supernatant. Resuspend the DNA in 20 μl water.

4. Ligation and transformation

(a) The ligation reaction

If the concentration of DNA fragments is known use a three-fold molar excess of fragments to vector. Otherwise try a range of different fragment concentrations.

Mix in a drawn-out capillary or 400-μl reaction tube:
   1 μl linearized vector (10 ng; approximately 2 fmol)
   1–5 μl DNA fragments (approximately 6 fmol)
   1 μl 10 mM ATP
   1 μl 10 × C buffer
   1 μl autoclaved gelatin (1 mg ml^{-1})
   1 μl T4 DNA ligase (diluted as determined empirically)
   water to give a final volume of 10 μl.

Incubate at 14°C for 3–12 h for sticky-end ligations, or for 24 h for blunt-end ligation.

A control ligation with no added DNA fragments must *always* be included in a set of ligation reactions to ensure that no spurious colourless plaques are formed. Occasionally, a control reaction with 10 ng of RFI vector DNA (CCC), and one with linearized vector but no ligase should be performed to test the efficiency of transformation, and to test the degree of linearization of the vector.

(b) Preparation of competent cells

Take a single colony of *E. coli* JM101 from minimal medium and grow up in 20 ml 2 × YT at 37°C with shaking.

When A_{550} = approximately 0.3, centrifuge the cells at 4°C for 2 min at 10 000 × **g** in a sterile tube.

Resuspend the pellet in 10 ml sterile 50 mM $CaCl_2$ at 0°C.

Leave for 20 min at 0°C then pellet the cells again.

Resuspend the cells in 2 ml sterile 50 mM $CaCl_2$.

The cells can be used immediately or kept at 0°C for up to 24 h. The cells may be used after several days, but their transformation efficiency declines after 24 h (Dagert and Ehrlich, 1979; Chapter 4).

(c) Transformation and plaque assay

Dispense 0.2 ml aliquots of competent cells in sterile 1.5-ml reaction tubes and add part or all of the ligation mix. For blunt-end ligations use all the ligation mix, and for sticky-end ligations use about one-fifth of the ligation mix, depending on the DNA preparation used.

Mix and incubate at 0°C for 40 min.

Heat shock the cells at 42°C for 2 min.

To 3 ml molten YT top agar at 42°C, add 30 μl IPTG, 30 μl X-gal solution, 0.2 ml exponentially growing JM101 and the transformed cells.

Mix and pour onto a dry YT agar plate (there should be no surface liquid and the plate should be at room temperature). Spread the top-agar by gently tilting and shaking the plate, and allow to set. Invert the plate and incubate at 37°C for 9–24 h.

5. Preparation of templates

Templates should be prepared within a few days of the plaque assay, and 24 templates can be conveniently prepared at one time using a 12-place microfuge.

In early experiments template should also be prepared from a blue plaque for use as a control template in the chain-termination sequencing.

(i) Add a drop of late exponential phase culture of JM101 to 25 ml 2 × YT. Dispense into 1-ml aliquots in culture tubes or universal bottles.

Using a sterile toothpick, Pasteur pipette or similar object, transfer a different colourless plaque into each 1-ml aliquot. Choose plaques well-separated from others and take care to touch only a single plaque.

Shake (300 r/min) at 37°C for 5–6 h. Longer incubations under these conditions may give poor template preparations due to host cell lysis.

(An alternative procedure is to add infected cells from the plaque directly to 1 ml of

$2 \times$ YT medium, with no added uninfected JM101. The 1-ml aliquots are kept at 4°C until late evening then shaken at 37°C overnight (maximum 16 h).)

(ii) Transfer the 1-ml culture to a 1.5-ml microfuge tube and centrifuge for 5 min at $10\ 000 \times$ **g**.

Take approximately 0.8 ml supernatant into another microfuge tube and add 0.2 ml 2.5 M NaCl, 20% PEG 6000. Mix well and leave at room temperature for 15 min.

Centrifuge for 5 min at $10\ 000 \times$ **g**.

Decant the supernatant and centrifuge the pellet for 1 min.

Remove ALL TRACES of the PEG supernatant using a drawn-out capillary or a piece of tissue. The PEG pellet should be visible.

(iii) Dissolve the pellet in 100 μl TE buffer and add 50 μl phenol (buffer-saturated). Vortex for 10 s, leave at room temperature for 10 min, vortex again and centrifuge for 1 min.

Transfer the upper aqueous layer to a new microfuge tube, using a drawn-out capillary or an automatic pipette.

Extract with 0.5 ml diethyl ether (water-saturated) to remove the phenol.

Ethanol precipitate the DNA (10 μl 3 M sodium acetate, 250 μl ethanol; -70°C for 5 min; centrifuge for 5 min and ethanol-wash the pellet).

Dry the pellet under vacuum.

Redissolve in 25 μl TE buffer.

Store the template DNA at -20°C. The presence of single-stranded DNA can be tested by running 2.5 μl on a 1% agarose gel stained with ethidium bromide (do not use xylene cyanol FF marker dye).

B. Chain-termination sequencing

1. Preparation of primer DNA

(a) Several universal primers are available for sequencing in M13mp derivatives. The simplest to obtain are the synthetic primers available commercially (from suppliers in Section VI). These yield good results if carefully titrated against a typical template preparation. Too little primer gives very weak autoradiograms; too much primer causes extra bands to appear on the autoradiogram making the sequence interpretation difficult.

(b) Double-stranded cloned primers are available. The plasmid pHM232 (Heidecker *et al.*, 1980) contains a 96 bp primer cloned in the *Eco*RI site of pBR325. The plasmid is prepared by standard dye–buoyant density centrifugation, and digested with *Eco*RI.

As pBR325 shows no extensive sequence homology with M13mp7, the primer fragment need not be separated from the vector DNA. We have sequenced pBR322 DNA fragments cloned in M13mp7 with no adverse interaction of pBR325 sequences in spite of the fact that pBR325 contains all of pBR322 (Bolivar, 1978).

The complete 96 bp primer gives a strong artefact band on the sequencing gel

(Schreier and Cortese, 1979; Sanger *et al.*, 1980). This is probably due to foldback and priming using the 5' end of the strand as template, and it can be avoided by treatment with exonuclease III:

80 μg *Eco*RI-cleaved pHM232 DNA
10 μk 10 × *Exo*III buffer
one unit exonuclease III
in 100 μl total volume.
Mix and incubate at room temperature for 20–30 min.
Heat at 70°C for 10 min to inactivate the enzyme.
Use at 1 μl per sequence without further treatment.

(The exonuclease III treatment should first be tested on a small scale to obtain the correct digestion time. Underdigestion gives a strong artefact band on the autoradiogram; overdigestion gives no bands at all!)

(c) Shorter cloned primers include those in the plasmids: pSP14 (released by *Eco*RI and *Bam*HI) and pSP16 (released by *Eco*RI) as described by Anderson *et al.* (1980). These can be used without exonuclease treatment. For optimal results they are best separated from the vector DNA. This can be done by acrylamide gel electrophoresis as described in Section III.A.3(e). We have prepared the 27-long *Eco*RI/*Eco*RI primer from a recombinant in M13mp2 (S. Anderson, unpublished data) by digestion with *Eco*RI, phenol-extraction, dilution to approximately 100 μg ml^{-1} and centrifugation at 100 000 × **g** overnight. The vector DNA sediments and the primer DNA remains in the supernatant and can be concentrated five-fold by 2-butanol extraction. Use approximately 1 μl per sequence. If the vector DNA is not removed a background ladder in all four channels is generated on the autoradiogram. This is presumably due to nicking of the vector DNA.

(d) Occasionally it may be desirable to use internal primers complementary to the DNA cloned into M13mp7. Such primers can be prepared from RFI DNA of other M13mp7 recombinants or from plasmids, etc. by restriction endonuclease digestion and purification of the primer fragment by gel electrophoresis as described in Section III.A.3(e). These primers can be exonuclease III-treated to obtain sequence internal to the primer, thus allowing useful sequence overlaps to be obtained. The primers should be used at a concentration of approximately 0.5 pmol μl^{-1}.

2. The sequencing reactions

Several sequences can be determined simultaneously.

(a) *Hybridization of primer and template*

The single-stranded template DNA and the primer DNA, whether double-stranded DNA or not, are denatured at 100°C to remove all secondary structure, then reannealed.

To a drawn-out glass capillary add:
    2.5 μl template DNA
    2 μl 10 × R buffer
    1 μl primer DNA
    4.5 μl water.
Mix by gently expelling the contents three times into a siliconized glass tube (50 mm × 13 mm).
Draw the mixture away from the tip of the capillary by gently heating the *top* of capillary until it just seals; the liquid is drawn up as the capillary cools. Seal the tip. Heat at 100°C for 3 min.
Place the capillary in a tube of water at 100°C and allow it to cool to room temperature over 20–30 min. (For internal primers longer than 100 nucleotides, anneal at 67°C for 20 min.) Use immediately.

(b) *The chain-termination reactions*

During the annealing reactions (above) dry down under vacuum 4 μCi of (α^{32}P) dATP (> 400 Ci mmol^{-1}; dATP*) in a siliconized glass tube for each sequence.

Note that errors in timing are not usually critical, whereas errors in volume may well be.

(i) Method 1

Resuspend the dATP* in the primer–template mix.
Add 2 μl to each of four drawn-out capillaries resting tip-down in 50 mm × 13 mm siliconized glass tubes, labelled T, C, G and A.
To capillary T add 1 μl T° mix and 1 μl ddTTP mix.
To capillary C add 1 μl C° mix and 1 μl ddCTP mix.
To capillary G add 1 μl G° mix and 1 μl ddGTP mix.
To capillary A add 1 μl A° mix and 1 μl ddATP mix.
Dilute DNA polymerase I (large fragment) in Klenow diluent to 0.2 unit per litre. Add 1 μl to each tube.
Mix the reagents by gently expelling them from the capillary three times.
Incubate 15 min at room temperature.
Add 1 μl 0.5 mM dATP to each tube. Mix well.
Incubate for 15 min at room temperature, then
either add 5 μl formamide–dye mix to each sample. Mix well, denature the DNA and run on a gel immediately (Section IV)
or freeze the samples at − 20°C
or in the rare cases in which the primer fragment must be removed before running the gel (e.g. for long internal primers), add 0.5 unit of the appropriate restriction endonuclease to each tube, and incubate at the temperature optimum for the enzyme for 10 min prior to adding formamide–dye mix or freezing the sample.

(ii) Method 2

This involves the use of microfuge tubes in place of the capillaries and siliconized glass tubes. Using a 40-place microfuge (e.g. the Eppendorf 5413) up to ten sequences can be done simultaneously.
During the annealing reactions (above) dry down under vacuum four samples of (α-^{32}P) dATP (> 400 Ci mmol^{-1}; dATP*), each containing 1 μCi per sequence (i.e. for ten sequences dry down 4 × 10 μCi dATP*).

Resuspend one sample of label in equal volumes of T mix and dTTP mix to a final concentration of 0.5 μCi μl^{-1} (i.e. for ten sequences resuspend in 10 μl T mix, 10 μl dTTP mix). This is T* mix.
Resuspend the other samples in C and ddCTP, G and ddGTP, A and ddATP mixes, respectively.
Cut the tops off 1.5-ml microfuge tubes and arrange them in the centrifuge in blocks of four, labelled T, C, G and A. The centrifuge must be at room temperature.
Add 2 μl primer–template mix to each tube in the block of four.
Add 2 μl T* mix to the first (T) tube in each block of four, 2 μl of C* mix to the second (C), etc.
Briefly centrifuge the tubes to bring the reagents to the bottom.
Add 2 μl of DNA polymerase I (large fragment) diluted in Klenow diluent to 0.1 unit μl^{-1} to each tube, and briefly centrifuge the tubes to start the reaction.
Incubate for 15 min at room temperature (the tubes can be left in the centrifuge)
Add 2 μl 0.5 mM dATP to each tube and centrifuge briefly.
Incubate for 15 min at room temperature, then
either add 5 μl formamide–dye mix, centrifuge briefly, denature the DNA and run on a gel immediately (Section IV)
or freeze the samples at -20 C
or in the rare case in which the primer fragment must be removed before running the gel, add 0.5 unit of the appropriate restriction endonuclease to each tube and incubate at the temperature optimum for the enzyme for 10 min prior to freezing the samples or adding formamide–dye mix.

(iii) Titration of dideoxynucleotide mixes
The length of the sequence that can be determined and the intensity of bands on the autoradiograph are functions of the ratio 2′,3′-dideoxyribonucleoside triphosphates to the corresponding 2′-deoxyribonucleoside triphosphate. The correct ratios must be determined empirically and are best done by keeping the X mixes the same and altering the ddX mix. With the reagents used in the author's laboratory those concentrations given in Section VI work well. The ratio should be chosen such that bands are seen well beyond the limit of resolution of the gel, or occasional problems will be found due to spurious bands in the resolved region. Too low a dideoxynucleotide concentration will result in weak exposures on autoradiography.

Separate ddX and X mixes have the advantage over a premixed solution in that the ratio ddX:dX can easily be changed to alter the length of readable sequence and the intensities of the bands on the autoradiograph (Smith, 1980).

3. T-channel screening

If a random cloning strategy is used to generate templates for sequence analysis, the frequency of occurrence of templates containing new or useful sequence information decreases as the project progresses. Initial screening of the templates using only the T-specific reaction allows the elimination of poor templates, of templates containing only a short inserted fragment, and of templates containing known sequence. The T-pattern is compared with the known sequence using a computer program (e.g. SEQFIT; Staden, 1977). The T-reaction is used, as the characteristic pattern of T residues in the vector distal to the cloning site is easily recognized on the autoradiograph (Fig. 7).

294 N. L. BROWN

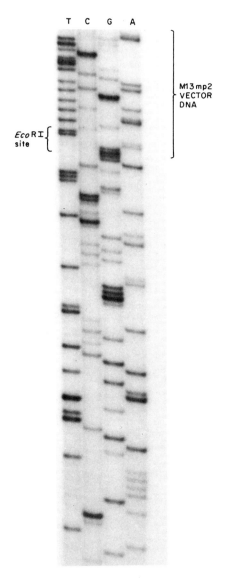

Fig. 7. Autoradiograph of a sequencing gel from the M13-cloning/chain-termination method. The sequence is from a small *Hae*III fragment of Tn*501* DNA cloned, using linkers, into the *Eco*RI site of M13mp2. The distal region of the vector DNA is marked and shows the characteristic pattern in the T-channel.

To screen 18 templates, set up 18 capillaries each resting tip-down in a siliconized glass tube.
Add 1 μl of a mixture containing 4 μl primer DNA, 4 μl 10 × R buffer, and 12 μl water to each.
Add 1 μl template DNA.
Seal the capillary and heat at 100 C for 3 min. Remove the capillary and allow it to cool to room temperature.
Meanwhile dry down 20 μCi (α-^{32}P) dATP (> 400 Ci mmol^{-1}; dATP*) in a siliconized glass tube. Dissolve this in 20 μl T mix, 20 μl ddTTP mix.
Open the capillaries, ensure that the liquid is at the tip and add 2μl of T -ddTTP-dATP* mix to each capillary.
Dilute four units of DNA polymerase I (large fragment) to 20 μl in Klenow diluent.
Add 1 μl to each capillary and mix.
Incubate at room temperature for 15 min.
Add 1 μl 0.5 mM dATP to each capillary, mix and blow the reaction mixture into the siliconized tube.
Incubate at room temperature for 15 min.
Add 3 μl formamide–dye mix.
Heat at 100 C for 5 min.
Load 2 μl of each sample onto a 6% acrylamide–7 M urea slab gel and electrophorese and autoradiograph this as described in Section IV.
After autoradiography each T-pattern can be read (as e.g. TxxTxTxxxxxTxxT) in a T-rich part of the sequence and compared to the known sequence. The complement of the T-pattern or of the known sequence must also be used in the comparison. The sequence distal to the cloning site in M13mp7 (TTcgTaaTcaTggTagcTgTTTccTgTgT) can be used to identity clones with small inserts, or with inserts of a specific size.

4. Reading a sequence

Following gel electrophoresis and autoradiography (Section IV) the DNA sequence can be read from the autoradiograph. The following points will assist in reading the sequence.

(a) Bands in each sequencing track are not of equal intensity. For doublets the following rules apply: (i) Upper C is always MORE intense than lower C; (II) Upper G is often MORE intense than lower G (and ALWAYS so if preceded by a T); (iii) Upper A is often LESS intense than lower A.

(b) Always read the spaces as well as the bands. Ensure that the proposed sequence fits into the available space on the gel [but see (d)].

(c) Occasionally, bands with the same mobility in all four channels are found on the gel. The known reasons for these include: (i) End-repair of double-stranded primer DNA (this will be in one region of the sequence only); (ii) DNA polymerase stopping immediately after a long (> 5) run of Gs; compressions (see below).

(d) Bands on the autoradiograph may be bunched together. Such a compression is due to persistent secondary structure in the radioactive DNA during electrophoresis. In an extreme case the bands are not resolved. Usually a compression is followed by a slight expansion of band spacing above the compression. This is a common and serious problem with GC-rich sequences, and may result in an incorrect sequence being read, or the sequence being unreadable. Usually this can be remedied by obtaining the sequence on the other strand, as the compression is displaced by a few residues. In some cases the compression involves sufficient residues that the compression in the other strand is coincident with that in the first. In such a case hot-formamide gels (Section IV.C.1) and/or the dITP-containing reactions (Section III.C.1) can be used.

(e) Problems in the interpretation of a sequencing gel can be allowed for by the use of an uncertainty code, such as the one shown in Fig. 8. This code covers all ambiguities that may arise on a sequencing gel and is very useful in conjunction with programs such as DBUTIL (Staden, 1980) which allow a record of the primary gel-reading data to be kept. The above list covers most

SYMBOL	MEANING			
1	Probably	C		
2	"	T		
3	"	A		
4	"	G		
D	Definitely	C	possibly	CC
V	"	T	"	TT
B	"	A	"	AA
H	"	G	"	GG
K	Definitely	C	possibly	CX
L	"	T	"	TX
M	"	A	"	AX
N	"	G	"	GX
R	A or G			
Y	C or T			
5	A or C			
6	G or T			
7	A or T			
8	G or C			
–	C or T or A or G			

Fig. 8. Uncertainty codes for DNA sequences for use with the DBUTIL series of programs (Staden, 1980).

usual deviations from the ideal of equal-intensity bands separated by regularly decreasing spacing. Some unusual deviations or problems are covered in Section V.

C. Outline of some specialized techniques

In addition to those combinations of methods described in Sections III.A and III.B, the following protocols will be useful for certain sequencing problems.

1. Deoxyinosine substitution

One of the common reasons for difficulty in determining a DNA sequence is the existence of compressions on the autoradiograph of the sequencing gel due to fold-back intrastrand base pairing. This base-pairing is more stable in GC-rich regions than in AT-rich regions, and this stability can be reduced by using dITP in place of dGTP in the chain-termination reactions.

The substitution of dITP for dGTP in the X° mixes can be made with only two major modifications to the protocol. The ratio of ddGTP to the corresponding deoxyribonucleotide (dITP) must be reduced about 25-fold; and a chase of 1 μl 0.5 mM dGTP should be added at the same time as the 0.5 mM dATP chase. The chase removes spurious bands due to the poor incorporation of dITP at some G residues.

2. Kilobase sequencing

Two workers have recently described a strategic modification of the M13-cloning method which avoids random cloning and can be used to walk along the DNA sequence. Both methods (Barnes *et al.*, 1982; Hong, 1982) are conceptually similar. A large fragment of DNA is cloned into an M13 derivative containing asymmetric restriction targets (e.g. M13mp9); a series of deletions are made from a fixed point in the vector into the insert DNA; the DNA is sequenced from the fixed point in the vector. The larger the deletion, the further into the original fragment the sequence is determined. By sequencing a series of deletions which have been separated according to size, the sequence of the large DNA fragment can be rapidly obtained.

The essential difference between the two methods is in the vector used and in the manner of generating the variable (distal) end of the deletion. Barnes *et al.* (1982) use the vector M13mWB2344, or similar, and generate the distal end of the deletion using quantitative digestion with DNAase I in the presence of ethidium bromide to nick the DNA, exonuclease III to form a gap and nuclease S1 to cleave the other strand. Hong (1982) uses the vectors M13mp8 or M13mp9, and generates the distal end of the deletion using partial digestion with DNAase I in the presence of Mn^{2+}. Both methods use a restriction site primer proximal to the cloning site to generate the fixed end of the deletion. It is important that this site is unique on the molecule, and vectors such as M13mp7 are therefore unsuitable as the cloning sites are paired either side of the insert.

Detailed protocols describing these methods are given in the original papers.

3. Fragment turn-around using M13mp8 and M13mp9

Confirmation of DNA sequence data often requires that the sequence of the complementary strand be obtained. This can easily be done for any DNA fragment which is cloned in the SmaI, BamHI, AccI or PstI sites of M13mp8 or M13mp9. These sites are flanked by unique EcoRI and HindIII sites, which can be used to excise the inserted fragment. Such a fragment from M13mp8 can be cloned in M13mp9, and vice versa, thus changing its orientation with respect to the primer. If the cloned fragment contains an EcoRI or HindIII site, only part of the fragment will be cloned.

A small amount of single-strand template DNA preparation can be used to directly transform competent JM101 cells. A plaque assay is performed as described in Section III.A.4(c), and infected cells are grown up in about 5 ml of $2 \times YT$ medium with shaking at $37°C$. The infected cells are harvested in late exponential phase, and RF DNA is prepared by a standard small-scale cleared lysate procedure (Chapter 2). The EcoRI–HindIII DNA fragment can be identified and isolated by gel electrophoresis, then cloned directly into the alternative vector cleaved with EcoRI and HindIII.

IV. Procedures for gel electrophoresis and autoradiography

A. Standard electrophoresis

Chain-termination reactions and the salt-free reactions from the chemical method can be run on thin (0.3-mm) acrylamide–urea gels (Sanger and Coulson, 1978). Thin gels increase band resolution on the autoradiograph as a simple geometric consequence of having the radioactive source close to the film. The gel concentration used depends on the experiment being performed. A 6% acrylamide gel (with 1 in 20 cross-linking with bis-acrylamide) is satisfactory for most purposes, except for sequencing within the first 15 nucleotides from the common end (i.e. the labelled end in the chemical method). In this case a 20% gel can be used. In all cases the gels are pre-electrophoresed to heat them up prior to loading the sample. This reduces problems caused by any persistence of secondary structure in the DNA fragments. Prerunning also removes electrolytes from 20% gels which would otherwise run with the smaller oligonucleotides and prevent the sequence being determined.

Making the gel
A variety of types of slab gel electrophoresis apparatus is available. We use commercially available apparatus of the Studier (1973) type. The gel plates must be very clean to prevent bubbles forming when the gel is poured. Each plate is cleaned with acetone, ethanol and distilled water each time it is used. The back plate (with a cut-out to provide electrical contact with the cathode buffer reservoir) is siliconized on its inside face to facilitate its removal from the gel. Siliconization is done using a commercially available solution of 2% dimethyldichlorosilane in 1,1,1-trichloroethane (e.g. Repelcote), and is repeated after the plate has been used several times. The front plate is soaked in detergent between uses.

Slot-formers and spacers are cut from 0.35-mm thick Plastikard. New Plastikard is coated with a substance that inhibits the polymerization of acrylamide, and this must be removed with neat detergent followed by thorough washing in water.

(i) Clean the gel plates with acetone, ethanol and water. Clamp the plates together with Plastikard spacers and seal the sides and bottom with yellow vinyl tape (Sellotape 1607); ensuring that there are no wrinkles in the tape, otherwise the gel may leak during pouring.

(ii) Make the gel mix.

	6%	20%
Urea (ultra-pure)	21 g	21 g
10 × TBE	5 ml	5 ml
Deionized 40% acrylamide (38:2)	7.5 ml	25 ml
1.6% ammonium persulphate	1.6 ml	1.6 ml

With *gentle* warming and stirring make up to 50 ml with H_2O.
Add 50 μl TEMED.

Pour the gel immediately, using a large volume pipette with a mechanical pipetting device, and with the plates at an angle of about 45°, run the solution down one of the side spacers until the gel mould is full. Lay the gel almost horizontal and insert the comb. Clamp the gel, or put weights over the wells to ensure that they form properly.
(iii) Leave 6% gels at least 1 h after setting before use; 20% gels are best left overnight, after layering buffer over the slot-former and covering with sealing film.

Running the gel

(i) Remove the tape from the bottom of the gel, and the comb from the top. Clamp the gel in the electrophoresis apparatus and fill the apparatus with 1 × TBE buffer. Prerun the gel for 30–60 min at 1.2 kilovolts for a 40-cm long 6% gel (this gives approximately 2 mA current per centimetre width of gel).

(ii) Add 5 μl of formamide–dye mix to the DNA-sequencing reactions if this has not already been done. Heat them at 100°C for 5 min. Rinse out the wells in the gel using a Pasteur pipette—this removes the urea that will have leached out of the gel. Load 2 to 3-μl sample per slot. Run the gel at 1.2 kilovolts.

(iii) The duration of the run depends on the sequence to be determined. On a 6% gel about 24-nucleotide fragments comigrate with the fast dye (bromophenol blue) and about 110-nucleotide long fragments run with the slow dye (xylene cyanol FF). Therefore, if the 96 bp primer is used for the chain-termination method, the slow dye should be run to the bottom of the gel.

B. Standard autoradiography

There are a number of ways of routinely autoradiographing gels. Two of the simplest are described below. First the back plate must be removed from the gel. If the back plate has been properly siliconized, the gel will remain attached to the front plate. The DNA fragments must be fixed in the gel in some way. This can be done using acid or by freezing.

1. Room-temperature autoradiography

Fix the gel for 5 min in 10% (v/v) acetic acid. Rinse well in water. Carefully blot the gel dry with paper towels. Cover the gel with Saran Wrap, and mark the gel with fluorescent paint or with radioactive ink. Put the gel in a cardboard folder, lay a sheet of X-ray film (see below) directly onto the gel, and leave to autoradiograph with a heavy metal plate on top to maintain close contact between the film and the gel.

If the cardboard folder is attached to a 2-mm thick mild steel plate, then several gels can be stacked on top of one another. It is relatively simple to arrange these in a light-proof cupboard or box in a darkroom.

2. Low-temperature autoradiography

This method has the advantage that the signal-to-noise ratio for ^{32}P autoradiography is higher at lower temperatures. A disadvantage is a potential loss of resolution, due to gel distortion when ice crystals form (Laskey, 1980). The gel is not acid fixed, but is immediately covered with Saran Wrap and marked with fluorescent paint or radioactive ink. The gel is placed in a metal cassette such as those used for medical X-rays. A sheet of X-ray film (see below) is placed directly on the gel. The cassette is closed and put at $-20°C$. Sequencing gels in metal cassettes can be stacked without problems from cross-exposure of films, although this is not always true of high-activity gels such as those used in strand separation in the chemical method described in Section II.A.2(c).

3. *Choice of autoradiography film*

Several films are available which are suitable for autoradiography of sequencing gels. We use Kodak Xomat AR, which is a high-sensitivity film with a clear base and a thin emulsion that can be developed in automatic processors. It is one of the more economical films, and can be used with blue-emitting intensifying screens for other purposes. Usually a 16-h exposure is sufficient to visualize a DNA sequence, but occasionally longer exposures are required. Indirect autoradiography (Section IV.C.2) is rarely required, and is disadvantageous due to its band-broadening effect, which reduces the resolution of bands on the autoradiograph.

C. Specialized procedures

1. *Formamide gels*

The problem of persistent regions of secondary structure causing compressions in the autoradiograph pattern of a sequencing gel may be circumvented by obtaining sequence data from the other strand. However, this is not always possible. The use of acrylamide–urea gels containing 25% deionized formamide often allows such regions to be sequenced. For reasons that are not clear, formamide gels do give rise to a number of problems including smearing of bands and track narrowing, which are not reproducible but occur sufficiently frequently to make it worth using formamide gels only infrequently to sequence through compressions.

Deionize the formamide by stirring with mixed-bed resin (e.g. Amberlite MB-1 or MB-3; 5 g 100 ml^{-1}) for about 40 min at room temperature.
For a 6% thin gel
Mix:
    21 g urea (ultrapure)
    7.5 ml deionized 40% acrylamide (38:2)
    12.5 ml deionized formamide
    5 ml 10 × TBE buffer
    1.6 ml 1.6% ammonium persulphate
with slight warming until the urea dissolves.
Adjust volume to 50 ml with water.
Add 50 μl TEMED and pour gel immediately.

The gel buffer (1 × TBE) is heated to 60–70°C, and the gel is heated at the same temperature for 1 h to ensure that the gel is hot before the sample is loaded. Prerunning is avoided with formamide gels to prevent undue deformation of the wells before the sample is loaded.

2. Indirect autoradiography

Techniques for the enhancement of autoradiographic images using intensifying screens are well established (Laskey and Mills, 1977; Laskey, 1980), and can be used for DNA sequencing gels. The advantage of enhancement of the image is offset by loss of resolution due to considerable broadening of the bands on the autoradiograph. The technique can be used to good effect when, for example, little DNA is available in the chemical method, or difficulty is encountered in obtaining good yields of a particular template in the M13-cloning methods. Due to the low resolution on indirect autoradiography, only short sequences close to the common end of the fragments will be obtained.

For indirect autoradiography, remove the back (i.e. cut-out) plate from the gel, leaving the gel on the front plate. Then take a piece of old X-ray film, cut to size, and put this on the gel. Turn the gel over and remove the glass plate, leaving the gel attached to the X-ray film. Cover this with Saran Wrap, and label it with radioactive ink. This is then put inside a metal X-ray cassette, or similar light-proof container. In the darkroom, a piece of suitable X-ray film (e.g. Fuji RX) is put on top of the gel, and exposed to a brief ($\leqslant 1$ ms) flash of light from a flash gun (with the safe lights turned off). An intensifying screen is placed face down on the film and the cassette is closed and placed at $-70°$C. After a suitable exposure, the film is developed in the normal way, except that no safelights are used.

There are several combinations of film and intensifying screen suitable for indirect autoradiography (Laskey and Mills, 1977; Laskey, 1980). We find Fuji RX film (15 cm × 40 cm) with Hannimex Mach-2 intensifying screen to be a good combination. (Kodak Xomat AR film, which is sensitive enough for direct autoradiography, is also suitable for indirect autoradiography.)

The preflashing step is critical. The exposure must be short ($\leqslant 1$ ms). A series of test exposures must be done in order to find conditions which will expose the film to an absorbance (A_{550}) of 0.15. We use a cheap electronic flash gun covered with a layer each of yellow and white papers at a sufficient distance (50 cm) to ensure near-uniform exposure of the film. A more sophisticated (and expensive) system might use Kodak Wratten, number 21 or 22 filters with a translucent diffuser. The yellow filter is effective in decreasing the intensity of the blue light to which the film is sensitive.

V. Problems

A. Chemical method

Several different problems that may be encountered in the sequencing protocols are considered in detail by Maxam and Gilbert (1980), and it would be mere plagiarism to consider them here.

Probably the most common difficulty with this method has been in obtaining 5′ end-labelled DNA fragments. Providing the chemical concentration of (γ-^{32}P)ATP is kept sufficiently high, and the protocols are followed exactly, little can go wrong at this step. With increasing numbers of restriction endonucleases giving 5′extensions becoming available, procedures for 3′ end-labelling with DNA polymerase and (α-^{32}P)dNTPs are probably the easiest procedures for end-labelling DNA.

B. M13-cloning/chain-termination method

Some problems and their cures are given below. This list is not comprehensive, but may indicate possible solutions to other problems.

1. No bands or few bands show up on autoradiogram

(a) *No primer DNA*. Is there a primer-specific band across all four tracks if using double-stranded non-exonuclease treated primer? Try fresh primer DNA. If preparing primer by using exonuclease III digestion, reduce the digestion conditions.

(b) *No template DNA*. Primer-specific band may be present. Was there a small pellet on PEG precipitation of the phage? Check the template preparation by running on an agarose gel containing ethidium bromide. Try a new template preparation.

(c) *Template DNA contains deletion of primer-complementary region*. Some lac⁻ plaques may be due to deletions in the *lacz* region of the M13 vector. Bizarrely, these deletions may occur only with added fragments and not in the appropriate control. Try other templates from the same batch, and try making and sequencing template DNA from a blue plaque.

(d) *Primer or template DNA is poisoned by impurities*. Make fresh DNAs.

(e) *No hybrid is formed on annealing*. Check the buffers used, and anneal by reducing the temperature slowly in a test-tube of boiling water which is allowed to cool to room temperature.

2. Several band patterns superimposed, and probably out of register

(a) *Template is not pure*. A mixed pattern of specific bands is due to two different template sequences being present. These can be repurified by transfection of competent cells with, say, 0.1–1 μl of template preparation, and making a fresh template preparation.

A non-specific background of bands may be due to non-removal of vector

DNA during preparation of the primer as described in Section III.B. (c). Alternatively, this effect may be due to lysis of cells during growth of the phage, and may be suppressed relative to the template sequence by increasing the ddNTP/dNTP ratio. Alternatively, the template can be repurified. Shorter growth time should be used to avoid cell lysis. This effect is also seen if the template DNA is randomly nicked by nucleases; all reagents should be checked as being nuclease-free.

(b) *Priming at more than one site.* This may happen if a primer other than the universal primer is used. The solution depends on whether there is more than one priming fragment, in which case the primer must be repurified; or whether there are two sites complementary to the primer, in which case another primer must be used. This effect is more likely to occur when the primer (the universal primer or another) is removed by restriction enzyme cleavage. If a second site for a restriction enzyme is present in the region sequenced, two families of fragments with different 5′ ends will be generated and give a mixed sequence. The single-site ribosubstitution method (Brown, 1978), or the use of a different restriction enzyme may circumvent this problem.

3. Bands appear as doublets or triplets

(a) *All bands in all channels.* Possibly the primer has a heterogeneous 5′ end caused by exonuclease activity during its preparation or its use. Check reactions for exonuclease activity or prepare new primer.

(b) *Some bands or channels.* Bands appear due to chain elongation stopping *before* the nucleotide to be incorporated due to the relatively low dNTP concentration. This is particularly noticeable in the inosine reactions (Section III.C.1), and in all channels if the 0.5 mM dATP chase is omitted; and it occasionally occurs elsewhere (e.g. T-channel). For inosine use a 1-μl 0.5 mM dGTP chase; for all channels make fresh dATP chase. For individual other channels, increasing the dNTP concentration (with or without altering the ddNTP/dNTP ratio) may remove the artefact.

4. The first 20–50 nucleotides from the primer are obscured

(a) *Self-priming on the primer.* During the denaturation and annealing step using the 96 bp primer, single strands can fold back on themselves to form a self-priming structure. This will incorporate nucleotides and chain terminate, using the 5′ end of the primer fragment as template. The products of this reaction will be superimposed on the template DNA sequence. This self-complementarity can be removed by pretreating the primer with exonuclease III to remove the 3′ end of each strand of the primer. Alternatively, reverse transcriptase, which requires perfect complementarity to prime can be used in the place of DNA polymerase I (large fragment).

(b) *Dark smear due to radioactive label.* Some batches of (α-^{32}P)dATP contain impurities which, when used with short (17–30 nucleotides) primers on 6% acrylamide gels, give rise to dark smears obscuring the sequence. This is intermittent and specific to one batch of label, and can be circumvented by using longer primers, using higher percentage gels or ordering fresh label.

5. A band or bands across all the lanes in a particular region of the gel

(a) *Reannealed double-stranded primer.* This can be end-repaired by the polymerase to give a labelled band at one or two positions in the sequence corresponding to the priming site. This does not usually interfere with the sequence determination. Increased exonuclease treatment will remove this. Using less primer may not be advantageous as there is always competition between the template and the homologous strand in the double-stranded primer for the complementary priming strand.

(b) *DNA polymerase cannot chain elongate through a particular sequence (e.g. at a run of Gs).* This is sequence-specific, and can be circumvented by sequencing the other strand, or by using reverse transcriptase instead of DNA polymerase. If the DNA polymerase has been diluted and kept in the wrong buffer it may give rise to a number of bands across the gel.

(c) *A site-specific nuclease in low amounts contaminating one of the reagents would also give this effect.* Change or repurify the reagent concerned. This can be a problem if the primer is removed by a restriction endonuclease which may be contaminated with, or intrinsically contain, a second activity (e.g. *Hind*III, contaminated with *Hind*II; or *Eco*RI and *Eco*RI* activity).

(d) *A severe compression.* See Section V.B.6.

6. A sudden decrease in band spacing, sometimes to zero (compression)

(a) *Secondary structure in single-stranded DNA during electrophoresis.* Fold-back structures at the end of the single-stranded DNA do not alter the hydrodynamic shape of the DNA in a progressive way and such structures tend to have similar mobilities and to run together on the gel. Running the gel at higher temperature (higher voltage) may remove small compressions. Sequencing the other strand will generally give rise to compressions in a different part of the sequence. However, it is not always trivial to sequence the other strand, and in G:C-rich regions with a high degree of symmetry the regions of compression on both strands may coincide. In such cases, hot formamide-containing gels should be used (Section IV.C), with normal chain-termination protocols or with deoxyinosine substitution (Section III.C.1). *In extremis*, procedures such as depurination analysis may prove useful (e.g. Brown and Smith, 1977).

VI. Buffers, reagents, equipment and suppliers

A. General purpose buffers and reagents

1. *Restriction enzyme buffers* (10 × RE buffer) unless otherwise stated all digestions were done in accordance with manufacturers' recommendations. Where a restriction enzyme is used simultaneously with another enzyme the buffer used is given.
2. *Phenol* is redistilled in air, and kept at -20°C in the dark. It is saturated with TE buffer (below) before use, and kept dark at 4°C (small aliquots of buffer-saturated phenol may be kept at -20°C).
3. *3 M sodium acetate* is adjusted to pH 6.5 before use.
4. *TE buffer*: 10 mM Tris-HCl, pH 7.5, 0.1 mM EDTA.
5. *10 × R buffer*: 500 mM NaCl, 100 mM Tris-HCl, pH 7.9, 100 mM 2-mercapto-ethanol, 100 mM $MgCl_2$.
6. *10 × TBE buffer*: 900 mM Tris-borate, pH 8.3, 25 mM EDTA (108 g l^{-1} Trizma base, 55 g l^{-1} boric acid, 9.3 g l^{-1} Na_2 EDTA; pH should be correct without further adjustment).
7. *Acrylamide*: 40% (380 g l^{-1} acrylamide, 20 g l^{-1} NN'-methylenebisacrylamide) for sequencing gels. 30% (290 g l^{-1} acrylamide, 10 g l^{-1} NN'-methylenebisacrylamide) for native gels. The acrylamide solution is stirred with 20 g l^{-1} Amberlite MB-1 or MB-3 mixed-bed resin for approximately 30 min, then the resin is removed by filtration. The acrylamide is further filtered through nitrocellulose filters, degassed and stored at 4°C. Degas before use.
8. *Formamide* is deionized by stirring with 5 g l^{-1} Amberlite MB-1 or MB-3 mixed-bed resin. Filter through sintered glass. When making formamide gels, the formamide should be freshly deionized and should be filtered through nitrocellulose filters.
9. *Formamide–dye mix* is made by dissolving xylene–cyanol FF and bromophenol blue to a concentration of about 0.03% (w/v) in deionized formamide and adding 0.1 volume of 0.25 M EDTA. The optimal dye concentration should be determined empirically.
10. *Native loading buffer*: 15% (w/v) Ficoll 400, 25 mM EDTA, 0.03% (w/v) bromophenol blue.
11. *Gel elution buffer*: 500 mM ammonium acetate, 10 mM magnesium acetate, 0.1% (w/v) SDS, 0.1 mM EDTA.
12. *Radioactive ink*: standard stationers' ink with ^{35}S-sulphate added to about 0.1 mCi ml^{-1} will be sufficient for general-purpose use. A small amount of 2 mCi ml^{-1} will be needed for short exposures (e.g. preparative separation of radioactive DNA fragments by gel electrophoresis). ^{35}S is a good isotope to use as it has a longer half-life than P^{32}, and it emits lower energy β-particles giving sharper definition.

B. Chemical method

1. *10 × Phosphatase buffer*: 100 mM Tris-Cl, pH 9.5, 1 mM EDTA, 10 mM spermidine-HCl.
2. *Calf Intestinal Phosphatase*: Boehringer, Grade I diluted to four units per millilitre

in 100 μg ml^{-1} Bovine Serum Albumin; 10 mM Tris-HCl, pH 7.9, 1 mM ZnCl$_2$, 1 mM MgCl$_2$ 50% (v/v) glycerol.

3. *10 × Kinase buffer*: 500 mM Tris-HCl, pH 9.5, 100 mM MgCl$_2$ 50 mM DTT, 5 mM spermidine-HCl, 0.5 mM EDTA.

4. *2 × Strand separation buffer*: 60% (v/v) DMSO, 1 mM EDTA, 0.03% (w/v) xylene cyanol, 0.03% (w/v) bromophenol blue.

5. *Strand separation gel*: 6 g acrylamide, 0.1 g bisacrylamide (N.B. 1 in 60 cross-linking), 6.7 ml 10 × TBE, 2 ml 1.6% (w/v) ammonium persulphate. Adjust volume to 120 ml with water; degas and start polymerization with 50 μl TEMED. Pour a 40 cm × 20 cm × 0.15 cm gel, using 1-cm wide sample wells.

6. *DMS buffer*: 50 mM sodium cacodylate, pH 8.0, 10 mM MgCl$_2$, 1 mM EDTA.

7. *Dimethyl sulphate*: store in a fume hood. With an automatic pipette dispense a small aliquot into stoppered bottle for each day's use. Dispose of small amount into 5 M NaOH.

8. *Hydrazine*: store in a tightly sealed bottle and disperse in a fume hood. With an automatic pipette dispense a small aliquot into a stoppered bottle for each day's work. Dispose of small amounts into 3 M ferric chloride.

9. *DMS stop*: 1.5 M sodium acetate, 1 M 2-mercaptoethanol, 1 mM EDTA. Store at 4°C. To 0.5 ml add 20 μl of 10 mg ml^{-1} tRNA immediately before use (enough for ten fragments).

10. *HZ stop*: 0.4 M sodium acetate, 0.1 mM EDTA. Store at 4°C. To 5 ml add 25 μl of 10 mg ml^{-1} tRNA immediately before use (enough for eight fragments).

11. *tRNA solutions*: dissolve in 1 mM Tris, pH 7.5, 0.1 mM EDTA. (Phenol-extract, ether-extract and dilute to about 10 mg ml^{-1} ($A_{260} = 200$). Store frozen.

12. *1.0 M piperidine*: make up fresh each time it is required. Store concentrated piperidine at 4°C. Dilute 0.2 ml into 1.8 ml chilled distilled water (do *not* use polycarbonate tubes), and rinse the piperidine out of the pipette several times. Mix well and store at 0°C.

C. The M13-cloning/chain-termination method

1. *Bacterial media*: all autoclaving is at 15 p.s.i. for 20 min.
   a. *5 × A salts*: 5.25% (w/v) K$_2$HPO$_4$
   2.25% (w/v) KH$_2$PO$_4$
   0.5% (w/v) (NH$_4$)$_2$SO$_4$
   0.25% (w/v) sodium citrate·2H$_2$O
   autoclave.
   b. *Minimal A–glucose plates*: autoclave 10 g agar in 400 ml H$_2$O.
   Add 100 ml sterile 5 × A salts
   0.5 ml sterile 20% (w/v) MgCl$_2$.7H$_2$O
   5 ml sterile 20% (w/v) glucose.
   c. *2 × YT medium*: 1.6% (w/v) bactotryptone
   1.0% (w/v) yeast extract
   1.0% (w/v) NaCl
   autoclave.
   d. *YT agar*: use half above concentrations and make 2% (w/v) agar for plates, or 0.5% (w/v) agar for top-agar overlaps. Top-agar can be heated to dissolve the solids then dispersed into 3-ml aliquots for autoclaving if desired.
   e. *X-gal solution*: weigh 20 mg on clean glassine paper. Dissolve in 1 ml dimethylformamide. Do not further sterilize. Store at −20°C.

    f. *IPTG solution*: weigh 24 mg on clean glassine paper. Dissolve in 1 ml autoclaved water. Do not further sterilize. Store at -20 C.

    g. *Other reagents* are sterilized by autoclaving (e.g. 50 mM $CaCl_2$ for making competent cells).

2. *DNA ligase dilution buffer*: 50% (v/v) glycerol, 50 mM KCl, 10 mM 2-mercaptoethanol, 100 μg ml^{-1} autoclaved gelatin, 10 mM potassium phosphate, pH 7.4, store at -20 C.

3. *ACE electrophoresis buffer*: 40 mM Tris-acetate, pH 8.0, 5 mM sodium acetate, 1 mM EDTA, 1 μg ml^{-1} ethidium bromide.

4. *G-75 High-salt buffer*: 750 mM NaCl, 10 mM Tris-HCl, pH 7.5, 1 mM EDTA.

5. *10 × C buffer* for ligations: 500 mM NaCl, 100 mM Tris-HCl, pH 7.5, 100 mM $MgCl_2$, 10 mM DTT.

6. *10 × ExoIII buffer*: 700 mM Tris-HCl, pH 8.0, 10 mM $MgCl_2$, 100 mM DTT.

7. *Commercial primer solutions* should be used according to the manufacturer's instructions. Too little primer gives no sequence, too much primer can cause only short sequences to be obtained.

8. *10 × R buffer*: 500 mM NaCl, 100 mM Tris-HCl, pH 7.9, 100 mM $MgCl_2$, 10 mM DTT.

9. *Nucleotide mixes*

    a. Dideoxynucleoside triphosphates are kept in water at -20 C. The working concentrations are determined empirically, but initially try:

            0.5 mM ddTTP

            0.3 mM ddCTP

            0.3 mM ddGTP

            0.1 mM ddATP

    b. T , C , G and A mixes are made up from 0.5 mM working solutions kept in water at -20 C.

	T	C	G	A
0.5 mM dTTP	1	20	20	20
0.5 mM dCTP	20	1	20	20
0.5 mM dGTP	20	20	1	20
50 mM Tris-HCl, pH 8.0, 1 mM EDTA	5	5	5	5

    c. 0.5 mM dATP for the chase is made up in 5 mM Tris-HCl, pH 8.0, 0.1 mM EDTA.

10. *Klenow diluent*: 50% (v/v) glycerol, 50 mM potassium phosphate, pH 7.0.

D. Sources of chemicals, enzymes and equipment

The products listed are those used in the author's laboratory, or listed in other papers (e.g. Maxam and Gilbert, 1980). This does not imply that they are superior to products from other suppliers, merely that they are satisfactory for their purpose.

    Reagents in addition to those listed below were obtained from a general chemical supply company (e.g. British Drug Houses Ltd), and are AnalaR grade where possible.

Bacterial media are obtained from Difco Laboratories Inc.

Radiochemicals are obtained from Amersham International plc, or New England Nuclear, GmbH.

Acrylamiade, bisacrylamide (electrophoresis grade); B.D.H. Ltd.
Agarose (low electroendosmosis): Sigma Chemical Co.
Amberlite MB-1, MB-3: B.D.H. Ltd.
DEAE-cellulose: Whatman Ltd.
Dimethyl sulphate: Aldrich Chemical Co.; N.E.N., GmbH.
DNA (calf thymus): Sigma Chemical Co.
Hydrazine: Eastman Organic Chemicals; N.E.N., GmbH.
IPTG: Sigma Chemical Co.
Linker oligonucleotides (EcoRI): Collaborative Research; B.R.L.
Piperidine: Fischer Scientific; N.E.N., GmbH.
Sephadex: Pharmacia.
Spermidine hydrochloride: Sigma Chemical Co.
tRNA: Boehringer Corporation Ltd.
Urea (ultra-pure): Bethesda Research Laboratories Ltd.
X-gal (5-bromo-4-chloro-3 indolylgalactoside): Sigma Chemical Co.

Universal primers for the M13-cloning/chain-termination method are available from Bethesda Research Laboratories Ltd (double-stranded DNA fragment), P-L Biochemicals Ltd (synthetic, single-stranded DNA) and New England Biolabs (synthetic single-stranded DNA). These primers have not been used in the author's laboratory.

Restriction endonucleases are available from many firms. Availability, purity and price are the factors most frequently determining choice of supplier; unfortunately there is great variation in all three factors.

The author's laboratory normally obtains other enzymes as listed below:

Calf intestinal phosphatase: Boehringer Corporation Ltd (405612).
DNA polymerase I (large fragment): Boehringer Corporation Ltd (104531).
Exonuclease III: P-L Biochemicals Ltd (0874).
Polynucleotide kinase: Boehringer Corporation Ltd (174645).
T4 DNA polymerase: P-L Biochemicals Ltd (0918).
T4 DNA ligase: Bethesda Research Laboratories (5224) or Boehringer Corporation Ltd (481220) or P-L Biochemicals Ltd (0870) or New England Biolabs (202).

E. coli strains and bacteriophage strains required for the M13-cloning method are available from Bethesda Research Laboratories Ltd or from P-L Biochemicals Ltd.

A DNA sequencing kit for the chemical method is available from N.E.N. (NEK-010).

Most of the equipment used in the methods described in this chapter can be obtained from normal general and specialist laboratory suppliers. A few notes describing important features of particular pieces of equipment are included below.

Plastikard (thickness 0.015 inch) is from Slaters' Plastikard Ltd, Temple Road, Matlock Bath, Derbyshire, U.K.
Vinyl Tape (No. 1607; 25 mm wide) is from D.R.G. Sellotape Products Ltd, Theobald Street, Boreham Wood, Hertfordshire, U.K.
Gel apparatus for sequencing gels is available from several suppliers (Bethesda

Research Laboratories, Raven Scientific Ltd, etc). It is very important that the gel plates are of high quality float glass to minimize variation in thickness of the gel.

Saran Wrap (Dow Chemical Corporation) proves superior to other domestic transparent film that we have tested, as it does not adhere to autoradiography film and cause film-blackening due to static electrical discharge on removing the film.

Capillary tubes for small-volume reactions are made by drawing-out open-ended melting point tubes. They are *not* siliconized, as losses by adsorbtion are minimal, and the surface tension holds the small volume of liquid in the capillary during incubations.

Microfuge tubes (1.5-ml) must have a good seal, yet open with relative ease. Those manufactured by Starstedt (No. 72.690) or Eppendorf (2236411-1) prove satisfactory.

VII. Concluding remarks

"Should I use the chemical method or the M13-cloning/chain-termination method?" is a question that can only be answered in a conditional way (it depends on the project) and in a subjective way (it depends on the experimentalist).

Many of the strongest arguments favouring the chemical method over the chain-termination method (e.g. use with double-stranded DNA) have been eliminated with the development of M13 vectors; whereas other arguments (e.g. detection of modified nucleotides) are still valid.

There is no doubt that some projects are best prosecuted by the chemical method. For example, if there are strong arguments against cloning some DNA fragments in M13; or if the sequence contains a protein-binding sequence that can be examined using chemical modification procedures (Siebenlist *et al.*, 1980). Other projects are best tackled by the M13-cloning/chain-termination method, especially those requiring large sequences to be determined. These can now be done by the kilobase-sequencing methods of Barnes *et al.* (1982) or Hong (1982). The majority of projects do not have strong arguments in favour of one method or the other. The advantage of rapidity in the M13-cloning/chain-termination method is sometimes offset by difficulties in obtaining clones in a specific region of sequence. The chemical method is more labour-intensive in the sequencing reactions, but the M13-cloning/chain-termination method requires that ligation, transformation and DNA preparation can all be performed satisfactorily. So the final choice of method usually depends on the expertise of the experimentalist and the advice of his acquaintances.

Acknowledgements

The author is indebted to colleagues for discussions on the trials and tribulations of DNA sequencing, as well as for their early communication of advances in methodology, in particular A. Bankier, W. Barnes, B. Barrell, A. Coulson, D. Fritzinger, J. Messing, D. Pridmore, E. Ruley, F. Sanger and R. Tizard. Work from the author's laboratory is supported by the Medical Research Council and The Royal Society. The author is a Royal Society E.P.A. Cephalosporin Fund Senior Research Fellow.

References

Anderson, S. (1981). *Nucleic Acids Res.* **9**, 3015–3027.
Anderson, S., Gait, M. J., Mayol, L. and Young, I. G. (1980). *Nucleic Acids Res.* **8**, 1731–1745.
Ansorge, W. and De Maeyer, L. (1980). J. *Chromatogr.* **202**, 45–53.
Atkinson, M. R., Deutscher, M. P., Kornberg, A., Russell, A. F. and Moffat, J. G. (1969). *Biochemistry* **8**, 4897–4904.
Barnes, W. M., Bevan, M. and Son, P. M. (1982). *In* "Methods in Enzymology" (R. Wu, Ed.), Vol. 101, pp. 98–122. Academic Press, New York.
Bolivar, F. (1978). *Gene* **4**, 121–136.
Brown, N. L. (1978). *FEBS Lett.* **93**, 10–15.
Brown, N. L. (1979). In "Companion to Biochemistry" (A. T. Bull, J. R. Lagnado, J. O. Thomas and K. F. Tipton, Eds), Vol. 2, pp. 1–48. Longmans, London.
Brown, N. L. and Smith, M. (1977). *J. Mol. Biol.* **116**, 1–28.
Brownlee, G. G. (1972). In "Laboratory Techniques in Biochemistry and Molecular Biology" (T. S. Work and E. Work, Eds), Vol. 3, pp. 1–265. North-Holland Publ., Amsterdam.
Dagert, M. and Ehrlich, S. D. (1979). *Gene* **6**, 23–28.
Friedmann, T. and Brown, D. M. (1978). *Nucleic Acids Res.* **5**, 615–622.
Garoff, H. and Ansorge, W. (1981). *Anal. Biochem.* **115**, 450–457.
Godson, G. N., Barrell, B. G., Staden, R. and Fiddes, J. C. (1978). *Nature (London)* **276**, 236–247.
Gronenborn, B. and Messing, J. (1978). *Nature (London)* **272**, 375–377.
Heidecker, G., Messing, J. and Gronenborn, B. (1980). *Gene* **10**, 69–73.
Hong, G. F. (1982). *J. Mol. Biol.* **158**, 539–549.
Laskey, R. A. (1980). In "Methods in Enzymology" (L. Grossman and K. Moldave, Eds), Vol. 65, pp. 363–371. Academic Press, New York and London.
Laskey, R. A. and Mills, A. D. (1977). *FEBS Lett.* **82**, 314–316.
Lis, J. T. (1980). *In* "Methods in Enzymology" (L. Grossman and K. Moldave, Eds), Vol. 65, pp. 347–353. Academic Press, New York and London.
Maxam, A. and Gilbert, W. (1977). *Proc. Natl. Acad. Sci. U.S.A.* **74**, 560–564.
Maxam, A. and Gilbert, W. (1980). *In* "Methods in Enzymology" (L. Grossman and K. Moldave, Eds), Vol. 65, pp. 499–560. Academic Press, New York and London.
Messing, J. (1979). *Recombinant DNA Technical Bulletin* **2**, 43–48.
Messing, J. and Vieira, J. (1982). *Gene* **19**, 269–276.

Messing, J., Gronenborn, B., Müller-Hill, B. and Hofschneider, P. H. (1977). *Proc. Natl. Acad. Sci. U.S.A.* **74**, 3642–3646.

Messing, J., Crea, P. and Seeburg, P. (1981). *Nucleic Acids Res.* **9**, 309–321.

Murray, K. (1974). *Int. Rev. Biochem.* **6**, 1–40.

Peacock, A. C. and Dingman, C. W. (1967). *Biochemistry* **6**, 1818–1827.

Ray, D. S. (1977). In "Comprehensive Virology" (H. Fraenkel-Conrat and R. R. Wagner, Eds), Vol. 7, pp. 105–178. Plenum, New York and London.

Roberts, R. J. (1982). *Nucleic Acids Res.* **10**, r117–r144.

Salser, W. (1974). *Annu. Rev. Biochem.* **43**, 923–965.

Sanger, F. and Coulson, A. R. (1975). *J. Mol. Biol.* **94**, 441–448.

Sanger, F. and Coulson, A. R. (1978). *FEBS Lett.* **87**, 107–110.

Sanger, F., Air, G. M., Barrell, B. G., Brown, N. L., Coulson, A. R., Fiddes, J. C., Hutchison, C. A. III, Slocombe, P. M. and Smith, M. (1977a). *Nature (London)* **265**, 687–695.

Sanger, F., Nicklen, S. and Coulson, A. R. (1977b). *Proc. Natl. Acad. Sci. U.S.A.* **74**, 5463–5467.

Sanger, F., Coulson, A. R., Friedmann, T., Air, G. M., Barrell, B. G., Brown, N. L., Fiddes, J. C., Hutchison, C. A. III, Slocombe, P. M. and Smith, M. (1978). *J. Mol. Biol.* **125**, 225–246.

Sanger, F., Coulson, A. R., Barrell, B. G., Smith, A. J. H. and Roe, B. A. (1980). *J. Mol. Biol.* **143**, 161–178.

Schreier, P. H. and Cortese, R. (1979). *J. Mol. Biol.* **129**, 169–172.

Siebenlist, U., Simpson, R. B. and Gilbert, W. (1980). *Cell* **20**, 269–281.

Skryabin, A. G., Zakharyev, V. M. and Bayev, A. A. (1978). *Doklady Akad. Nauk. USSR.* **241**, 488–492.

Smith, A. J. H. (1980). In "Methods in Enzymology" (L. Grossman and K. Moldave, Eds), Vol. 65, pp. 560–580. Academic Press, New York and London.

Staden, R. (1977). *Nucleic Acids Res.* **4**, 4037–4051.

Staden, R. (1980). *Nucleic Acids Res.* **8**, 3673–3694.

Studier, F. W. (1973). *J. Mol. Biol.* **79**, 237–248.

Tu, C.-P. D. and Cohen, S. N. (1980). *Gene* **10**, 177–183.

Weaver, R. F. and Weissman, C. (1979). *Nucleic Acids Res.* **7**, 1175–1193.

Note added in proof

As anticipated in the Introduction to this Chapter, there has been a number of significant changes in the methodology of DNA sequence analysis. References to these, but no details, are given in this note.

Several new M13mp vectors with additional cloning sites are available; e.g. M13mp10 to M13mp19 (Norrander *et al.*, 1983). JM103 has been found to be a P1 lysogen and has been superseded by JM105, a *hsd*R⁻ strain. The strain TG1 (Gibson, 1984) is an alternative *hsd*R⁻ mutant of JM101. There are several new restriction endonucleases suitable for DNA fragmentation, cloning and labelling (Roberts, 1984), and there are more efficient methods for transformation (Hanahan, 1983).

Fundamental changes include the use of adenosine 5'-(α-[³⁵S]-thio)triphosphate as the radioactive label to increase the sharpness of bands on the autoradiograph, thus increasing the resolution higher up the gels, and the use of buffer-gradient gels which alter the progressive separation of fragments, thus allowing more sequence to be read from a single gel. The gels are dried before autoradiography. The procedures are described by Biggin *et al.* (1983). The use of microtitre plates for sequence analysis in place of microfuge tubes (Section III.B.2.(ii)) allows the facile manipulation of a large number of samples at one time. The use of a digitizing tablet to read gels directly into automatic computer programs (Staden, 1982, 1984) has removed much of the error and cross-checking when reading sequences. Technical improvements have been made: such as the use of a cup-horn sonication probe, in which DNA can be sonicated in a sealed microfuge tube, thus reducing contamination between samples or by the metal of the probe.

References

Biggin, M. D., Gibson, T. J. and Hong, B. F. (1983). *Proc. Natl. Acad. Sci. USA.* **80**, 3963–3965.
Gibson, T. J. (1984). Ph.D. Thesis, University of Cambridge.
Hanahan, D. (1983). *J. Mol. Biol.* **166**, 557–580.
Norrander, J., Kempe, T. and Messing, J. (1983). *Gene* **26**, 101–106.
Roberts, R. J. (1984). *Nucleic Acids Res.* **12**, r167–r204.
Staden, R. (1982). *Nucleic Acids Res.* **10**, 4731–4751.
Staden, R. (1984). *Nucleic Acids Res.* **12**, 499–503.

Index

Contents of published volumes